EVOLUTIONARY MACHINE DESIGN:
Methodology & Applications

EVOLUTIONARY MACHINE DESIGN:
Methodology & Applications

Edited By

Nadia Nedjah
Luiza de Macedo Mourelle

Nova Science Publishers
New York 2005

For permission to use material from this book please contact us:
Telephone 631-231-7269; Fax 631-231-8175
Web Site: http://www.novapublishers.com

ISBN 1-59454-405-0

Published by Nova Science Publishers, Inc. ✢ New York

Contents

List of Figures

List of Tables

List of Algorithms

Preface

In recent years, genetic programming has attracted many researcher's attention and so became a consolidated methodology to automatically create new competitive computer programs. Concise and efficient synthesis of a variety of systems has been generated by evolutionary computations.

Evolvable hardware is a growing discipline. It allows one to evolve creative and novel hardware architectures given the expected input/output behavior. There are two kinds of evolvable hardware: extrinsic and intrinsic. The former relies on a simulated evolutionary process to evaluate the characteristics of the evolved designs while the latter uses hardware itself to do so. Usually, reconfigurable hardware such FPGA and FPAA are exploited.

One of the main problems that still researchers are faced with in the field of evolutionary machine design is the scalability. This book is devoted to reporting innovative and significant progress in automatic machine design. Theoretical as well as practical chapters are contemplated. The scalability problem in evolutionary machine designs is addressed.

The content of this book is divided into two main parts: evolvable hardware and genetic programming; and evolutionary designs. In the following, we give a brief description of the main contribution of each of the included chapters.

Part I: Evolvable Hardware and Genetic Programming

In Chapter 1, which is entitled *Routine High-Return Human-Competitive Evolvable Hardware*, the authors, **John R. Koza, Martin A. Keane and Matthew J. Streeter**, review the use of genetic programming as an automated invention machine for the synthesis of both the topology and sizing of analog electrical circuits. It makes the point that genetic programming now routinely delivers high-return human-competitive machine intelligence.

In Chapter 2, which is entitled *Using Generative Representations to Evolve Robots*, the author, namely **Gregory S. Hornby**, claims that for automated design systems to scale in complexity they must use a representation which allows for the hierarchical creation and reuse of modules, which we call a generative representation. The author also proves that not only is the ability to reuse modules necessary for functional scalability, but it is also valuable for improving efficiency in testing and construction.

In Chapter 3, which is entitled *Intrinsic Evolutionary Design of Analog Building Blocks for Fuzzy Logic Controllers*, the authors, namely **José Franco M. do Amaral, Jorge Luís M. do Amaral, Ricardo Tanscheit, Marco A. C. Pacheco and Marley M. B. R. Vellasco**, discuss the use of an Evolvable Hardware platform in the synthesis of analog electronic circuits for Fuzzy Logic Controllers. To prove the soundness of their work, the authors present four case studies: a type Z membership function, a type S membership function, a fuzzy logic operator and an output circuit (defuzzifier).

In Chapter 4, which is entitled *Improving the Search by Encoding Multiple Solutions in a Chromosome*, the author, namely **Mihai Oltean**, investigates the possibility of encoding multiple solutions of a problem in a single chromosome. Three Genetic Programming techniques are analyzed: Multi-Expression Programming, Linear Genetic Programming and Infix Form Genetic Programming. Using some numerical experiments, the author shows that encoding multiple solutions in a single chromosome greatly improves the search process.

PART II: EVOLUTIONARY DESIGNS

In Chapter 5, which is entitled *Real-World Evolutionary Designs: Secure Evolvable Hardware for Public-Key Cryptosystems*, the authors, namely **Nadia Nedjah and Luiza de Macedo Mourelle**, propose a methodology based on genetic programming to automatically generate data-flow based specifications for hardware designs of combinational digital circuits. The aim consists of allowing automatic generation of balanced hardware specifications for a given input/output behaviour. To emphasize the applicability of the methodology to real-world problems, the authors use genetic programming as an alternative methodology to automatically generate secure and minimal hardware designs of RSA-based public-key cryptosystems.

In Chapter 6, which is entitled *Automated Discovery of Innovative Designs of Mechanical Components Using Evolutionary Multi-Objective Algorithms*, the authors, namely **Kalyanmoy Deb and Shamik Chaudhuri**, study the design task as a simultaneous optimization of two or more conflicting objectives and use an evolutionary algorithm for finding multiple trade-off optimal solutions.

In Chapter 7, which is entitled *Toward Efficient Topological Synthesis of Dynamic Systems Using Genetic Programming*, the authors, namely **Jianjun Hu, Kisung Seo, Erik D. Goodman and Ronald Rosenberg**, concentrate on building a topologically open-ended evolutionary synthesis engine. Using a set of scalable benchmark problems, the eigenvalue placement problems for bond-graph-based synthesis of mechatronic systems, the authors investigate the representation issues and knowledge incorporation approaches critical for efficient automated synthesis of mechatronic systems by genetic programming.

In Chapter 8, which is entitled *The Role of Simulated Evolution in Bioinformatics*, the authors namely, **Andy Auyeung and Ajith Abraham**, introduce evolutionary computation applications in bioinformatics. The authors first give an overview of some key concepts and classical problems in bioinformatics. Then, illustrate their work using two case studies:

Genome Reversal Distance Estimation and The Largest Compatible Subset Problem for Phylogenetic Data.

ACKNOWLEDGEMENT

As editors of this book, we wish to thank all the contributors for their hard work and their promptness. Also, our special thanks go to the reviewers that provided us with the right feedback at the right time. This allowed us to fulfill our aim with the expected quality and delays.

Nadia Nedjah, Ph.D.

Department of Electronics Engineering & Telecommunication
Faculty of Engineering
State University of Rio de Janeiro
nadia@eng.uerj.br
http://www.eng.uerj.br/ nadia

Luiza de Macedo Mourelle, Ph.D.

Department of System Engineering & Computation
Faculty of Engineering
State University of Rio de Janeiro
ldmm@eng.uerj.br
http://www.eng.uerj.br/ ldmm

Part I

EVOLVABLE HARDWARE & GENETIC PROGRAMMING

In: Evolutionary Machine Design: Methodology & Applications ISBN 1-59454-405-0
Editors: N. Nedjah & L. Mourelle, pp:3-32

Chapter 1

ROUTINE HIGH-RETURN HUMAN-COMPETITIVE EVOLVABLE HARDWARE

John R. Koza, Martin A. Keane[†]*, Matthew J. Streeter*[‡]

Biomedical Informatics Program,
Department of Electrical Engineering, Stanford University
Stanford, California USA
koza@stanford.edu

[†]Econometrics Inc. Chicago, Illinois USA
mak@sportsmrkt.com

[‡]Genetic Programming Inc., Mountain View, California USA
(Currently Carnegie Mellon University)
matts@cs.cmu.edu

This chapter reviews the use of genetic programming as an automated invention machine for the synthesis of both the topology and sizing of analog electrical circuits. It makes the point that genetic programming now routinely delivers high-return human-competitive machine intelligence. The chapter also makes the point that genetic programming has delivered a progression of qualitatively more substantial results in synchrony with five approximately order-of-magnitude increases in the expenditure of computer time. The chapter shows six examples where genetic programming has synthesized a circuit that duplicates the functionality or infringes a 21st-century patented electrical circuit. Finally, the chapter discusses how genetic programming can be enhanced in order to potentially enable it to deliver more complex results and commercially useful results.

1.1 Introduction

One of the central challenges of computer science is to get a computer to solve a problem without explicitly programming it to do so. Paraphrasing Arthur Samuel, founder of the field of machine learning, this challenge (1959) is

> "How can computers be made to do what needs to be done, without being told exactly how to do it?"

Samuel described the criterion for success for the above challenge in his 1983 talk entitled "AI: Where It Has Been and Where It Is Going":

> "[T]he aim [is] ... to get machines to exhibit behavior, which if done by humans, would be assumed to involve the use of intelligence."

Genetic programming starts from a high-level statement of what needs to be done and then automatically creates a computer program to solve the problem. Section 1.2 provides background on genetic programming. It shows how genetic programming can be used to automatically create programs that yield both the topology and sizing of analog electrical circuits. Section 1.3 of this chapter makes the point that genetic programming now routinely delivers high-return human-competitive machine intelligence. Section 1.4 makes the point that genetic programming has delivered a progression of qualitatively more substantial results in synchrony with five approximately order-of-magnitude increases in the expenditure of computer time. Sections 1.5 and 1.6 demonstrate that genetic programming is an automated invention machine for the synthesis of both the topology and sizing of analog electrical circuits. These sections show six examples where genetic programming has synthesized a circuit that duplicates the functionality or infringes a 21st-century patented electrical circuit. Section 1.7 discusses how the techniques used in the previous sections can be enhanced in order to potentially enable genetic programming to deliver more complex results and commercially useful results. Section 1.8 summarizes this chapter.

1.2 Automatic Circuit Synthesis by Means of Genetic Programming

Genetic programming is an extension of the genetic algorithm [14] into the arena of computer programs. Genetic programming starts from a high-level statement of what needs to be done and automatically creates a computer program to solve the problem. Genetic programming uses the Darwinian principle of natural selection and analogs of recombination (crossover), mutation, gene duplication, gene deletion, and certain mechanisms of developmental biology to progressively breed an improved population over many generations [2, 20, 22, 22, 24].

The design process for electrical circuits begins with a high-level description of the circuit's desired behavior and characteristics. The process entails creation of both the topology and the sizing of a satisfactory circuit. The *topology* of a circuit comprises:

- the total number of components in the circuit,
- the type of each component (e.g., resistor, capacitor, transistor) at each location in the circuit,
- a list of all the connections that exist between the leads of the circuit's components, input ports, output ports, power sources, and ground.

The *sizing* of a circuit consists of the component value, if any, associated with each component. The sizing of a component is usually numerical.

Genetic programming was first used to automatically synthesize both the topology and sizing of analog electrical circuits in 1995 [23]. Numerous examples of the automatic synthesis of analog electrical circuits composed of transistors, capacitors, resistors, inductors, and other components are found in [24].

Our approach to the problem of automatically creating both the topology and sizing of an electrical circuit by means of genetic programming involves

- establishing a developmental representation for electrical circuits involving program trees, and
- defining a fitness measure that measures how well the behavior and characteristics of a candidate circuit satisfy high-level design requirements.

During the run of genetic programming, the evaluation of the fitness of each individual in the population involves

- converting each individual program tree in the population into a netlist for an electrical circuit using the developmental process,
- ascertaining the circuits behavior and characteristics, and
- using the circuits behavior and characteristics to calculate a value of fitness.

Electrical circuits are ordinarily represented as labeled graphical structure with cycles (circuit diagrams). However, the program trees ordinarily used in genetic programming are acyclic graphs. Our approach to the automatic synthesis of circuits using genetic programming employs a developmental process to overcome this representational difference.

The developmental process used for automated synthesis of circuits by means of genetic programming transforms a program tree (an acyclic graph) into a fully developed electrical circuit (a graph structure with cycles). This approach is inspired by the principles of developmental biology, the innovative work of [18] on using developmental genetic algorithms to evolve neural networks, and the creative work of [11] on using developmental genetic programming (cellular encoding) to evolve neural networks. For additional background of the use of developmental processes in the context of genetic programming, the reader is also referred to early work on ontogenetic programming by Spector and [35] and on evolving Lindenmayer rules for creating structures [21].

The developmental process used for automated synthesis of circuits by means of genetic programming entails the execution of functions in a circuit-constructing program tree. These functions include component-creating functions, topology-modifying functions, development-controlling functions, arithmetic-performing functions, and automatically defined functions.

The starting point for our developmental process consists of a simple initial circuit. The initial circuit consists of an embryo, and a test fixture. The embryo contains at least one modifiable wire. All development originates from the embryos modifiable wire(s).

An electrical circuit is developed by progressively applying the functions in a circuit-constructing program tree to the modifiable wires of the original embryo and, as the circuit grows, to the modifiable wires and modifiable components that sprout from it. The execution of the functions in the program tree transforms the initial circuit into a fully developed circuit. That is, the functions in the circuit-constructing program tree progressively side-effect the embryo and its successor structures until a fully developed circuit eventually emerges.

A test fixture (external to the entity that is being automatically created) facilitates measurement of the fully developed circuit. The test fixture is a hard-wired structure composed of nonmodifiable wires and nonmodifiable electrical components. The test fixture feeds external input(s) into the circuit that is being evaluated. It also enables the circuits output(s) to be probed. The test fixture supplies the measurements that enable the fitness measure to assign a single numerical value of fitness to the behavior and characteristics of the fully developed circuit.

The functions in the circuit-constructing program trees are divided into five categories:

- component-creating functions that insert components (e.g., resistors, capacitors, transistors) into the developing circuit,

- topology-modifying functions (e.g., series division, parallel division, cut, via to connect two distant points in a circuit, via to connect a point in the circuit to ground, via to connect a point to a power supply, via to connect a point to the incoming signal, via to connect a point to an output port) that modify the topology of the developing circuit,

- development-controlling functions that control the developmental process by which the embryo and its successor structures are converted into a fully developed circuit (e.g., the development-ending function),

- arithmetic-performing functions (e.g., addition, subtraction) that may appear in a value-setting subtree that is an argument to a component-creating function and that specifies the numerical value of the component, and

- automatically defined functions that enable certain substructures to be reused (including parameterized reuse).

The component-creating functions generally have value-setting subtree(s) that establish the value of the component (e.g., the capacitance of a capacitor). Many of the component-creating and topology-modifying functions possess one or more construction-continuing subtrees. The terminals in the circuit-constructing program trees may include

- constant numerical values,
- perturbable numerical values,
- symbolic values (used, for example, to create discrete alternatives for certain components),
- zero-argument functions (e.g., the development-ending function, zero-argument automatically defined functions), and
- externally supplied free variables (used, for example, when a circuit is to be parameterized by an external value).

In the usual implementation of genetic programming, all the individual program trees in the initial random population (generation 0) of the population are syntactically valid executable programs. All the genetic operations used in genetic programming (i.e., crossover, mutation, reproduction, and the architecture-altering operations) operate so as to create syntactically valid executable programs from syntactically valid executable programs. Thus, all the individuals encountered during the run (including, in particular, the best-of-run individual produced upon completion of the run) are necessarily syntactically valid executable programs.

Each circuit-constructing program tree in a run of genetic programming for automatic circuit synthesis is created in accordance with a constrained syntactic structure (strong typing) that imposes grammatical limits on how the available functions and terminals may be combined. For example, a value-setting subtree establishing the numerical value of a capacitor is permitted to appear only as a designated argument of the capacitor-creating function. All the individuals in generation 0 of a run of genetic programming comply with the constrained syntactic structure appropriate for automated circuit synthesis. All the genetic operations that are performed during the run operate so as to preserve the constrained syntactic structure. Thus, all the individuals encountered during the run (including the best-of-run individual) comply with the constrained syntactic structure.

Our developmental approach is more than just a mechanism for mapping an acyclic graph (the circuit-constructing program tree) into a graphical structure with cycles (the fully developed circuit). That is, the developmental approach does far more than just enable us to overcome a representation obstacle.

The developmental process has the advantage of preserving the electrical validity of the circuit. There are no unconnected leads in the initial circuit. Each component-creating, topology-modifying, and development-controlling function operates so as to preserve this connectivity at each stage of the developmental process. The result is that there are no unconnected leads in the fully developed circuit.

To summarize the foregoing points, every developmental step associated with every individual circuit in every generation of the population of a run of genetic programming using our approach is

- syntactically valid,
- executable,
- compliant with required constrained syntactic structure, and
- electrically valid (connected).

The developmental approach has the additional advantage of preserving locality. Most of the component-creating, topology-modifying, and development-controlling functions intentionally operate on a small local area of the circuit. Subtrees within a program tree therefore tend to operate locally. The crossover operation (the main workhorse of genetic programming and genetic algorithms) transplants subtrees. It should be remembered that the premise behind the crossover operation in genetic programming (and the genetic algorithm) is that individuals with relatively high fitness are likely to contain some local substructures which, when recombined, may (at least some of the time) create offspring with even higher fitness. In genetic programming, the conventional crossover operation recombines a subtree from one parents program tree with the second parents program tree. Over many generations, functions and terminals that are close together in a tree program tend to be differentially and preferentially preserved by crossover. In particular, smaller subtrees are preserved to a greater degree than larger ones. Moreover, when circuits are represented by circuit- constructing program trees containing the functions that we use, a subtree tends to represent a local area in the fully developed circuit. Thus, the crossover operation works in conjunction with the developmental process in preserving locality. The mutation operation and architecture-altering operations similarly work in conjunction with the developmental process in preserving locality.

Useful parts of a circuit-constructing program tree can be reused. Real-world circuits are replete with reuse. Reuse eliminates the need to "reinvent the wheel" on each occasion when a particular sequence of steps may be useful. Reuse makes it possible to exploit a problem's modularities, symmetries, and regularities and thereby potentially accelerate the problem- solving process [25].

The efficiency of genetic programming in the domain of automatic circuit synthesis stems from the combined effects of the

- preservation of syntactic validity,
- preservation of executability of the circuit-constructing program trees,
- preservation of constrained syntactic structure,
- preservation of electrical connectivity,

- preservation of locality during crossover (and other operations), and
- the facilitation of reuse.

Early work in the field of evolvable includes [12, 13]. The genetic algorithm has been successfully used to automatically synthesize analog circuits since the mid-1990's [10, 28] and to programming a digital field-programmable gate array to perform analog functions [36–39]. Nonetheless, the genetic algorithm does not usually deliver the above benefits of locality and validity and facilitation of reuse. For example, the ordinary crossover operation in the genetic algorithm rarely preserves syntactic validity when chromosome strings are used to represent complex structures such as electrical circuits. When syntactic validity is not preserved, the user is usually faced with three choices concerning the syntactically invalid offspring:

- deletion,
- penalization, or
- repair.

For complex structures such as circuits, deletion is rarely a practical option because the percentage of syntactically valid offspring after a crossover is so low (in the space of allowable circuits) that virtually every individual would be deleted. For the same reason, penalization has the disadvantage that practically every individual must be penalized. Thus, in practice, repair is the most common way to deal with the initial invalidity of offspring produced by crossover in the genetic algorithm. However, when repair is undertaken, it is no longer true all genetic material in the offspring comes from one or the other parent. To the extent that the crossover almost always dramatically alters the characteristics of the swapped genetic material, it acquires the characteristics of the mutation operation. Because crossover rarely preserves syntactic validity when chromosome strings are used to represent circuits, virtually every crossover operation becomes a mutation operation. This, in turn, means that the problem-solving effectiveness of the crossover operation is reduced to the lesser level that can be delivered by the mutation operation [26].

A second problem arises from the fact that most practical systems in the real world typically contain massive regularity, symmetry, homogeneity, and modularity. For example, non-trivial analog electrical circuits almost always contain multiple occurrences of certain subcircuits (e.g., current mirrors, voltage gain stages, Darlington emitter-follower sections, cascodes, voltage divider subcircuits). At a higher level, analog circuits often also contain multiple occurrences of various more complex entities, such as filters, amplifiers, and phase-locked loops. Similarly, digital circuits almost always contain multiple occurrences of certain standard cells and multiple occurrences of higher-level entities (e.g., counters, registers, multiplexers). The design of large circuits would be considerably more difficult (and perhaps even impractical) if the designer had to separately think through the design of each subcircuit from the first principles of electrical engineering on each occasion when the subcircuit is needed. Reuse enables the designer to solve a particular problem once and, thereafter, simply reuse the solution.

Reuse of a subcircuit can be realized in the context of genetic programming in several different ways. In one type of reuse, the circuit-constructing functions responsible for a useful subcircuit may reside in an automatically defined function (ADF). In this kind of reuse, the automatically defined function resembles a subroutine in an ordinary computer program [19, 20, 22, 27]. Multiple occurrences of the subcircuit result when the automatically defined function is repeatedly invoked. Reuse by means of automatically defined functions is described and illustrated in connection with electrical circuits in chapters 27 and 28 of Genetic Programming III: Darwinian Invention and Problem Solving [24]. The ability of genetic programming to reuse useful substructures is contrasted with the capabilities of the conventional genetic algorithm in this regard in Section 16.2.2 of Genetic Programming IV. Routine human-competitive Machine Intelligence [26].

A second (often overlooked) way by which reuse an be realized is that the ordinary crossover operation in genetic programming may work as a mechanism for reusing a subtree that is responsible for a useful subcircuit. Multiple occurrences of a useful subcircuit may be created when the subtree responsible for the useful subcircuit (being part of a reasonably fit individual) is included in a crossover fragment that the crossover operation inserts into another (reasonably fit) individual that already produces the subcircuit. The ability of the crossover operation in genetic programming to reuse useful substructures in this way is contrasted with the capabilities of the conventional genetic algorithm in this regard in Chapter 16 of [26].

1.3 Genetic Programming Now Routinely Delivers High-Return Human-Competitive Machine Intelligence

We begin by defining what we mean by "human-competitive", "high-return", and "routine".

Human-Competitive. In attempting to evaluate an automated problem-solving method, the question arises as to whether there is any real substance to the demonstrative problems that are published in connection with the method. Demonstrative problems in the fields of artificial intelligence and machine learning are often contrived toy problems that circulate exclusively inside academic groups that study a particular methodology. These problems typically have little relevance to any issues pursued by any scientist or engineer outside the fields of artificial intelligence and machine learning. To make the idea of human-competitiveness concrete, we say that a result is "human-competitive" if it satisfies one or more of eight criteria enumerated in [26]. One of the eight criteria (and the one that is most relevant to this chapter) is

> "The result was patented as an invention in the past, is an improvement over a patented invention, or would qualify today as a patentable new invention."

All of the criteria have the desirable attribute of being at arms-length from the fields of artificial intelligence, machine learning, and genetic programming. That is, a result cannot acquire the rating of "human-competitive" merely because it is considered interesting by researchers *inside* the specialized fields that are attempting to create machine intelligence. Instead, a result produced by an automated method must earn the rating of "human-competitive" *independent* of the fact that it was generated by an automated method.

Based on this definition, there are now 36 instances where genetic programming has produced a human-competitive result. Of these, 21 (Table 1.1) are previously patented inventions of electrical circuits, networks, or controllers. In addition, there are two instances where genetic programming has created a patentable new invention [17]. Also, there are 14 other instances (not shown in Table 1.1 of human-competitive results that are not patent-related.

High-Return. What is delivered by the actual automated operation of an artificial method in comparison to the amount of knowledge, information, analysis, and intelligence that is pre-supplied by the human employing the method?

We define the *AI ratio* (the "artificial-to-intelligence" ratio) of a problem-solving method as the ratio of that which is delivered by the automated operation of the *artificial* method to the amount of *intelligence* that is supplied by the human applying the method to a particular problem.

The AI ratio is especially pertinent to methods for getting computers to automatically solve problems because it measures the value added by the artificial problem-solving method. Manifestly, the aim of the fields of artificial intelligence and machine learning is to generate human-competitive results with a high AI ratio.

Ascertaining the return of a problem-solving method requires measuring the amount of A that is delivered by the method in relation to the amount of I that is supplied by the human user.

Because each of the results in Table 1.1 is a human-competitive result, it is reasonable to say that genetic programming delivered a high amount of A in each case. The question thus arises as to how much I was supplied by the human user in order to produce these 36 results. Answering this question requires the discipline of carefully identifying the amount of analysis, intelligence, information, and knowledge that was supplied by the intelligent human user prior to launching a run of genetic programming. To do this, we make a clear distinction between the problem-specific preparatory steps and the problem- independent executional steps of a run of genetic programming.

The *preparatory steps* are the problem-specific and domain-specific steps that are performed by the human user prior to launching a run of the problem-solving method. The preparatory steps establish the I component of the AI ratio (i.e., the denominator).

The *executional steps* are the problem-independent and domain-independent steps that are automatically executed during a run of the problem-solving method. These steps include the creation of the initial (usually random population) of individuals; the evaluation of fitness of each individual in the population; the selection of individuals from the popula-

Table 1.1. Twenty-one previously patented inventions that have been reinvented by genetic programming

Invention	Date	Inventor	Institution	Patent
Darlington emitter-follower section	1953	Sidney Darlington	Bell Telephone Laboratories	2,663,806
Ladder filter	1917	George Campbell American	Telephone and Telegraph	1,227,113
Crossover filter	1925	Otto Julius Zobel	American Telephone and Telegraph	1,538,964
"*M*-derived half section" filter	1925	Otto Julius Zobel	American Telephone and Telegraph	1,538,964
Cauer (elliptic) topology for filters	1934, 1936	Wilhelm Cauer	University of Gottingen	1,958,742, 1,989,545
Sorting network	1962	Daniel G. O'Connor and Raymond J. Nelson	General Precision, Inc.	3,029,413
Computational circuits	NA	Numerous	Numerous	Numerous
Electronic thermometer	NA	Numerous	Numerous	Numerous
Voltage reference circuit	NA	Numerous	Numerous	Numerous
60 dB and 96 dB amplifiers	NA	Numerous	Numerous	Numerous
Second-derivative controller	1942	Harry Jones	Brown Instrument Company	2,282,726
Philbrick circuit	1956	George Philbrick	George A. Philbrick Researches	2,730,679
NAND circuit	1971	David H. Chung and Bill H. Terrell	Texas Instruments Incorporated	3,560,760
PID (proportional, integrative, and derivative) controller	1939	Albert Callender and Allan Stevenson	Imperial Chemical Limited	2,175,985
Negative feedback	1937	Harold S. Black	American Telephone and Telegraph	2,102,671
Low-voltage balun circuit	2001	Sang Gug Lee	Information and Communications University	6,265,908
Mixed analog-digital variable capacitor circuit	2000	Turgut Sefket Aytur	Lucent Technologies Inc.	6,013,958
High-current load circuit	2001	Timothy Daun-Lindberg and Michael Miller	International Business Machines Corporation	6,211,726
Voltage-current conversion circuit	2000	Akira Ikeuchi and Naoshi Tokuda	Mitsumi Electric Co., Ltd.	6,166,529
Cubic function generator	2000	Stefano Cipriani and Anthony A. Takeshian	Conexant Systems, Inc.	6,160,427
Tunable integrated active filter	2001	Robert Irvine and Bernd Kolb	Infineon Technologies AG	6,225,859

tion on the basis of fitness to participate in the genetic operations (i.e., crossover, mutation, reproduction, and the architecture-altering operations); and the iteration of the steps of fitness evaluations, selection, and application of the genetic operations. The results produced by the executional steps provide the *A* component of the AI ratio (i.e., the numerator).

The five major preparatory steps for genetic programming require the human user to specify

1. the set of terminals (e.g., the independent variables of the problem, zero-argument functions, and random constants) for each branch of the to-be-evolved computer program,

2. the set of primitive functions for each branch of the to-be-evolved computer program,

3. the fitness measure (for explicitly or implicitly measuring the fitness of candidate individuals in the population),

4. various parameters for controlling the run, and

5. a termination criterion and method for designating the result of the run.

The amount of *I* required to use genetic programming to solve a problem of circuit synthesis is contained in the primitive ingredients of the to-be-created computer program (the first and second preparatory steps), the problems fitness measure (the third preparatory step containing the high-level statement of what needs to be done), and the runs control parameters and termination procedures (the fourth and fifth preparatory steps).

We identified the functions and terminals required for any problem of circuit synthesis in the previous section. We identify the fitness measure for six illustrative problems later in this chapter. Thus, it is reasonable to say that, in practice, only a de *minimus* amount of knowledge, information, analysis, and intelligence is pre-supplied by the human employing genetic programming for a problem of circuit synthesis. In any event, the amount of *I* required by genetic programming is certainly not greater than that required by any other method of artificial intelligence and machine learning of which we are aware. Indeed, we know of no other problem-solving method (automated or human) that does not start with primitive elements of some kind, does not incorporate some method for specifying what needs to be done to guide the methods operation, does not employ administrative parameters of some kind, and does not contain a termination criterion of some kind.

In view of the high amount of *A* in the numerator and the small amount of *I* in the denominator, we can see that the AI ratio is high for the results in Table 1.1 produced by genetic programming.

Routine. Generality is a precondition to what we mean when we say that an automated problem-solving method is "routine." Once the generality of a method is established, "routineness" means that relatively little human effort is required to get the method to successfully handle new problems within a particular domain and to successfully handle new problems from a different domain. The ease of making the transition to new problems lies at the heart of what we mean by "routine."

The vast majority of present-day electrical circuits on silicon chips are composed of transistors, capacitors, and resistors. Once these primitive ingredients are identified, new problems of circuit synthesis can be handled merely by changing the fitness measure. Thus, after solving one problem of automatically synthesizing both the topology and tuning of a circuit, the transition to each new problem of circuit synthesis involves providing genetic programming with a different specification of what needs to be done—that is, a different fitness measure. Relatively little effort is required to make an intra-domain transition among problems of analog circuit synthesis.

Similarly, virtually all controllers are built from the same primitive ingredients (e.g., integrators, differentiators, gains, adders, subtractors, and signals representing the plant output and the reference signal). Once these primitive ingredients are identified, new problems of controller synthesis can be handled merely by changing the statement of what needs to be done. Thus, after solving one problem of automatically synthesizing both the topology and tuning of a controller (say, the controller patented by Callender and Stevenson in 1939 shown in Table 1.1), the transition to each new problem of controller synthesis (say, the controller patented by Jones in 1942 in Table 1.1) involves providing genetic programming with a different fitness measure. That is, relatively little effort is required to make an intra-domain transition among problems of controller synthesis.

In making the inter-domain transition from problems of automatic synthesis of controllers to problems of automatic synthesis of analog electrical circuits, the primitive ingredients change from integrators, differentiators, gains, and the like to transistors, resistors, capacitors, and the like. In addition, the fitness measure changes from one that minimizes a controller's integral of time-weighted absolute error, minimizes overshoot, and maximizes disturbance rejection to one that is based on the analog circuits amplification, suppression or passage of a signal, elimination of distortion, and the like. That is, relatively little effort is required to make an inter-domain transition.

For these reasons, we say that genetic programming now routinely delivers high-return human-competitive machine intelligence.

1.4 Progression of Qualitatively More Substantial Results Produced in Synchrony with Increasing Computer Power

Numerous questions naturally arise in connection with any proposed approach to machine intelligence (including, specifically, genetic programming).

- Is the method formulated with sufficient precision to enable it to be implemented (or is it vagueware)?
- Has the method been successfully demonstrated on a specific single problem (or is it promiseware)?
    - Was the method applied to a difficult demonstrative problem (or is it toyware)?

  - Did the method top out after succeeding on a single demonstrative problem?

- Has the method solved multiple problems (or is it soloware)?
  - Are the multiple problems difficult?
  - Did the method top out at this stage?

- Has the method solved problems from multiple domains (or is it nicheware)?
  - Are the domains difficult?
  - Did the method top out at this stage?

- Were the results human-competitive?

- Can the method profitably take advantage of the increased computational power available by means of parallel processing (or is it serialware)?

- Or, is the method Mooreware—able to take advantage of the exponentially increasing computational power made available by the relentless iteration of Moore's law?

Genetic Programming: On the Programming of Computers by Means of Natural Selection [20] demonstrated that genetic programming is not vagueware, promiseware, soloware, or nicheware. The numerous human-competitive results produced by genetic programming (Table 1.1) dispose the issue of whether genetic programming is toyware. The last two questions in the above list address the issue of the future potential of a proposed approach (including, specifically, genetic programming).

Table 1.2 lists the five computer systems used to produce our group's reported work on genetic programming in the 15-year period between 1987 and 2002. Column 3 of this table shows the duration in petacycles (1015cycles) per day for system. Speed-up1 is over previous row while speed-up2 is over first system in this table. The system was used for work reported in the given reference (column 6 of the table). Column 7 shows the number of human-competitive results generated by each computer system.

The first entry in Table 1.2 is a serial computer. The four subsequent entries are parallel computer systems. The presence of four increasingly powerful parallel computer systems in the table reflects the fact that genetic programming has successfully taken advantage of the increased computational power available by means of parallel processing (thereby avoiding a pitfall that often constrains other proposed approaches to machine intelligence). The increasing number of human-competitive results in Table 1.2 reflect the increasing computational power. Table 1.2 shows the following:

- There is an order-of-magnitude speed-up (column 4) between each successive computer system in the table. Note that, according to Moore's law, exponential increases in computer power correspond approximately to constant periods of time.

- There is a 13,900-to-1 speed-up (column 5) between the fastest and most recent machine (the 1,000-node parallel computer system) and the slowest and earliest computer system in the table (the serial LISP machine).

Table 1.2. Human-competitive results produced by genetic programming with five computer systems

System	Period	Peta-cycles	Speed-up1	Speed-up2	Reference	Results
Serial Texas Instruments LISP machine	1987–1994	0.00216	1(base)	1(base)	*Genetic Programming I*, *Genetic Programming II*	0
64-node Transtech transputer parallel machine	1994–1997	0.02	9	9	A few problems in *Genetic Programming III*	2
64-node Parsytec parallel machine	1995–2000	0.44	22	204	Most problems in *Genetic Programming III*	12
70-node Alpha parallel machine	1999–2001	3.2	7.3	1,481	A minority (8) of problems in *Genetic Programming IV*	2
1,000-node Pentium II parallel machine	2000–2002	30.0	9.4	13,900	A majority (28) of the problems in *Genetic Programming IV*	12

- The slower early machines generated few or no human-competitive results, whereas the faster more recent machines have generated numerous human-competitive results.

Four successive order-of-magnitude increases in computer power are explicitly shown in Table 1.2. An additional order-of-magnitude increase was achieved by making extraordinarily long runs on the largest machine in the table (the 1,000-node Pentium ®II parallel machine). The length of the run that produced a genetically evolved patentable controller [17] was 28.8 days - almost an order-of-magnitude increase (9.3 times) over the 3.4-day average for most other runs that our group has made in recent years. If this final 9.3-to-1 increase is counted as an additional speed-up, the overall speed-up between the first and last entries in the table is 130,660-to-1.

Table 1.3 presents the five just-explained order-of-magnitude increases in the expenditure of computing power. Column 4 of this table characterizes the qualitative nature of the results produced by genetic programming. The table shows the progression of qualitatively more substantial results produced by genetic programming in terms of five order-of-magnitude increases in the expenditure of computational resources. Note that the speed-up is over the previous row.

The order-of-magnitude increases in computer power shown in Table 1.3 correspond closely (albeit not perfectly) with the following progression of qualitatively more substantial results produced by genetic programming:

- toy problems,
- human-competitive results not related to patented inventions,
- 20th-century patented inventions,
- 21st-century patented inventions (described later in this chapter), and

Table 1.3. Progression of qualitatively more substantial results

System	Period	Speed-up	Qualitative nature of the results produced by genetic programming
Serial Texas Instruments LISP machine	1987–1994	1 (base)	• Toy problems of the 1980s and early 1990s from the fields of artificial intelligence and machine learning
64-node Transtech transputer parallel machine	1994–1997	9	• Two human-competitive results involving one-dimensional discrete data (not patent-related)
64-node Parsytec parallel machine	1995–2000	22	• One human-competitive result involving two-dimensional discrete data • Numerous human-competitive results involving continuous signals analyzed in the frequency domain • Numerous human-competitive results involving 20th-century patented inventions
70-node Alpha parallel machine	1999–2001	7.3	• One human-competitive result involving continuous signals analyzed in the time domain • Circuit synthesis extended from topology and sizing to include routing and placement (layout)
1,000-node Pentium II parallel machine	2000–2002	9.4	• Numerous human-competitive results involving continuous signals analyzed in the time domain • Numerous general solutions to problems in the form of parameterized topologies • Six human-competitive results duplicating the functionality of 21st-century patented inventions
Long (4-week) runs of 1,000-node Pentium II parallel machine	2002	9.3	• Generation of two patentable new inventions

- patentable new inventions.

This progression demonstrates that genetic programming is able to take advantage of the exponentially increasing computational power made available by iterations of Moore's law.

1.5 DESCRIPTION OF SIX 21st-CENTURY PATENTED CIRCUITS

There are now 21 instances where genetic programming has duplicated the functionality of a previously patented invention (including infringing a previously issued patent). Specifically, there are 15 instances where genetic programming has created an entity that either infringes or duplicates the functionality of a previously patented 20th-century invention and six instances where genetic programming has done the same with respect to a previously patented 21st-century invention.

To make the foregoing points concrete, this section presents the six post-2000 instances where genetic programming automatically created both the topology (graphical structure) and sizing (numerical component values) for patented analog electrical circuits composed of transistors, capacitors, and resistors. The six inventions are the six inventions in Table 1.1 that are dated 2000 or 2001. In each instance, genetic programming started from a high-level statement of a circuit's desired behavior and characteristics (e.g., its desired output given its input). In producing results, genetic programming used only de minimus knowledge about analog circuits. Specifically, genetic programming employed a circuit simulator (e.g., SPICE) for the *analysis* of candidate circuits, but did not use any deep knowledge or expertise about the *synthesis* of circuits.

The function and terminal sets for all six problems (described below) permit the construction of any circuit composed of transistors, resistors, and capacitors.

The main difference among the runs of genetic programming for the six problems is that we supplied a different fitness measure for each problem. Construction of a fitness measure requires translating the problem's high-level requirements into a precise computation. We read the patent document to find the performance that the invention was supposed to achieve. We then created a fitness measure reflecting the invention's performance and characteristics. The fitness measure specifies the time-domain output value(s) that is desired given various time-domain input value(s). For each problem, a test fixture consisting of certain fixed components (such as a source resistor, a load resistor) is connected to the desired input port(s) and the desired output port(s). Circuits may be simulated using a simulator such as SPICE [31].

We supplied models for transistors appropriate to the problem. We used the commercially common 2N3904 (*npn*) and 2N3906 (*pnp*) transistor models unless the patent document called for a different model. We used 5-Volt power supplies unless the patent specified otherwise.

The control parameters and termination criterion were the same for all six problems, except that we used different population sizes to approximately equalize each runs elapsed time per generation. We now describe the six fitness measures.

Low-Voltage Balun Circuit. The purpose of a balun (balance/unbalance) circuit is to produce two outputs from a single input, each output having half the amplitude of the input, one output being in phase with the input while the other is 180 degrees out of phase with the input, with both outputs having the same DC offset. The patented balun circuit uses a power supply of only 1 Volt. The fitness measure consisted of *(i)* a frequency sweep analysis designed to ensure the correct magnitude and phase at the two outputs of the circuit and *(ii)* a Fourier analysis designed to penalize harmonic distortion.

Mixed Analog-Digital Register-Controlled Variable Capacitor. This mixed analog-digital circuit has a capacitance that is controlled by the value stored in a digital register. The fitness measure for this problem employed 16 time-domain fitness cases. The 16 fitness cases ranged over all eight possible values of a 3-bit digital register for two different analog input signals.

Voltage-Current Conversion Circuit. The purpose of the voltage-current conversion circuit is to take two voltages as input and to produce a stable current whose magnitude is proportional to the difference of the voltages. We employed four time-domain input signals (fitness cases) in the fitness measure. We included a time-varying voltage source beneath the output probe point to ensure that the output current produced by the circuit was stable with respect to any subsequent circuitry to which the output of the circuit might be attached.

High-Current Load Circuit. The patent for the high-current load circuit covers a circuit designed to sink a time-varying amount of current in response to a control signal. The patented circuit employs a number of FET transistors arranged in parallel, each of which sinks a small amount of the desired current. The fitness measure for this problem consisted of two time-domain simulations, each representing a different control signal.

Low-Voltage Cubic Signal Generator. The patent for the low-voltage cubic signal generator covers an analog computational circuit that produces the cube of an input signal as its output. The circuit is *compact* in that it contains a voltage drop across no more than two transistors. The fitness measure for this problem consisted of four time-domain fitness cases using various input signals and time scales. The compactness constraint was enforced by providing only a 2-Volt power supply.

Tunable Integrated Active Filter. The patent for the tunable active filter covers a tunable integrated active filter that performs the function of a lowpass filter whose passband boundary is dynamically specified by a control signal. The circuit has two inputs: a to-be-filtered incoming signal and a control signal. The fitness measure for this problem consisted of a performance penalty and a parsimony penalty. The passband boundary, f, ranges over nine values between 441 and 4,414 Hz. The performance penalty is a weighted sum, over 61 frequencies for each of the nine values of f, of the absolute weighted deviation between

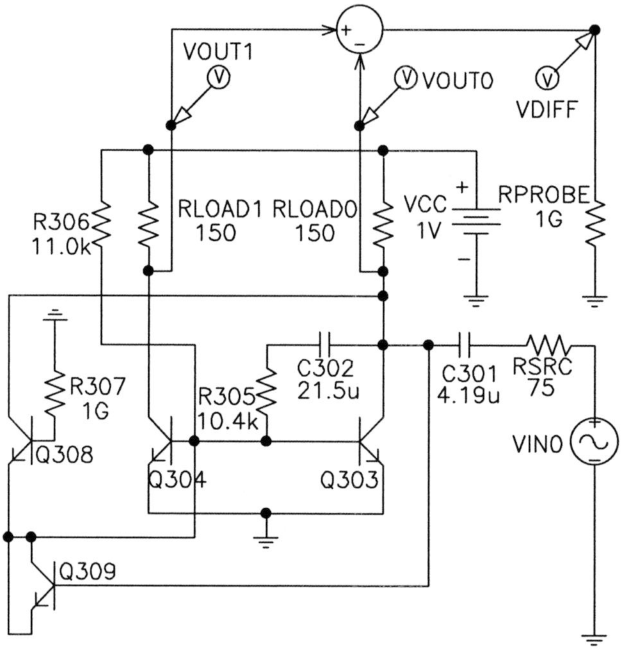

Figure 1.1. Best-of-run balun circuit

the output of the individual candidate circuit at its probe point and the target output. The parsimony penalty is equal to the number of components in the circuit.

Additional details on these six problems can be found in [26].

1.6 RESULTS FOR SIX 21st-CENTURY PATENTED CIRCUITS

Low-Voltage Balun Circuit. Genetic programming automatically created the circuit shown in Figure 1.1. This best-of-run evolved circuit was produced in generation 97 and has a fitness of 0.429. The patented circuit has a fitness of 1.72. That is, the evolved circuit is roughly a fourfold improvement (less being better) over the patented circuit in terms of our fitness measure. In addition, the evolved circuit is superior to the patented circuit both in terms of its frequency response and its harmonic distortion.

In the patent documents, [30] shows a previously known conventional (prior art) balun circuit. This previously known circuit is shown as Figure 1.2 of this chapter.

Lee's patented low-voltage balun circuit is shown in Figure 1.3 of this chapter. Lee in [30] states that the essential difference between the prior art and his invention is a coupling capacitor C_2 located between the base and the collector of the transistor Q_2. Lee explains the essence of his invention as follows:

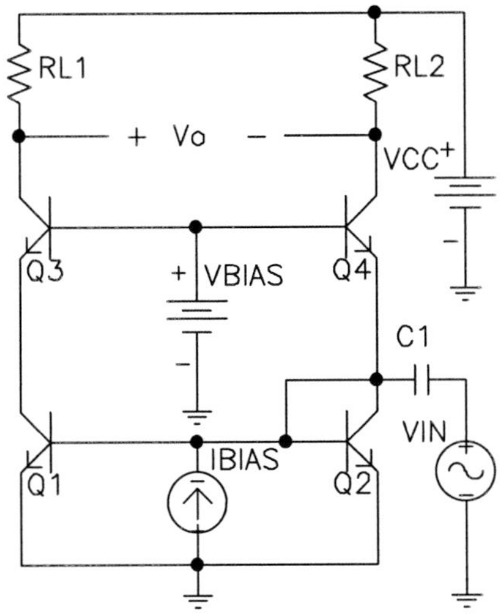

Figure 1.2. Prior art balun circuit shown in U.S. patent 6,265,908

> "The structure of the inventive balun circuit shown in [Figure 1.3 of this chapter] is identical to that of [Figure 1.2 of this chapter] except that a capacitor C^2 are further provided thereto. The capacitor C_2 is a coupling capacitor disposed between the base and the collector of the transistor Q_2 and serves to block DC components which may be fed to the base of the transistor Q_2 from the collector of the transistor Q_2."

As can be seen, the best-of-run genetically evolved circuit (Figure 1.1 possesses the very feature that Lee identifies as the essence of his invention, namely the coupling capacitor called C_{302} in Figure 1.1 and called C_2 in Figure 1.3.

The genetically evolved circuit also reads on three additional elements of claim 1 of Lee's 2001 patent. However, the genetically evolved circuit achieves the circuit's remaining functionality in a manner different from that specified by the remaining elements of Lee's patent. Thus, although the evolved circuit captures the essence of Lee's invention and many of the secondary features of Lee's circuit, the evolved circuit does not infringe Lee's patent. This suggests that genetic programming can be used to create new inventions as well as to engineer around existing patents.

Mixed Analog-Digital Register-Controlled Variable Capacitor. Over our 16 fitness cases, the patented circuit has an average error of 0.803 millivolts. In generation 95, a circuit emerged with average error of 0.808 millivolts, or approximately 100.6% of the average error of the patented circuit. During the course of this run, we harvested the smallest individuals produced on each processing node with a certain maximum level of error. Examination of these harvested individuals revealed a circuit from generation 98 Figure 1.4

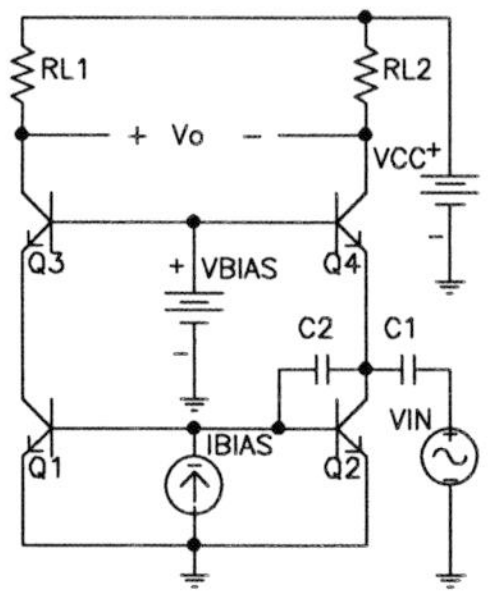

Figure 1.3. Lee's low voltage balun circuit shown in patent 6,265,908

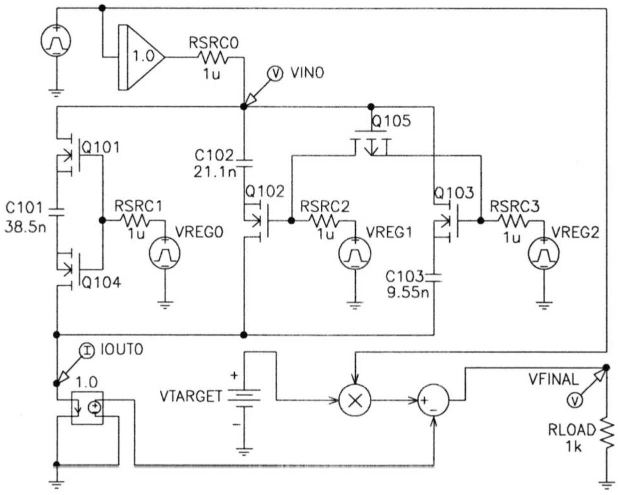

Figure 1.4. Evolved compliant register-controlled capacitor circuit

that approximately matches the topology of the patented circuit (without infringing). The genetically evolved circuit reads on all but one of the elements of claim 1 of the patented circuit (and hence does not infringe the patent).

Voltage-Current Conversion Circuit. A circuit emerged on generation 109 of our run of this problem with a fitness of 0.619 (so that the evolved circuit has about 62% of the average weighted error of the patented circuit). The evolved circuit was subsequently tested on unseen fitness cases that were not part of the fitness measure and outperformed the patented circuit on these new fitness cases. The best-of-run circuit solves the problem in a different manner than the patented circuit.

High-Current Load Circuit. On generation 114, a circuit emerged that duplicated Daun-Lindberg and Miller's [6] parallel FET transistor structure. This circuit has a fitness (weighted error) of 1.82 (so that the evolved circuit has about 182% of the weighted error of the patented circuit).

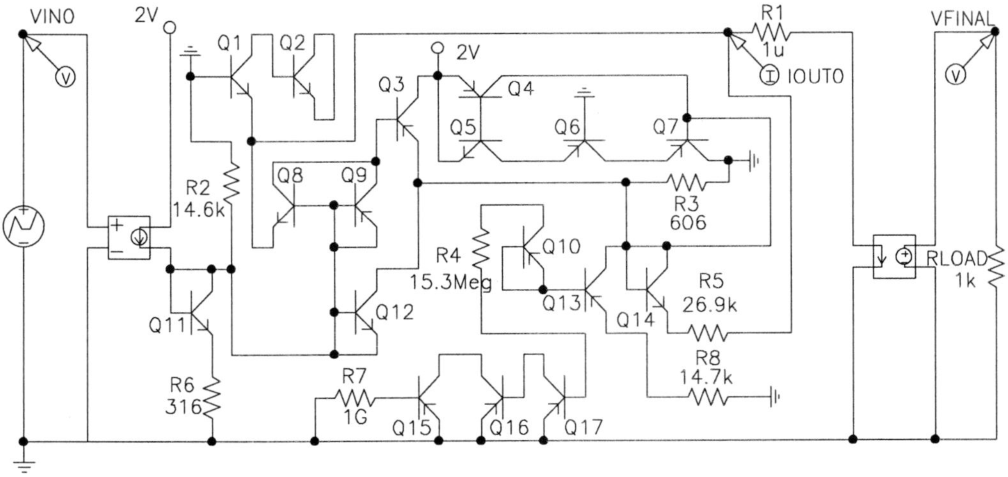

Figure 1.5. Best-of-run cubic signal generation circuit

The genetically evolved circuit shares the following features found in claim 1 of U.S. patent 6,211,726:

> "A variable, high-current, low-voltage, load circuit for testing a voltage source, comprising: . . ."

> "a plurality of high-current transistors having source-to-drain paths connected in parallel between a pair of terminals and a test load."

However, the remaining elements of claim 1 in U.S. patent 6,211,726 are very specific and the genetically evolved circuit does not read on these remaining elements. In fact, the remaining elements of the genetically evolved circuit bear hardly any resemblance to the patented circuit. In this instance, genetic programming produced a circuit that duplicates the functionality of the patented circuit using a different structure.

Low-Voltage Cubic Signal Generator. The best-of-run evolved circuit (Figure 1.5) was produced in generation 182 and has an average error of 4.02 millivolts. The patented circuit had an average error of 6.76 millivolts. That is, the evolved circuit has approximately 59% of the error of the patented circuit over our four fitness cases.

The claims in U.S. patent 6,160,427 amount to a very specific description of the patented circuit. The genetically evolved circuit does not read on these claims and, in fact, bears hardly any resemblance to the patented circuit. In this instance, genetic programming produced a circuit that duplicates the functionality of the patented circuit and does so using a very different structure.

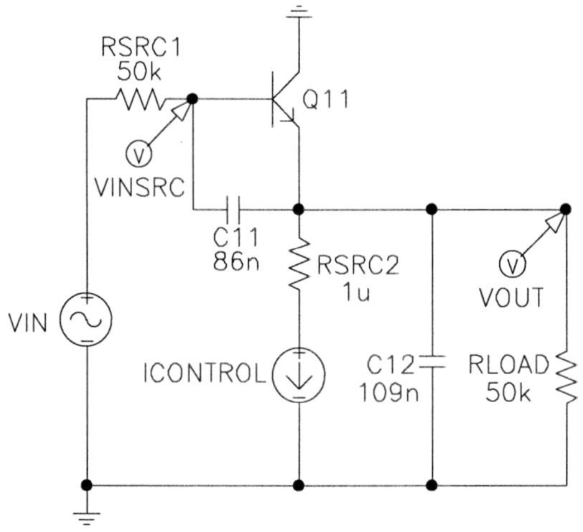

Figure 1.6. Best-of-run circuit for the tunable integrated active filter

Tunable Integrated Active Filter. Averaged over the nine values of frequency, the best-of-run circuit from generation 50 (Figure 1.6) has 72.7 millivolts average absolute error for frequencies in the passband and 0.39 dB average absolute error for other frequencies.

The best-of-run genetically evolved circuit reads on every element of claim 1 of U.S. patent 6,225,859 and therefore infringes the patent.

Table 1.4 summarizes the results for the six problems involving the post-2000 patented inventions in terms of their novelty.

1.7 Commercial Practicality of Genetic Programming for Automated Circuit Synthesis

The previous section demonstrated that genetic programming can automatically synthesize analog circuits that duplicate the functionality of six circuits that were patented after January 1, 2000.

Table 1.5 tallies the computer time consumed by the 11 runs of the six post-2000 patented circuits. Column 2 of this table shows the product of the total population size, M, and the number of generations $i+1$ run before the best-of-run individual was encountered. Column 3 shows the length of the run in hours.

As can be seen from Table 1.5, the average number of hours for runs involving each of the six post-2000 patented circuits is 25, 88, 99, 83, 170, and 14, respectively. The average of these averages is 80 hours (3.3 days). (We use the average of the averages here because we happened to make four runs of the problem that took the least computer time).

All six problems were run on a home-built parallel computer system consisting of 1,000 350-MHz Pentium II processors (appearing as the last row of Table 1.2). This system operates at an overall rate of 3.5×10^{11} Hz. A 3.3-day (80-hour) run represents about 1017 cycles (i.e., 100 petacycles).

Table 1.4. Summary of the six post-2000 patented inventions

Problem	Result
Low-voltage balun circuit	The evolved circuit captures the essence of the previously patented circuit and many of its secondary features, but does not infringe the existing patent.
Mixed analog-digital variable capacitor	The evolved circuit reads on all but one of the elements of claim 1 of the patented circuit, but does not infringe the existing patent.
Voltage-current conversion circuit	The evolved circuit duplicates the functionality of the patented circuit, but in an entirely different way.
High-current load circuit	The evolved circuit duplicates the functionality of the patented circuit, but in an entirely different way.
Cubic function generator	The evolved circuit duplicates the functionality of the patented circuit, but in an entirely different way.
Tunable integrated active filter	The evolved circuit is an infringing duplicate of the previously patented circuit.

Table 1.5. Computer time consumed by 11 runs of the six post-2000 patented inventions

Run	$M*(i+1)$	Hours
Low-voltage balun circuit	490,000,000	25
Mixed analog-digital variable capacitor	198,000,000	88
High-current load circuit–1st run	230,000,000	134
High-current load circuit–2nd run	432,000,000	67
Voltage-current conversion circuit	550,000,000	83
Cubic function generator–1st run	915,000,000	206
Cubic function generator–2nd run	654,000,000	135
Tunable integrated active filter–1st run	142,000,000	23
Tunable integrated active filter–2nd run	102,000,000	14
Tunable integrated active filter–3rd run	78,000,000	12
Tunable integrated active filter–4th run	56,000,000	6

The relentless iteration of Moore's law promises increased availability of computational resources in future years. If available computer capacity continues to double approximately every 18 months over the next decade, a computation requiring 80 hours will require only about 1% as much computer time (i.e., about 48 minutes) a decade from now.

Aside from the promise of increased availability of computational resources in the future, there are two reasons why we are currently not near the boundary of the current capability of genetic programming to automatically synthesize analog circuits.

One reason is that multiple runs of a probabilistic algorithm are often necessary to solve a problem. However, all 11 runs involving the six post-2000 patented circuits (ignoring partial runs used for debugging purposes) produced a satisfactory solution. This success rate of 100% is unusual with a probabilistic algorithm. This high rate, over six problems involving 21st-century patented inventions, suggests that we are currently not near the boundary of the current capability of genetic programming.

A second reason is the (intentional) uniformity (and hence inefficiency) of our runs of the six problems involving 21st-century patented circuits. In approaching the six problems, our goal was to use as little problem-specific human-supplied knowledge, information, analysis, and intelligence as possible. This "clean hands" orientation is, of course, entirely irrelevant to a practicing engineer interested in the commercial practicality of automatic circuit synthesis.

The authors believe that runs of genetic programming for problems of analog circuit synthesis problems can be accelerated in the following ways.

First, many pieces of elementary knowledge helpful to the construction of useful circuits were not made available to the runs of the six problems involving 21st-century patented circuits. For example, the initial population of individuals in a run of genetic programming is typically created at random. As the run proceeds, new individuals are created by probabilistic problem-independent operations (e.g., crossover, mutation). Consequently, many individuals in the population (although syntactically correct) represent unrealistic or impractical electrical circuits. One particularly egregious characteristic of the circuits that appear in unrestricted runs of genetic programming is that the circuit draws preposterously large amounts of current. To cull circuits of this type from the population, each circuit in the population can be examined for the current drawn by the circuit's positive power supply and negative power supply. If the current exceeds a certain generous maximum (e.g., an absolute value of 250 milliamperes), the circuit is penalized (or perhaps eliminated).

Second, a threshold requirement for a functioning circuit is that the circuit connect to all input signals, all output signals, and all necessary sources of power (e.g., the positive power supply and the negative power supply). A circuit can be tested for this characteristic by first randomly choosing one occurrence of the INPUT0 function (i.e., the topology- modifying function that make a connection to input port 0). If the circuit has no occurrence of this function, it receives a high penalty value of fitness that effectively eliminates it. If there is at least one occurrence of this function, a graph traversal is made of the circuit. If there is not at least one reachable occurrence of every other INPUT function, OUTPUT function, and power supply, the circuit receives a high penalty value of fitness.

Third, the components that are inserted into a developing circuit need not be as primitive as a single transistor, a single resistor, or a single capacitor. Instead, the set of component-creating functions can be expanded to include numerous frequently-occurring, known-useful combinations of components. Examples include current mirrors, voltage gain stages, Darlington emitter-follower sections, cascodes, three-ported voltage divider subcircuits composed of two resistors in series, and three-ported subcircuits consisting of two resistors (or capacitors) with their common point connected to power or ground. In this vein the authors of [9] have proposed a promising set of frequently occurring combinations of transistors that are known to be useful in analog circuitry. For certain problems, the set of primitives can also be expanded to include higher-level entities, such as filters, op amps, oscillators, voltage-controller current sources, multipliers, and phase-locked loops.

Fourth, although the runs of the six post-2000 patented circuits were intentionally done in a uniform way, a practicing engineer has no reason to enforce such uniformity. For example, we did not use automatically defined functions (subroutines) for any of the six problems involving post-2000 patented circuits. However, most practical electrical circuits are replete with reuse. A practicing engineer would recognize that reuse is particularly relevant in at least two of the six problems (namely the mixed analog-digital integrated circuit for variable capacitance and the low-voltage high-current transistor circuit for testing a voltage source). The practicing engineer would have no reason to forgo the manifest benefits of reuse and automatically defined functions. Automatically defined functions are described in [19,20,22,27].

Fifth, considerable work has been done in recent years to accelerate the convergence characteristics of circuit simulators. There are numerous commercially available simulators that are considerably more efficient than the simulator used for the runs of the six problems here. We used a version of the SPICE3 simulator [31] that we modified in various ways (as described in [24]. Speedups of up to 10-to-1 are reportedly possible today.

Sixth, there are numerous opportunities to incorporate problem-specific knowledge into a run of genetic programming. For example, the developmental process need not start merely with modifiable wires. A substructure of known utility for a particular problem can be hard-wired into the embryo, thereby relieving genetic programming of the need to reinvent it. For example, the search for a high-performance amplifier might begin with an embryo containing a balanced voltage gain stage or a differential pair (along with more modifiable wires) as the starting point (as opposed to merely a single modifiable wire).

Seventh, it is possible to integrate general knowledge of electrical engineering into a run of genetic programming. For example, Sripramong and Toumazou (2002) combine current-flow analysis into runs of genetic programming for the purpose of automatically synthesizing CMOS amplifiers.

Eighth, the authors believe that the efficiency of runs of genetic programming can, in general, be improved by adapting several of the principles set forth in *The Design of Innovation: Lessons from and for Competent Genetic Algorithms* [8] to the domain of genetic programming.

Ninth, because there usually are multiple competing elements in the fitness measures of most practical problems of circuit synthesis, the authors believe that the efficiency of runs of genetic programming can be improved by using some of the recently published new techniques of multiobjective optimization [5, 7, 40].

Tenth, the authors believe that the efficiency of runs can be improved by adapting some of the innovative ideas in *Efficient and Accurate Parallel Genetic Algorithms* [3] to the domain of genetic programming.

Eleventh, there has been an outpouring of theoretical work in the past few years on the theory of genetic algorithms and genetic programming. In particular, the authors believe that many of the insights in *Foundations of Genetic Programming* [29] can be used to improve the efficiency of runs of genetic programming.

Looking forward, we believe that genetic programming will be increasingly used to automatically generate ever-more complex human-competitive results.

1.8 SUMMARY

As far as we know, genetic programming is, at the present time, unique among methods of artificial intelligence and machine learning in terms of its duplication of numerous previously patented results, unique in its generation of patentable new results, unique in the breadth and depth of problems solved, unique in its delivery of routine high-return, human-competitive evolvable hardware.

Bibliography

[1] Aytur and Turgut Sefket, *Integrated Circuit with Variable Capacitor*. U. S. patent 6,013,958. Filed July 23, 1998. Issued January 11, 2000.

[2] Banzhaf, Wolfgang, Nordin, Peter, Keller, Robert E., and Francone, Frank D., *Genetic ProgrammingAn Introduction*. San Francisco, CA: Morgan Kaufmann and Heidelberg: dpunkt, 1998.

[3] Cantu-Paz, Erick., *Efficient and Accurate Parallel Genetic Algorithms*. Boston: Kluwer Academic Publishers, 2000.

[4] Cipriani, Stefano and Takeshian, Anthony A., *Compact cubic function generator*. U. S. patent 6,160,427. Filed September 4, 1998, Issued December 12, 2000.

[5] Coello Coello, Carlos A., Van Veldhuizen, David A., and Lamont, Gary B., *Evolutionary Algorithms for Solving Multi-Objective Problems*. Boston: Kluwer Academic Publishers, 2002.

[6] Daun-Lindberg, Timothy Charles and Miller; Michael Lee., *Low Voltage High-Current Electronic Load*. U. S. patent 6,211,726. Filed June 28, 1999, Issued April 3, 2001.

[7] Deb, Kalyanmoy, *Multi-Objective Optimization using Evolutionary Algorithms*. Boston: Kluwer Academic Publishers, 2001.

[8] Goldberg, David E., *The Design of Innovation: Lessons from and for Competent Genetic Algorithms*. Boston: Kluwer Academic Publishers, 2002.

[9] Graeb, Helmut E., Zizala, S., Eckmueller, J., and Antreich, K., The sizing rules method for analog circuit design. *Proceedings of the IEEE/ACM International Conference on Computer Aided Design*. Piscataway, NJ: IEEE Press. Pages 343349, 2001.

[10] Grimbleby, J. B., Automatic analogue network synthesis using genetic algorithms. *Proceedings of the First International Conference on Genetic Algorithms in Engineering Systems: Innovations and Applications (GALESIA)*. London: Institution of Electrical Engineers. Pages 5358, 1995.

[11] Gruau, Frederic., Genetic synthesis of Boolean neural networks with a cell rewriting developmental process. In Schaffer, J. D. and Whitley, Darrell (editors). *Proceedings of the Workshop on Combinations of Genetic Algorithms and Neural Networks 1992. Los Alamitos*, CA: The IEEE Computer Society Press, 1992.

[12] Higuchi, Tetsuya, Niwa, Tatsuya, Tanaka, Toshio, Iba, Hitoshi, de Garis, Hugo, and Furuya, Tatsumi., Evolving hardware with genetic learning: A first step towards building a Darwin machine. In Meyer, Jean-Arcady, Roitblat, Herbert L. and Wilson, Stewart W. (editors). From Animals to Animats 2: *Proceedings of the Second International Conference on Simulation of Adaptive Behavior*. Cambridge, MA: The MIT Press. 1993. Pages 417424, 1993.

[13] Higuchi, Tetsuya, Niwa, Tatsuya, Tanaka, Toshio, Iba, Hitoshi, de Garis, Hugo, and Furuya, Tatsumi., Evolvable HardwareGenetic-Based Generation of Electric Circuitry at Gate and Hardware Description Language (HDL) Levels. *Electrotechnical Laboratory technical report 93-4*. Tsukuba, Japan: Electrotechnical Laboratory, 1993.

[14] Holland, John H., *Adaptation in Natural and Artificial Systems*. Ann Arbor, MI: University of Michigan Press, 1975.

[15] Ikeuchi, Akira and Tokuda, Naoshi., *Voltage-Current Conversion Circuit*. U. S. patent 6,166,529. Filed February 24, 2000 in U. S. Issued December 26, 2000 in U. S. Filed March 10, 1999 in Japan.

[16] Irvine, Robert and Kolb, Bernd., *Integrated Low-Pass Filter*. U.S. patent 6,225,859. Filed September 14, 1998. Issucd May 1, 2001.

[17] Keane, Martin A., Koza, John R., and Streeter, Matthew J., Automatic synthesis using genetic programming of an improved general-purpose controller for industrially representative plants. In Stoica, Adrian, Lohn, Jason, Katz, Rich, Keymeulen, Didier, and Zebulum, Ricardo (editors) 2002. *Proceedings of NASA/DoD Conference on Evolvable Hardware*. Los Alamitos, CA: IEEE Computer Society. Pages 113122, 2002.

[18] Kitano, Hiroaki., *Designing neural networks using genetic algorithms with graph generation system*. Complex Systems. 4(1990) 461476.

[19] Koza, John R., Genetic Programming: A Paradigm for Genetically Breeding Populations of Computer Programs to Solve Problems. *Stanford University Computer Science Department technical report* STAN-CS-90-1314, June 1990.

[20] Koza, John R., *Genetic Programming: On the Programming of Computers by Means of Natural Selection*. Cambridge, MA: MIT Press, 1992.

[21] Koza, John R., Discovery of rewrite rules in Lindenmayer systems and state transition rules in cellular automata via genetic programming. *Symposium on Pattern Formation (SPF-93)*, Claremont, California. February 13, 1993.

[22] Koza, John R., *Genetic Programming II: Automatic Discovery of Reusable Programs*. Cambridge, MA: MIT Press, 1994.

[23] Koza, John R., Bennett III, Forrest H, Andre, David, and Keane, Martin A., *Automated design of both the topology and sizing of analog electrical circuits using genetic programming*. In Gero, John S. and Sudweeks, Fay (editors). Artificial Intelligence in Design '96. Dordrecht: Kluwer Academic Publishers. Pages 151170, 1996.

[24] Koza, John R., Bennett III, Forrest H, Andre, David, and Keane, Martin A. 1999. *Genetic Programming III: Darwinian Invention and Problem Solving*. San Francisco, CA: Morgan Kaufmann.

[25] Koza, John R., Keane, Martin A., and Streeter, Matthew J., The importance of reuse and development in evolvable hardware. In Lohn, Jason, Zebulum, Ricardo, Steincamp, James, Keymeulen, Didier, Stoica, Adrian, and Ferguson, Michael I. (editors). 2003. *Proceedings of 2003 NASA/DoD Conference on Evolvable Hardware*. Los Alamitos, CA: IEEE Computer Society. Pages 3342, 2003.

[26] Koza, John R., Keane, Martin A., Streeter, Matthew J., Mydlowec, William, Yu, Jessen, and Lanza, Guido., *Genetic Programming IV*. Routine Human-Competitive Machine Intelligence. Kluwer Academic Publishers, 2003.

[27] Koza, John R., and Rice, James P., Genetic generation of both the weights and architecture for a neural network. *In Proceedings of International Joint Conference on Neural Networks*, Seattle, July 1991. Los Alamitos, CA: IEEE Press. Volume II. Pages 397404, 1991.

[28] Kruiskamp, Marinum Wilhelmus and Leenaerts, Domine., DARWIN: CMOS opamp synthesis by means of a genetic algorithm. *Proceedings of the 32nd Design Automation Conference*. New York, NY: Association for Computing Machinery. Pages 433438, 1995.

[29] Langdon, William B. and Poli, Riccardo., *Foundations of Genetic Programming*. Berlin: Springer-Verlag, 2002.

[30] Lee, Sang Gug., *Low Voltage Balun Circuit*. U. S. patent 6,265,908. Filed December 15, 1999. Issued July 24, 2001.

[31] Quarles, Thomas, Newton, A. R., Pederson, D. O., and Sangiovanni-Vincentelli, A., *SPICE 3 Version 3F5 Users Manual*. Department of Electrical Engineering and Computer Science, University of California. Berkeley, CA. March 1994.

[32] Samuel, Arthur L., Some studies in machine learning using the game of checkers. *IBM Journal of Research and Development*. **3**(3): 210229, 1959.

[33] Samuel, Arthur L., AI: Where it has been and where it is going. *Proceedings of the Eighth International Joint Conference on Artificial Intelligence*. Los Altos, CA: Morgan Kaufmann. Pages 1152 1157, 1983.

[34] Sripramong, Thanwa and Toumazou, Christofer., The invention of CMOS amplifiers using genetic programming and current-flow analysis. *IEEE Transactions on Computer-Aided Design of Integrated Circuits and Systems*. **21**(11). November 2002. Pages 12371252.

[35] Spector, Lee and Stoffel, Kilian., Ontogenetic programming. In Koza, John R., Goldberg, David E., Fogel, David B., and Riolo, Rick L. (editors). 1996. Genetic Programming 1996: *Proceedings of the First Annual Conference*, July 28-31, 1996, Stanford University. Cambridge, MA: MIT Press. Pages 394399, 1996.

[36] Thompson, Adrian. 1995. Evolving electronic robot controllers that exploit hardware resources. In Moran, Federico; Moreno, Alvaro; Merelo, Juan Julian; and Chacon, Pablo (eds.)., *Advances in Artificial Life: Third European Conference on Artificial Life*, Granada, Spain, June 1995, Proceedings. Lecture Notes in Computer Science Vol.929. Berlin: Springer-Verlag. pp.640656, 1995.

[37] Thompson, Adrian., An evolved circuit, intrinsic in silicon, entwined with physics. In Higuchi, Tetsuya; Iwata, Masaya; and Liu, Weixin (eds.). *Proceedings of International Conference on Evolvable Systems: From Biology to Hardware (ICES-96)*. Lecture Notes in Computer Science. Berlin: Springer-Verlag. Vol.1259. pp.390405, 1996

[38] Thompson, Adrian., *Hardware Evolution: Automatic Design of Electronic Circuits in Reconfigurable Hardware by Artificial Evolution*. Ph.D. thesis. School of Cognitive and Computing Sciences, University of Sussex, 1996.

[39] Thompson, Adrian., Silicon evolution. In Koza, John R., Goldberg, David E., Fogel, David B., and Riolo, Rick L. (editors). 1996. Genetic Programming 1996: *Proceedings of the First Annual Conference*, July 2831, 1996, Stanford University. Cambridge, MA: MIT Press. Pages 444452.

[40] Zitzler, Eckart, Deb, Kalyanmoy, Thiele, Lothar, Coello Coello, Carlos A., and Corne, David (editors). Evolutionary Multi-Criterion Optimization, *First International Conference*, EMO 2001, Zurich, Switzerland, March 2001, Proceedings. Lecture Notes in Computer Science. Volume 1993. Berlin, Germany: Springer-Verlag.

In: Evolutionary Machine Design: Methodology & Applications ISBN 1-59454-405-0
Editors: N. Nedjah & L. Mourelle, pp:33-58

Chapter 2

USING GENERATIVE REPRESENTATIONS TO EVOLVE ROBOTS

Gregory S. Hornby

QSS Group Inc., NASA Ames Research Center,
Mail Stop 269-3, Moffett Field, CA 94035-1000, USA
hornby@email.arc.nasa.gov, http://ic.arc.nasa.gov/people/hornby/

Recent research has demonstrated the ability of evolutionary algorithms to automatically design both the physical structure and software controller of real physical robots. One of the challenges for these automated design systems is to improve their ability to scale to the high complexities found in real-world problems. Here we claim that for automated design systems to scale in complexity they must use a representation which allows for the hierarchical creation and reuse of modules, which we call a *generative representation*. Not only is the ability to reuse modules necessary for functional scalability, but it is also valuable for improving efficiency in testing and construction. We then describe an evolutionary design system with a generative representation capable of hierarchical modularity and demonstrate it for the design of locomoting robots in simulation. Finally, results from our experiments show that evolution with our generative representation produces better robots than those evolved with a non-generative representation.

2.1 INTRODUCTION

Computer-automated design systems using evolutionary algorithms have been used to evolve a variety of static objects – such as antennas [11], load cells [16], trusses [14] and more [1,2] – software controllers for robots [3, 6, 15, 20], and both the controller and structure of robots [10, 12, 17, 21]. For the most part the designs that have been produced are fairly simple, which has led to a concern with how well this method will scale to the high complexities necessary for real-world robot designs. In engineering and software development, complex artifacts are achieved by exploiting the principles of regularity, modularity, hierarchy and reuse [19] [8] [13]. These features can be summarized as the hierarchical reuse of building blocks.

Here we claim that for automatic design systems to scale in complexity the designs they produce must be made of reused modules. While the evolutionary algorithm can affect the degree of reuse in an evolved design, the ability to create structures which reuse subassemblies is limited by the ability of the representation to encode them. We define *generative representations* as the class of representations which allow building-blocks encoded in the genotype of a design to be reused in the actual design.

An evolutionary design system using a generative representation would start with a library of basic parts and would iteratively create new, more powerful modules from ones already in its library. This principle of modularity is well accepted as a general characteristic of good design since it typically promotes decoupling and reduces complexity [18]. Another advantage of reusing modules throughout a design is that a design built with a library of standard modules requires less time to verify and test because it consists of fewer unique components. Also, fewer unique components and reduced complexity should simplify manufacturing, and also leads to a smaller stockpile of spare parts necessary for maintenance and repair.

Generative representations improve the scalability of evolutionary design systems because the hierarchical reuse of modules captures some types of design dependencies and increases the ability of the search engine to navigate large design spaces. The reuse of elements in a design allows a generative representation to capture design dependencies by giving it the ability to make coordinated changes in several parts of a design simultaneously. For example, if all the legs of a robot reuse the same component, then changing the length of that component will change the length of all legs simultaneously. Navigation of large design spaces is improved through the ability to manipulate assemblies of components as units.

For example, if adding/removing an assembly of m parts would make a design better, this would require the manipulation of m elements of a design encoded with a non-generative representation. With a generative representation the ability to add/remove copies of a previously created module allows for selecting these m parts in a more meaningful way than choosing them at random.

Having presented an argument for the use of generative representations, the rest of this chapter gives a detailed description of our evolutionary design system for creating robots and gives a comparison between evolution with a generative representation and a non-generative representation.

2.2 Generative Representations

Generative representations are any type of representation that allows for the creation and reuse of organizational units in a design. Within this definition there are many different methods by which reuse can be achieved. The generative representation used here is a kind of computer language within which design-construction programs are written. This language consists of a framework for designing construction rules and a set of these rules defines a program for a design. Designs are created by compiling a design program into an assembly procedure of construction commands and then executing this assembly procedure in the module which constructs designs. Since it is a general framework for encoding designs the person using this framework must supply the set of design-construction commands and a design constructor.

A design encoded with our generative representation consists of a set of rules for constructing a design and an initial command to start the execution of this set of rules. Each rule consists of a rule head followed by a number of condition-body pairs. For example in the following rule,

$$A(n0,n1) : n1 > 5 \rightarrow B(n1+1)cD(n1+0.5,n0-2)$$

the rule head is A(n0, n1), the condition is $n1 > 5$ and the body is B(n1+1) c D(n1+0.5, n0-2). The following is an example of a complete encoding of a design:

$$P0(4)$$
$$P0(n0): \quad n0 > 1.0 \rightarrow [\,P1(n0*1.5)\,]\; a(1)\; b(3)\; c(1)\; P0(n0-1)$$

$$P1(n0): \quad n0 > 1.0 \rightarrow \{\;[\,b(n0)\,]\; d(1)\;\}(4)$$

This example contains the starting command, $P0(4)$ and two rules, $P0$ and $P1$, both of which take a single argument and have a single condition-successor pair.

To produce an actual design from its encoding, the set of rules is first compiled into an assembly procedure. This assembly procedure is an intermediate stage between encoded design, the *genotype*, and actual design, the *phenotype*. An assembly procedure is produced by taking the starting command from the design's genotype and then iteratively rewriting rule heads with the appropriate successor. In addition to rewriting, this representation has a looping feature which replicates symbols that are enclosed within parentheses. The expression $\{$ *block* $\}(n)$ repeats the enclosed block of symbols n times and $\{abc\}(3)$ compiles to, *abcabcabc*. The above program is compiled as follows:

1. *P0(4)*
2. *[P1(6)] a(1) b(3) c(1) P0(3)*
3. *[{ [b(6)] d(1) }(4)] a(1) b(3) c(1) [P1(4.5)] a(1) b(3) c(1) P0(2)*
4. *[{ [b(6)] d(1) }(4)] a(1) b(3) c(1) [{ [b(4.5)] d(1) }(4)] a(1) b(3) c(1) [P1(3)] a(1) b(3) c(1) P0(1)*
5. *[{ [b(6)] d(1) }(4)] a(1) b(3) c(1) [{ [b(4.5)] d(1) }(4)] a(1) b(3) c(1) [{ [b(3)] d(1) }(4)] a(1) b(3) c(1)*
6. *[[b(6)] d(1) [b(6)] d(1) [b(6)] d(1) [b(6)] d(1)] a(1) b(3) c(1) [[b(4.5)] d(1) [b(4.5)] d(1) [b(4.5)] d(1) [b(4.5)] d(1)] a(1) b(3) c(1) [[b(3)] d(1) [b(3)] d(1) [b(3)] d(1) [b(3)] d(1)] a(1) b(3) c(1) b(3)*

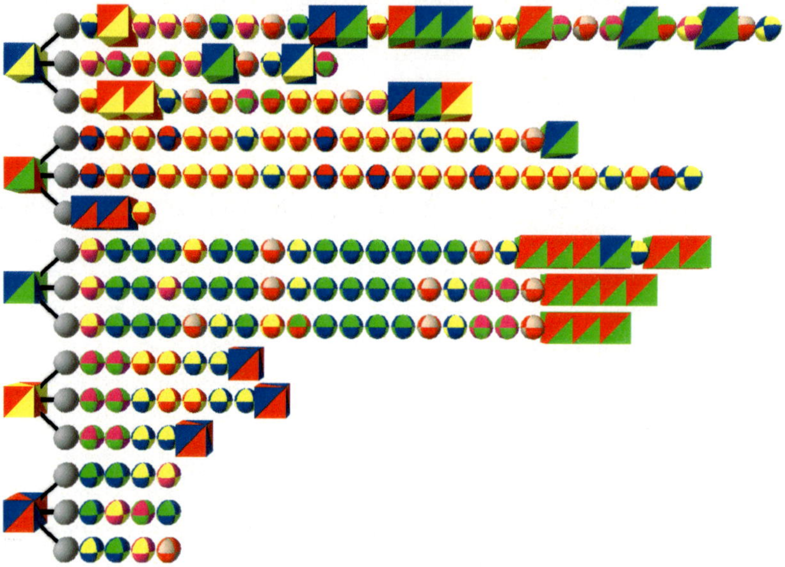

(a)

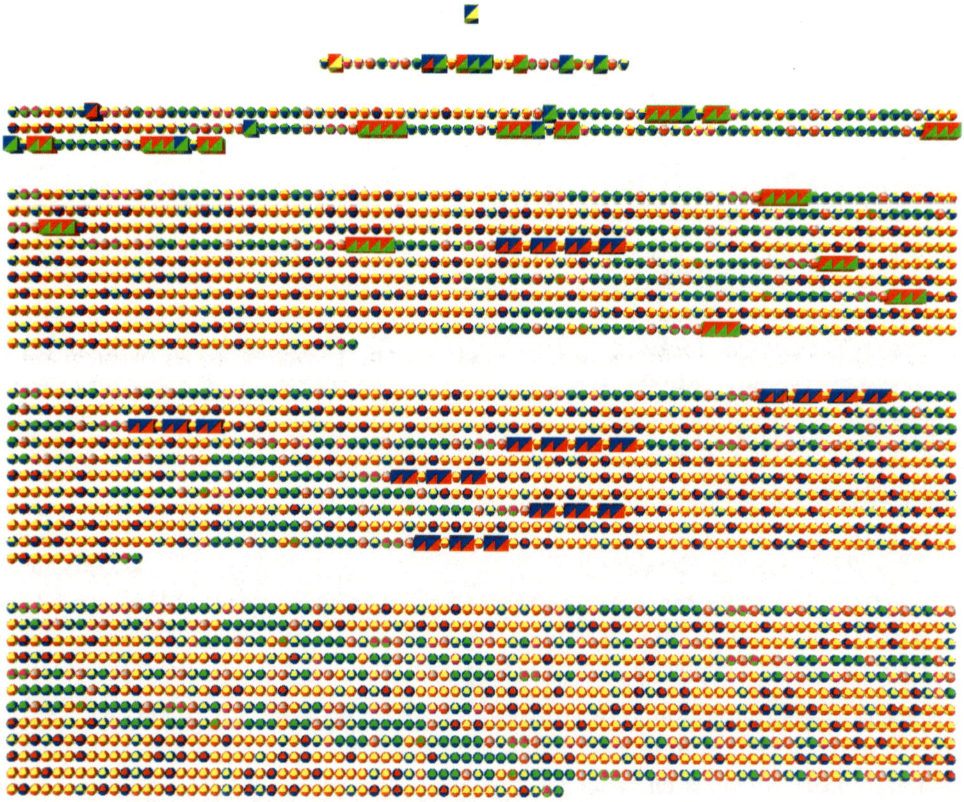

(b)

Figure 2.1. Graphical version of the generative representation, (a); along with the sequence of strings produced, (b).

A program for encoding a design can be shown graphically by representing the different parts and symbols of a program with different shapes and colors. The images in figure 2.1 show a larger set of rules for a design, figure 2.1.a, as well as the sequence of assembly procedures that are generated in the compilation process, figure 2.1.b. In these images rule-head symbols are represented by cubes with lines connecting them to their condition-body pairs, grey spheres represent the condition and the symbols following it are the body. The sequence is started with the first cube (here a blue and yellow one) and the sequence of symbols below it are the assembly procedures generated after each iteration of parallel replacement.

2.3 ENCODING ROBOTS WITH A GENERATIVE REPRESENTATION

To create designs with the generative representation of the previous section, the non-rule-head symbols are interpreted as construction commands in a design construction language. The class of robots which we evolve consist of Tinker-Toy^{TM}-like rods of regular length and both fixed and actuated joints. Since these robots are evolved using a generative representation we call them *genobots*, for *gen*eratively *en*coded r*obots*. For these robots there are two types of controllers which are used to drive them: simple oscillators, and neural-networks.

2.3.1 Oscillator Controlled Genobots

The command set for constructing oscillator-controlled genobots consists of operators for attaching fixed rods and actuated rods as well as operators for controlling the oscillation of the actuated rods. To know where to add the next part the robot-construction module maintains the current construction state, which consists of the current position and orientation on the robot body and also the relative phase offset for oscillators. The commands *turn-left/right/up/down/clockwise/counter-clockwise(n)* rotate the current heading about the appropriate axis in units of 90°. Rods are added to the robot with the command *forward*, which adds a rod in the forward direction if none exists or moves the current position to the end of the rod if one does exist. The command *back* moves the current position back to the other end of the current rod. Actuated rods are added with a set of commands which specify the joint type to use and its oscillation rate. *Revolute-1(n)* creates a joint which oscillates from 0° to 90° about the Z-axis with speed *n*, *revolute-2(n)* creates a joint which oscillates from −45° to 45° about the Z-axis with speed *n*, *twist-90(n)* creates a joint which oscillates from 0° to 90° about the X-axis with speed *n*, and *twist-180(n)* creates a joint which oscillates from −90° to 90° about the X-axis with speed *n*. These actuated-rod commands specify the rate of oscillation, to control the relative phase of the oscillating joints the construction state maintains an offset value that is assigned to newly created actuated joints. This phase-offset value is changed with the commands increase-offset(n) and decrease-offset(n), which adjust the phase-offset value in increments of 25%. To allow for a kind of branching in executing robot-construction assembly procedures there are commands, [and], for pushing and popping the construction state to/from a stack.

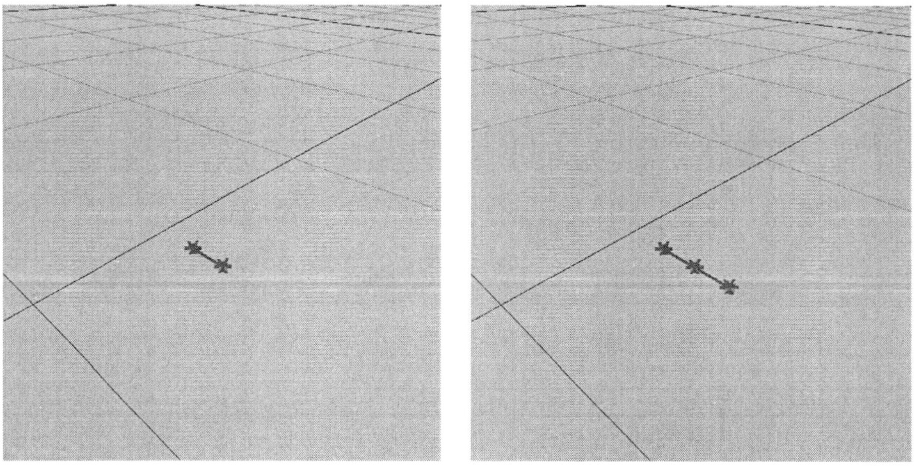

(a) (b)

Figure 2.2. Building and simulating a three-dimensional robot.

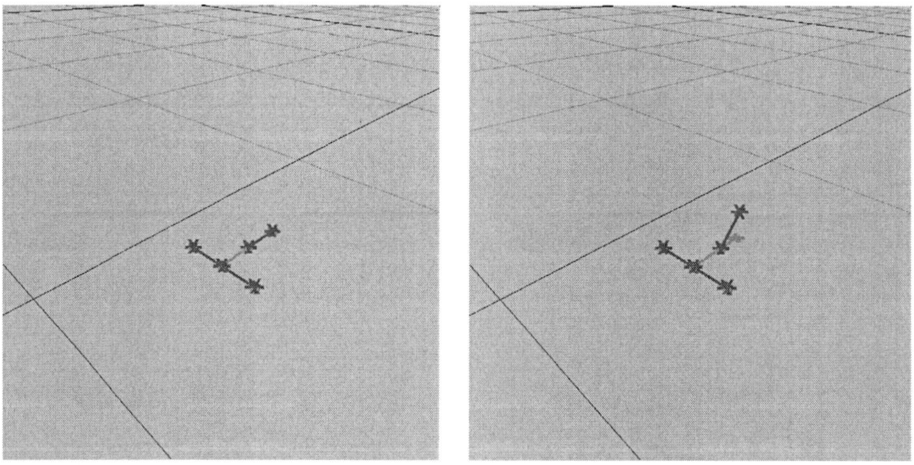

(c) (d)

Figure 2.3. Building and simulating a three-dimensional robot (*continued*).

Figure 2.2 and Figure 2.3 contain images of intermediate steps in building a genobot, as well as part of its animation, from the following command sequence,

[left(1) forward] [right(1) forward] revolute-1(1) forward

The single bar in figure 2.2.a is built from the string, *[left(1) forward]*, and the two bar structure in figure 2.2.b is built from, *[left(1) forward] [right(1) forward]*. The final robot is made from the command sequence, *[left(1) forward] [right(1) forward] revolute-1(1) forward*, and is shown in figure 2.3.c, where it is displayed part-way through its movement cycle. Figure 2.3.d displays the robot with the actuated joint moved half-way through its joint range.

2.3.2 Neural Networks

The method for constructing the neural-network controllers starts with a single node and edge and adds new nodes/edges through the execution of network-construction commands. Commands for constructing the network operate on links between neurons and use the most recently created link as the current one. *Push* and *pop* operators, '[' and ']', are used to store and retrieve the current link – consisting of the from-neuron, the to-neuron and index of the link into the to-neuron (for when there are multiple links between neurons) – to and from the stack. This stack of edges allows a form of branching to occur in an encoding – an edge can be pushed onto the stack followed by a sequence of commands and then a pop command makes the original edge the current edge again. For the following list of commands the current link connects from neuron A to neuron B.

- decrease-weight(n) – Subtracts n from the weight of the current link. If the current link is a virtual link, it creates it with weight $-n$.
- duplicate(n) – Creates a new link from neuron A to neuron B with weight n.
- increase-weight(n) – Add n to the weight of the current link. If the current link is a virtual link, it creates it with weight n.
- loop(n) – Creates a new link from neuron B to itself with weight n.
- merge(n) – Merges neuron A into neuron B by copying all inputs of A as inputs to B and replacing all occurrences of neuron A as an input with neuron B. The current link then becomes the nth input into neuron B.
- next(n) – Changes the from-neuron in the current link to its nth sibling.
- output(n) – Creates an output-neuron, with a linear transfer function, from the current from-neuron with weight n. The current-link continues to be from neuron A to neuron B.
- parent(n) – Changes the from-neuron in the current link to the nth input-neuron of the current from-neuron. Often there will not be an actual link between the new from-neuron and to-neuron, in which case a virtual link of weight 0 is used.

- reverse – Deletes the current link and replaces it with a link from B to A with the same weight as the original.
- set-function(n) – Changes the transfer function of the to-neuron in the current link, B, with: 0, for sigmoid; 1, linear; and 2, for oscillator.
- split(n) – Creates a new neuron, C, with a sigmoid transfer function, and moves the current link from A to C and creates a new link connecting from neuron C to neuron B with weight n.

Neurons in the network are initialized to an output value of 0.0 and are updated sequentially by applying a transfer function to the weighted sum of their inputs with their outputs clipped to the range ± 1. The different transfer functions are: sigmoid, using $tanh(sum\ of\ inputs)$; linear; and an oscillator. Oscillator units maintain a state which is increased by 0.01 after each update. The output of an oscillator unit is mapped to the range -1 to 1 by applying a triangle wave function, with a period of four, to the sum of its inputs and its state. The initial activation value for neurons with the sigmoid and linear transfer functions is 0.0 and the initial activation value for oscillator units is 1.0.

2.3.3 Neural-Network Controlled Genobots

A genobot's morphology and neural controller are constructed by combining the command sets for constructing body and brain into one language and then building body and brain simultaneously. Since actuated joints are controlled by the neural network the commands for modifying the phase offset, increase-offset(n) and decrease-offset(n), are not included. The resulting design language consists of the commands: [,], (,), forward, back, revolute-1, revolute-2, twist-90, twist-180, left(n), right(n), up(n), down(n), clockwise(n), clockwise(n), counter, decrease-weight(n), duplicate(n), increase-weight(n), loop(n), merge(n), next(n), parent(n), reverse, set-function(n), and split(n). This language has two push/pop commands with two stacks: ( ), for pushing/popping the link-state to the link stack; and [ ], for pushing/popping both the morphology and link states to a stack. A robot's body and brain are joined together by attaching the current input-neuron to the newly created actuated joint each time a joint command – *revolute-1*, *revolute-2*, *twist-90*, or *twist-180* – is executed. By defining joint-creation commands in a way that affects both controller and morphology a connection between body and brain is induced.

An example of an assembly procedure using this language is,

[right(1.0) forward right(1.0) forward right(1.0) forward right(1.0) forward] duplicate(0.25) split(0.4) reverse revolute-1(1.0) duplicate(0.25) split(0.4) reverse revolute-1(1.0) left(1.0) right(1.0) forward right(1.0) forward right(1.0) forward right(1.0) forward

Figure 2.4 contains a sequence of images showing intermediate stages in the construction of this assembly procedure. Before any commands are processed a robot consists

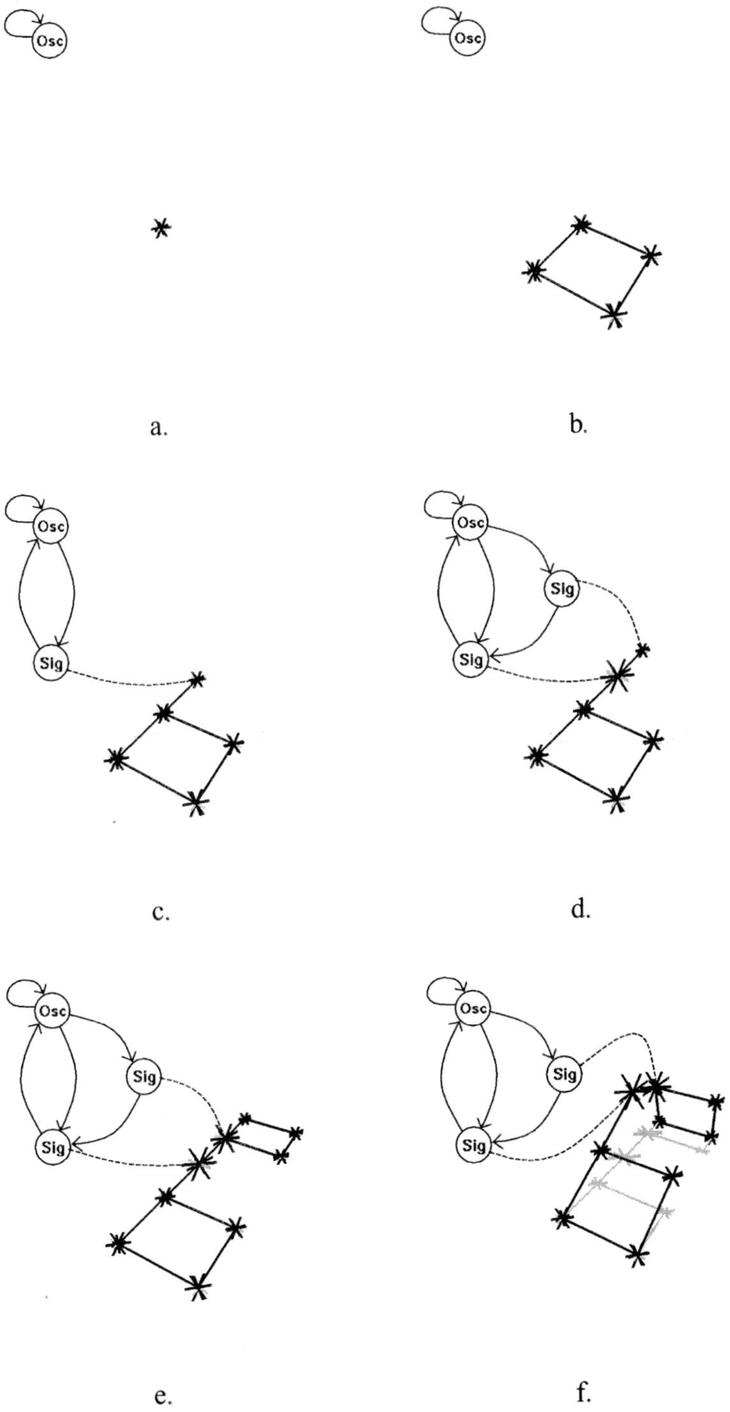

Figure 2.4. Constructing a neural-network controlled genobot

of a single oscillating neuron and a point, figure 2.4.a. After executing the commands, *[right(1.0) forward right(1.0) forward right(1.0) forward right(1.0) forward]* , the robot consists of a square of four rods and the oscillating neuron, figure 2.4.b. After executing, *duplicate(0.25) split(0.4) reverse revolute-1(1.0)*, a second neuron is created and it is attached to the actuated joint at the end of the newly created rod, figure 2.4.c. The commands, *duplicate(0.25) split(0.4) reverse revolute-1(1.0)*, are repeated and a third neuron is created and it is attached to another actuated joint, figure 2.4.d. The last commands, *left(1.0) right(1.0) forward right(1.0) forward right(1.0) forward right(1.0) forward* , attach another square onto the end of the last revolute-1 joint, figure 2.4.e. Figure 2.4.f shows the genobot with the joints halfway through their movement range.

2.3.4 Generative Representation Example for Neural-Network Controlled Genobots

Having presented construction languages for oscillator-controlled robots, neural networks and neural-network controlled robots we now give an example going from genotype to phenotype of a neural-network controlled robot. The encoding for this genobot consists of the starting command $P0(4)$, two production rules, each with two condition-successor pairs, and uses the command set for constructing neural-network controlled genobots:

$$
\begin{aligned}
&P0(4)\\
&P0(n0): \quad n0 > 3.0 \rightarrow \quad P1(5.0)\ P0(n0-2.0)\ left(1.0)\ P1(4.0)\\
&\qquad\qquad\ \ n0 > 0.0 \rightarrow \quad \{\ duplicate(0.25)\ split(0.4)\ \textit{reverse}\\
&\qquad\qquad\qquad\qquad\qquad\quad \textit{revolute-1(1.0)}\ \}(2.0)\\
&P1(n0): \quad n0 > 4.0 \rightarrow \quad [\ P1(4.0)\ ]\\
&\qquad\qquad\ \ n0 > 0.0 \rightarrow \quad \{\ right(1.0)\ forward\ \}(n0)
\end{aligned}
$$

To produce the assembly procedure for constructing the genobot the rule-system is compiled starting with the command *P0(4)*:

1. *P0(4)*
2. *P1(5.0) P0(2.0) left(1.0) P1(4.0)*
3. *[P1(4.0)] { duplicate(0.25) split(0.4) reverse revolute-1(1.0) }(2.0) left(1.0) { right(1.0) forward }(4.0)*
4. *[{ right(1.0) forward }(4.0)] { duplicate(0.25) split(0.4) reverse revolute-1(1.0) }(2.0) left(1.0) { right(1.0) forward }(4.0)*
5. *[right(1.0) forward right(1.0) forward right(1.0) forward right(1.0) forward] duplicate(0.25) split(0.4) reverse revolute-1(1.0) duplicate(0.25) split(0.4) reverse revolute-1(1.0) left(1.0) right(1.0) forward right(1.0) forward right(1.0) forward right(1.0) forward*

This last sequence of commands is the assembly procedure from the example in section 2.3.3 and produces the genobot in figure 2.4.f.

2.4 Robot Simulator

Once an assembly procedure for constructing a robot has been executed and the resulting robot is constructed, its behavior is evaluated in a quasi-static, kinematics simulator. The kinematics are simulated by computing successive frames of moving joints in small angular increments of 0.001 radians toward the desired angle. This angle is determined by either an oscillator or a neuron. Oscillators cycle between -1 and 1 and this is scaled to the joint's range of motion. Similarly, the output value of a neuron falls within the range of -1 and 1 and this is scaled to the joint's range of motion. After each update the structure is then settled by determining whether or not the robot's center of mass falls outside its footprint and then repeatedly rotating the entire structure about the edge of the footprint nearest the center of mass until it is stable.

To achieve robot designs that are robust to transferal to the real world, noise is added to evolved structures similar to the method of [9] and [7]. A robot design is evaluated by simulating it three times, once without noise and twice with different amounts of construction noise applied to joint angles. Noise is applied to all connections that are not part of a cycle and is a random rotation in the range of ± 0.1 radians about each of the three coordinate axis. The returned fitness of an evolved individual is the worst fitness score from the three trials. By adding construction noise to a robot and evaluating it multiple times with different random noise each time, evolved robots are made robust to imperfections in real-world construction.

2.5 Evolutionary Design System

To demonstrate the advantages of generative representations we use GENRE, an evolutionary design system for creating designs [4]. GENRE consists of several design constructors and fitness functions, the compiler for the generative representation and an evolutionary algorithm (EA) for searching the design spaces. The EA is the module that drives GENRE and it operates by processing a population of designs (members of which are called *individuals*) encoded with the generative representation. Search is started by creating an initial random population of individuals and evaluating each of these with a user-defined *fitness function*, a mathematical expression for scoring the goodness of a design. The EA then creates successive new populations by selecting the better individuals of the current population and applying small amounts of variation to their encoding to produce new individuals in a new population.

The two variation operators that are used to produce new individuals are *mutation* and *recombination*. Mutation creates a new individual by copying the parent individual and making a small change to it, such as by replacing one command with another, perturbing the parameter in a command by adding/subtracting a small value to it, or adding/deleting a sequence of commands in a rule body. Recombination takes two individuals as parents and creates a new individual by making a copy of the first parent and then either exchanging a rule with the second parent, or randomly replacing a sequence of commands in one body with a sequence from the second parent.

Designs can be encoded with either the generative representation described in section 2.2 or a non-generative representation. For designs encoded with the generative representation the design program is first compiled into a sequence of construction commands called an assembly procedure. This assembly procedure is then executed by the design constructor to produce the encoded design. For the non-generative representation each individual in the population is an assembly procedure which specifies how to construct the design. We implement this assembly procedure as a degenerate version of the generative representation which has only a single rule in which the condition always succeeds and the body consists only of construction commands. Implementing the non-generative representation in the same way as the generative representation allows us to use the same evolutionary algorithm and the same variation operators; the only difference between the two representations is the ability to hierarchically reuse elements of encoded designs. Once a design has been constructed, using either the generative or non-generative representation, it is evaluated for how good it is with the user-defined fitness function.

2.6 Evolution of Oscillator Controlled Robots

To demonstrate the advantages of generative representations for robot design we first compare the generative representation of section 2.2 against the non-generative representation described in section 2.5 for the evolution of oscillator controlled robots. For this comparison the non-generative representation is implemented as a degenerate type of generative representation with one production rule, no arguments, one condition-successor pair whose condition always succeeds, and without the repeat operator or the ability to call production rules. The maximum length of the production body is set to ten thousand symbols, allowing assembly procedures of up to ten thousand operators to be evolved. The generative representation has fifteen production rules, three condition-successor pairs, and two parameters for each production rule. For the generative representation, the maximum length of production body is set to fifteen commands and the maximum allowed length of a compiled assembly procedure is set to ten thousand operators – the same length as with the non-generative representation. The evolutionary algorithm used a population of one hundred individuals and was run for five hundred generations and results are the average over ten trials.

The design problem for this comparison is to produce robots that move across the ground as fast as possible with fitness being a function of the distance moved by the robot's center of mass. In order to discourage sliding, fitness was reduced by the distance that points of the robot's body were dragged along the ground. Since the kinematics simulator detects collisions but cannot handle them like a physical dynamics simulator would, robots that have collisions between body parts are given a fitness of zero. Finally, a robot was given zero fitness if it had a sequence of four or more rods in which none of the rods was part of a closed loop with other rods. This constraint was intended to keep the system from producing spindly robots which would not function well in reality. The graph in figure 2.5 plots the fitness of the best individual in the population, averaged over ten trials, for both

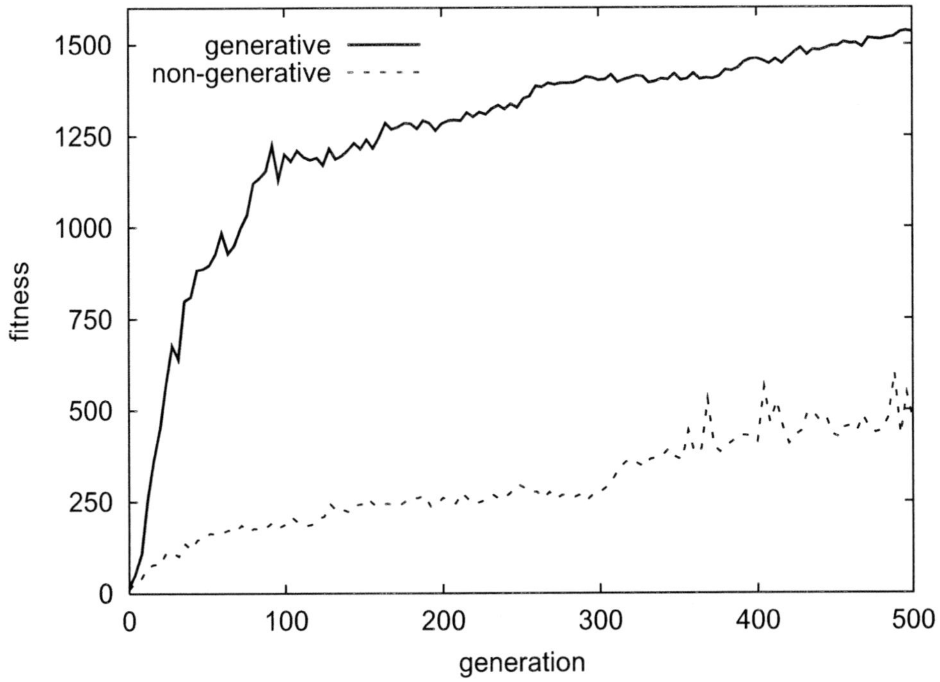

Figure 2.5. Performance comparison between the non-generative and generative representations on evolving robots with oscillator networks for controllers.

the non-generative and generative representations. This graph shows that far better robots are evolved with the generative representation (with an average best fitness of just over fifteen hundred) than with the non-generative representation (with an average best fitness of approximately five hundred).

Robots evolved with the non-generative representation tended to have few parts, moved awkwardly and had little regularity in their structure. The two main forms of locomotion found were using one or more appendages to push along or having two main body parts connected by a sequence of rods that twisted in such a way that first one half of the robot would rotate forward, then the other. The two fastest robots evolved with the non-generative representation are shown in figure 2.6.a (fitness 1188 with 49 rods and moves by twisting) and figure 2.6.b (fitness 1000 with 31 rods which moves by pushing).

Genobots evolved with the generative representation not only had higher average fitness, but tended to move in a more continuous manner. As with evolution using the non-generative representation, the genobots created at the beginning of an evolutionary run had a few rods and joints that would slowly slide on the ground. In most evolutionary runs, faster genobots were evolved by repeating rolling segments to smoothen out gaits or by increasing the size of segments/appendages to increase the distance moved in each oscillation period. Of these, the two fastest are the genobot in figure 2.7.a, whose segments

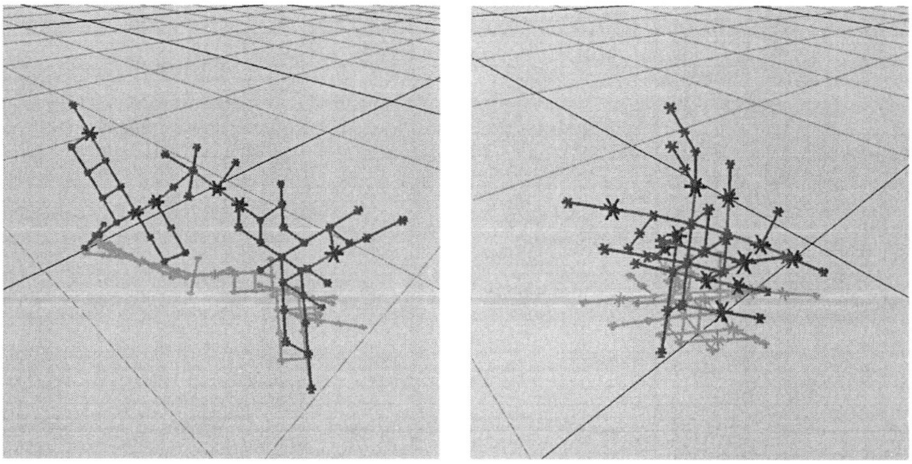
(a) (b)

Figure 2.6. The two best oscillator controlled robots evolved using the non-generative representation.

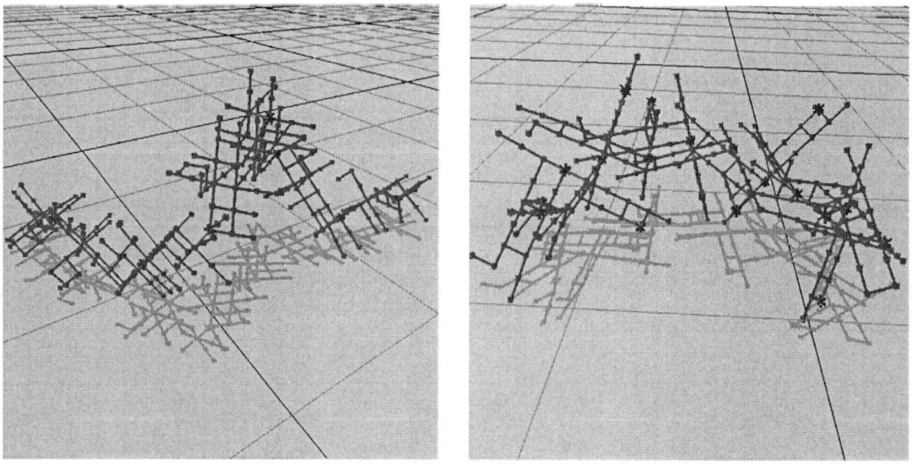
(a) (b)

Figure 2.7. The two best oscillator controlled genobots evolved using the generative representation.

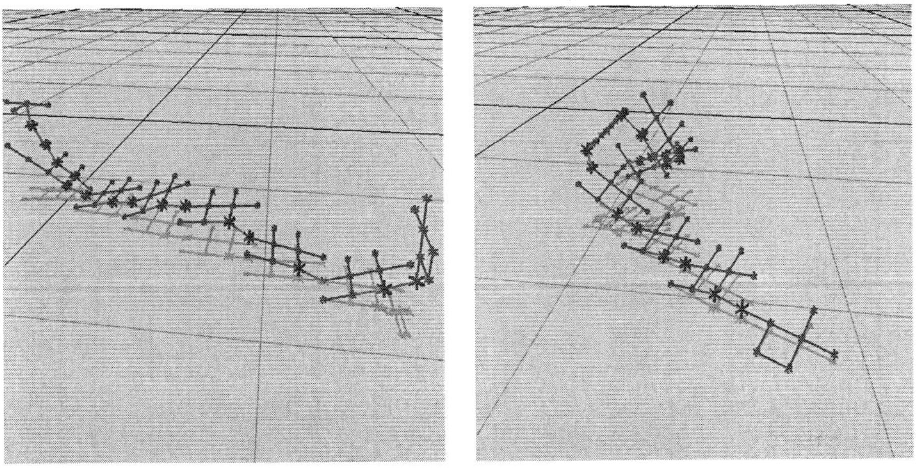

(a) (b)

Figure 2.8. Part of the locomotion cycle of an oscillator-controlled genobot.

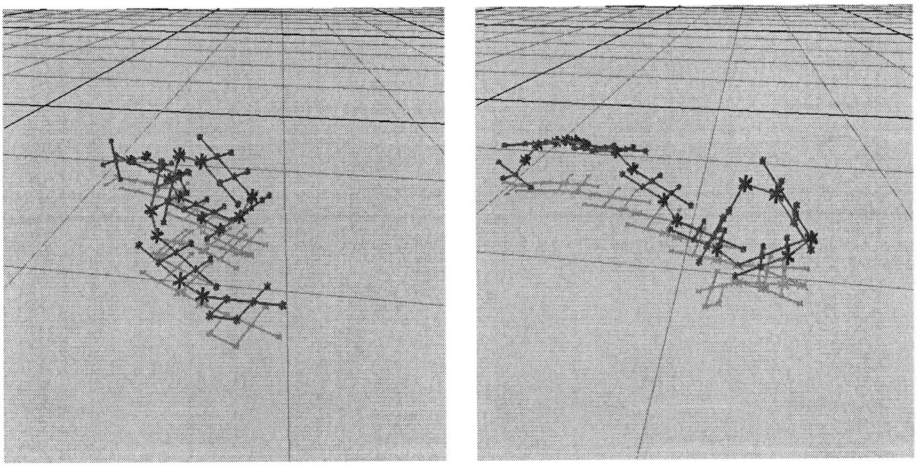

(c) (d)

Figure 2.9. Part of the locomotion cycle of an oscillator-controlled genobot (*continued*).

are shaped like a coil and it moves by rolling sideways with fitness of 3604 and 325 rods, and the genobot in figure 2.7.b, a sequence of interlocking X's that rolls along with fitness 2754 and 268 rods. An example of the movement cycle of a genobot produced with the generative representation is in figure 2.8 and 2.9.

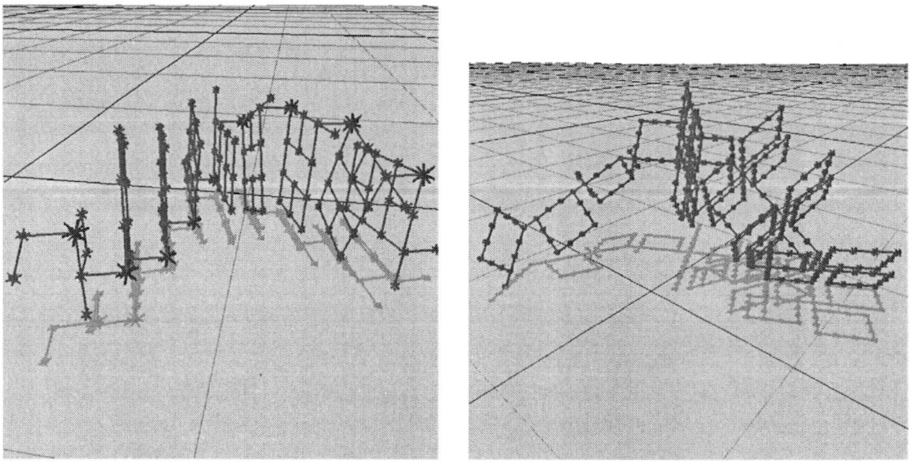

(a) (b)

Figure 2.10. A variety of evolved 3D oscillator robots.

The robot variety of Figure 2.10 and Figure 2.11 consists of: *a*, a sequence of rolling rectangles with 169 bars; *b*, an asymmetric rolling genobot with 306 bars; *c*, an undulating serpent with 339 bars; *d*, a four-legged walking genobot with 629 bars. While additional runs with the non-generative representation failed to produce designs more interesting than those in figure 2.6, additional runs with the generative representation produced a variety of genobots with different styles of locomotion. The most common form of movement for evolved oscillator-controlled genobots was to roll along sideways, as done by the chains in 2.10.a and 2.10.b. The genobot in 2.11.c moves like an undulating sea-serpent. One of the larger genobots that evolved is the one in figure 2.11.d which uses four legs in an awkward walk.

2.7 Evolution of Neural-Network Controlled Robots

Next we compare the generative representation against the non-generative representation on evolving neural-network controlled robots. The same fitness function, a measure of distance travelled, is used as with the experiments for oscillator-controlled robots and both the generative and non-generative representation are configured in the same way. The results for this comparison are shown in figure 2.12, which contains a graph of the fitness (averaged over ten trials) of the best individuals evolved with the non-generative representation and the generative representation. After ten generations the generative representation achieved

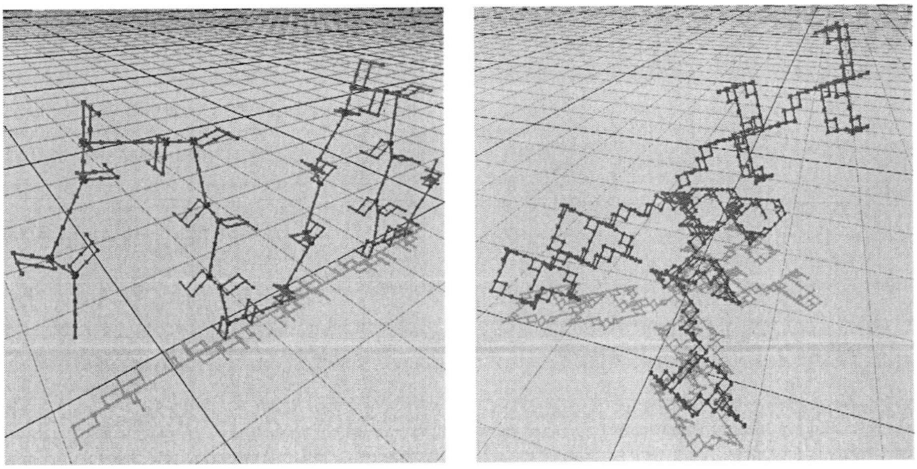

(c) (d)

Figure 2.11. A variety of evolved 3D oscillator robots (*continued*).

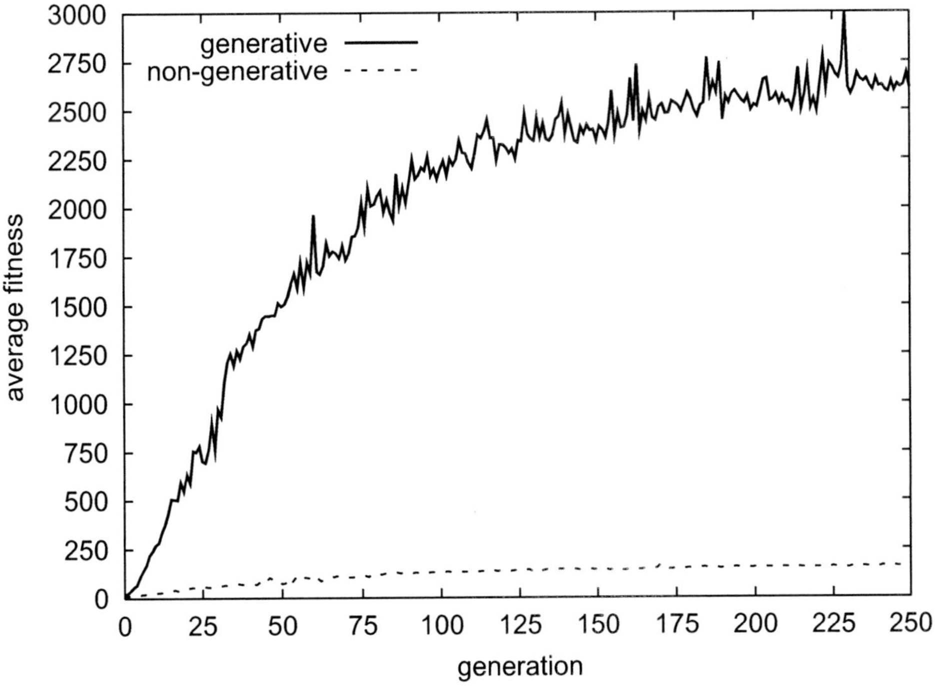

Figure 2.12. Performance comparison between the non-generative representation and the generative representation on evolving robots with neural networks for controllers.

a higher average fitness than runs with the non-generative representation did after 250 generations and the final genobots evolved with the generative representation were on average more than ten times faster than robots evolved with the non-generative representation.

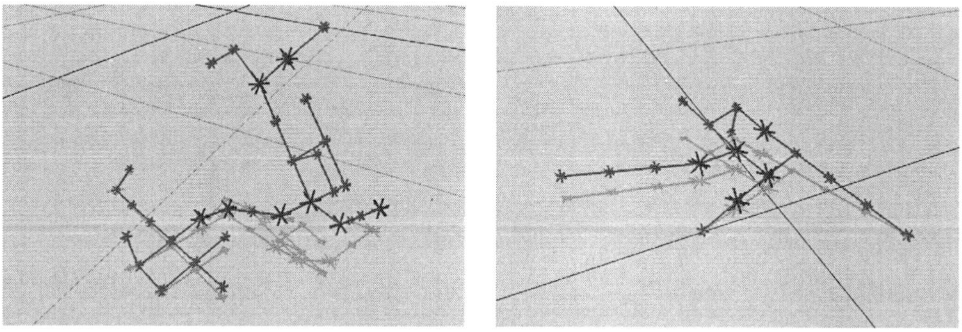

(a) (b)

Figure 2.13. The two best neural-network controlled robots evolved with the non-generative representation.

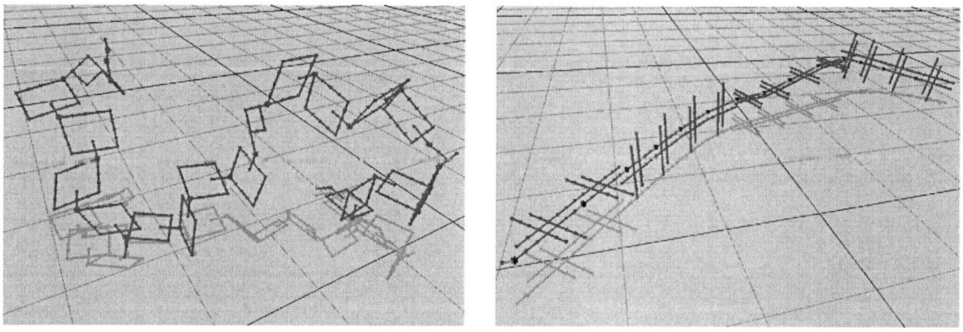

(a) (b)

Figure 2.14. The two best neural-network controlled genobots evolved with the generative representation.

Figure 2.13 shows the two best individuals evolved with the non-generative representation and Figure 2.14 shows the two best genobots evolved with the generative representation. From the images it can be seen that the robots evolved with the non-generative representation are irregular and have few components, whereas the genobots evolved with the generative representation are more regular and, in some cases, have two or more levels of reused assemblies of components.

As with the oscillator-controlled robots, further runs with the generative representation produced robots with different styles of locomotion but failed to produce new varieties of robots with the non-generative representation. The images in Figure 2.15 and Figure 2.16

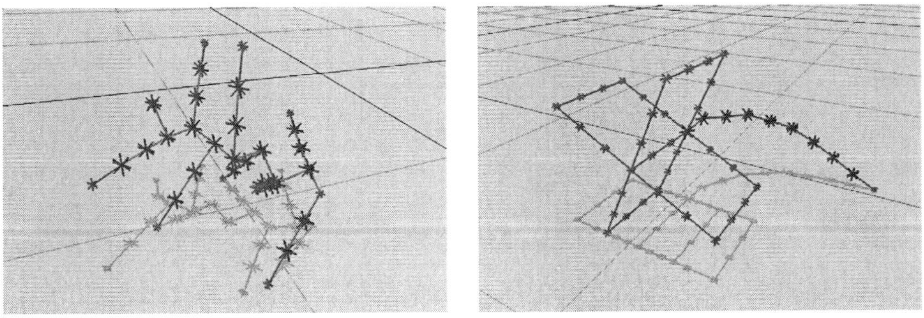

(a) (b)

Figure 2.15. Other genobots evolved using the generative representation on runs with no constraints on limb lengths.

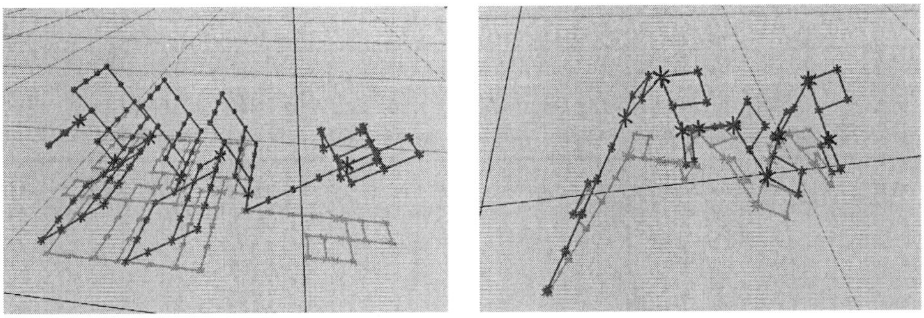

(c) (d)

Figure 2.16. Other genobots evolved using the generative representation on runs with no constraints on limb lengths. (*continued*) are examples of other neural-network controlled robots evolved with the generative representation. The genobot in Figure 2.15.a is comprised almost entirely of actuated joints and moves by alternating between pulling all its limbs in tight to its body and extending them while twisting its torso. In another evolutionary run a wheel-like genobot was evolved that moves by using its tail to continually turn its body over and over, Figure 2.15.b. The robot in Figure 2.16.c has articulated joints between body segments for a kind of inchworm-like motion and is similar to early versions of the undulating serpent of Figure 2.11.c. Finally, the robot in Figure 2.16.d is an example of a rolling chain of segments which is the method of locomotion most commonly evolved for both oscillator and neural-network controlled genobots.

2.8 Advantages of a Generative Representation

The central claim of this chapter is that using generative representations improves the evolvability of designs by capturing design dependencies and improving the ability of the search algorithm to navigate through large design spaces in a meaningful way. This can be intuitively understood by looking at some examples of robots evolved with a generative representation.

An advantage of the design encodings that are found with a generative representation is in the changes that can be made to this encoding that can not be made to designs encoded with a non-generative representation. The images in figure 2.17 are an example which shows the benefits of reuse through variations applied to the genobot in figure 2.14.b. Changing the genotype to add rods to an assembly of parts results in the change to all occurrences of that part in the design, Figure 2.17.b, and a single change to the genotype can cause the addition/subtraction of a large number of parts, figure 2.17.c. With a non-generative representation, these changes would require the simultaneous changes of multiple symbols in the encoding. Some of these changes must be done simultaneously for the resulting design to be viable – changing the height of only one leg of a walking robot can result in a significant loss of fitness – and so these changes are not evolvable with a non-generative representation. Others, such as producing a new body-segment, are viable with a series of single-rod changes. Yet, in the general case this could result in a significantly slower search speed in comparison with a single change to a robot encoded with a generative representation.

The graphs in figure 2.18 are scatter plots of the command difference between a parent and child's assembly procedures against their change in fitness on the robot design problem. These graphs show that as the size of change in the resulting design increases it is more likely to be an improvement on designs encoded with a generative representation than those encoded with a non-generative representation. This means that search algorithms are better able to use large movements in the design space to navigate through the design space with the generative representation.

That the evolutionary design system is taking advantage of the ability to make coordinated changes with a generative representation is demonstrated by individuals taken from

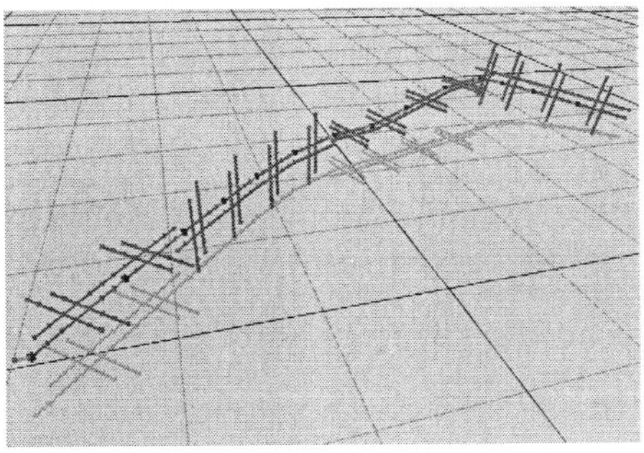

(a)

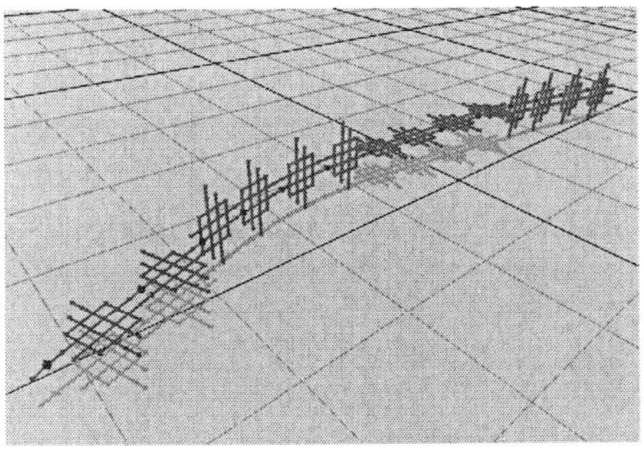

(b)

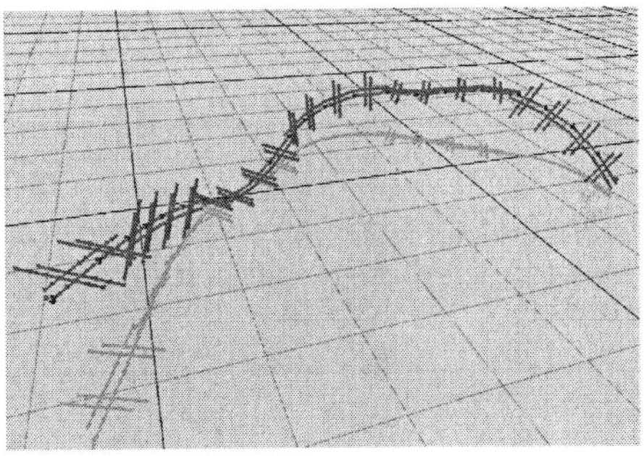

(c)

Figure 2.17. Mutations of a genobot:(a), the genobot from figure 2.14.b; (b), a change to a low-level component of parts results in all occurrences of this part to have the change; (c), a single change to the genotype changes the number of high-level components in the genobot from four to six.

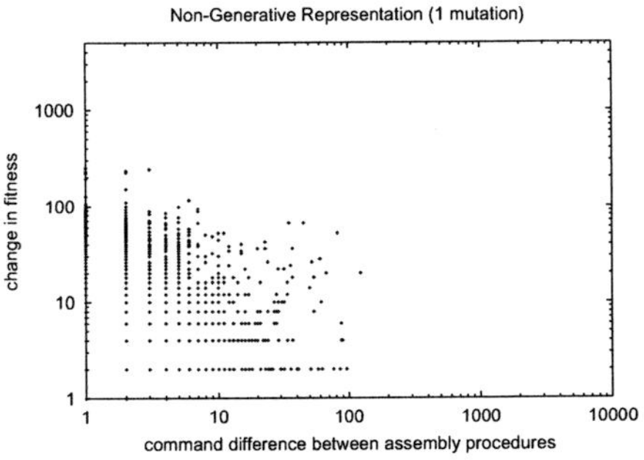

(a)

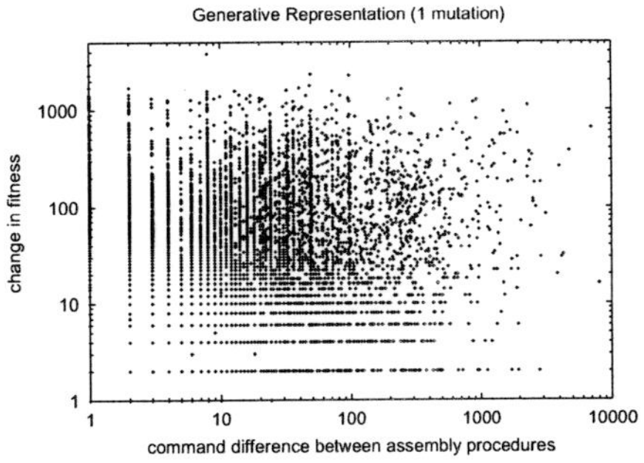

(b)

Figure 2.18. Plot of amount of change in assembly procedures from parent to child versus change in fitness for trials evolving robots.

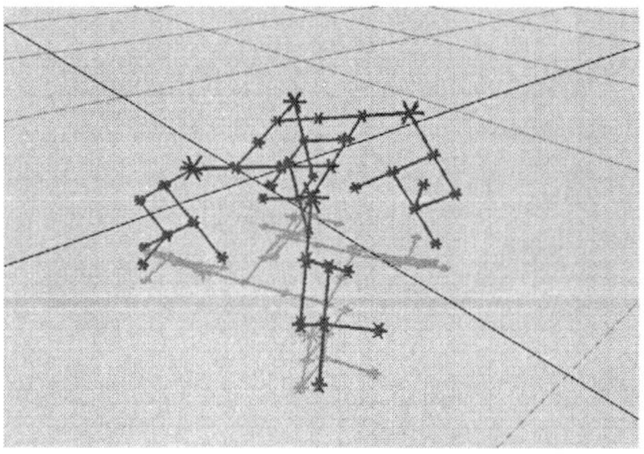

(a) Fitness: 348.

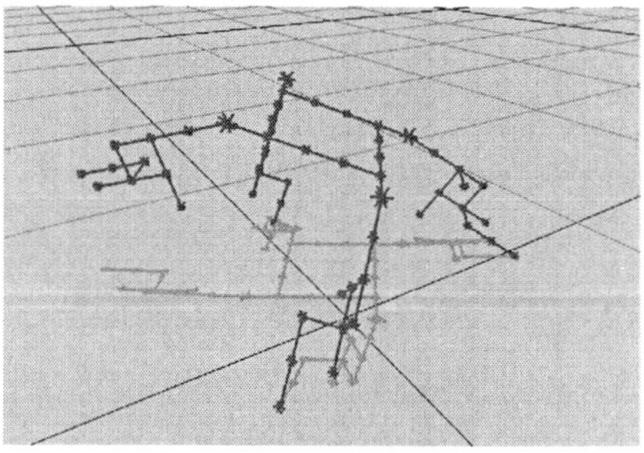

(b) Fitness: 780.

Figure 2.19. Evolution of a four-legged walking genobot.

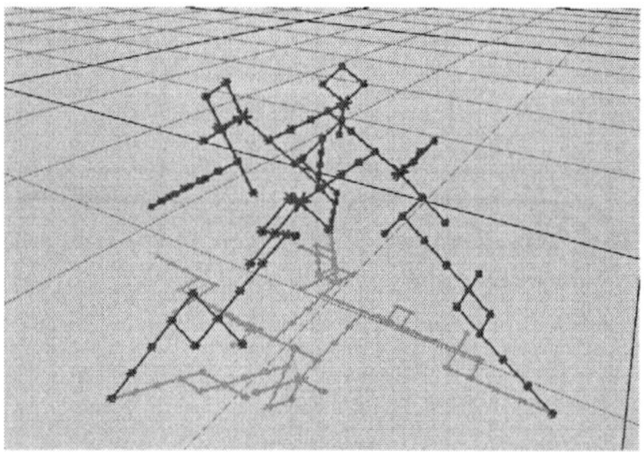

(c) Fitness: 1450.

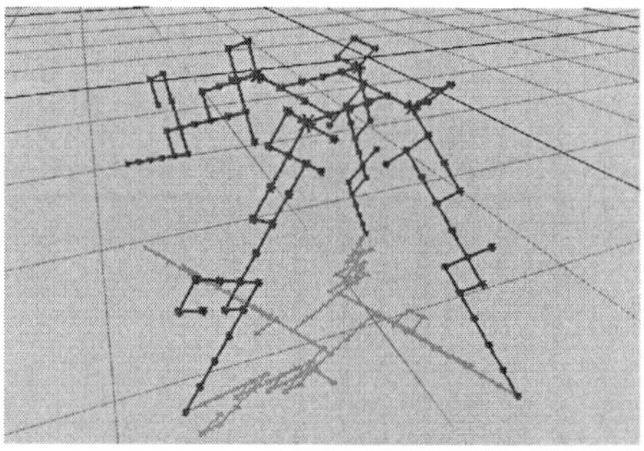

(d) Fitness: 2192.

Figure 2.20. Evolution of a four-legged walking genobot (*continued*).

different generations of the evolutionary process. The sequence of images in Figure 2.19 and Figure 2.20, which are of the best individual in the population taken from different generations, show two changes occurring. First, the rectangle that forms the body of the genobot goes from two-by-two (figure 2.19.a), to three-by-three (figure 2.19.b), before settling on two-by-three (figures 2.20.c-d). These changes are possible with a single change on a generative representation but cannot be done with a single change on a non-generative representation. The second change is the evolution of the genobot's legs. That all four legs are the same in all four images strongly suggests that the same module in the encoding is being used to create them. As with the body, changing all four legs simultaneously can be done easily with the generative representation by changing the one module that constructs them, but would require simultaneously making the same change to all four occurrences of the leg assembly procedure in the non-generative representation.

(a) (b)

Figure 2.21. Two tables from a family of designs.

One other advantage of using a generative representation is that by encoding an object through a set of reusable rules for constructing it, it is possible to encode a class of designs. By evaluating an individual with different parameters to its starting command families of designs can be evolved, such as the tables in figure 2.21 [5].

2.9 SUMMARY

Only in the last few years has the computer-automated design of robots succeeded in transferring designs that are produced in simulation to the real-world [12]. The next challenge has been in creating such systems that can produce designs of complexities comparable to real-world robots. Existing systems for designing robots have been limited by the representation they use to encode designs. As with both traditional engineering and software design, for evolutionary design systems to be able to scale they must be able to hierarchically reuse modules throughout a design. For designs to be able to reuse modules the representation scheme for encoding them must allow it.

Here we have defined generative representations as the class of representations which allow modules encoded in the genotype to be reused in producing the actual design and have claimed that evolution with generative representations will improve scalability. To support this claim we described a generative representation and an automated design system for creating robots. Using this system we evolved oscillator-controlled and neural-network controlled robots for a locomotion task using both a non-generative and a generative representation. The results of this comparison showed that better robots were evolved with the generative representation than with the non-generative representation, and that robots encoded with the generative representation had a modular structure with a reuse of assemblies of components.

This comparison has shown how important the representation is for an evolutionary design system to scale to complex, high-part count designs. The next step in automated design is in producing design representations that can hierarchically create and reuse assemblies of parts in ever more powerful ways. As continuing work expands the range and power of generative representations, while maintaining evolvability, we expect to see ever more progress toward general purpose evolutionary design systems.

Acknowledgements

Images and graphs are copyright Gregory S. Hornby and used with permission.

Bibliography

[1] P. J. Bentley, editor. *Evolutionary Design by Computers*. Morgan Kaufmann, San Francisco, 1999.

[2] P. J. Bentley and D. W. Corne, editors. *Creative Evolutionary Systems*. Morgan Kaufmann, San Francisco, 2001.

[3] R. Grzeszczuk and D. Terzopoulos. Automated learning of muscle-actuated locomotion through control abstraction. In *SIGGRAPH 95 Conference Proceedings*, Annual Conference Series, pages 63–70, Los Angeles, California, August 1995. In *Computer Graphics* Annual Conf. Series, 1995.

[4] G. S. Hornby. *Generative Representations for Evolutionary Design Automation*. PhD thesis, Michtom School of Computer Science, Brandeis University, Waltham, MA, 2003.

[5] G. S. Hornby. Generative representations for evolving families of designs. In E. Cantu-Paz et al., editor, *Proc. of the Genetic and Evolutionary Computation Conference*, LNCS 2724, pages 1678–1689, Berlin, 2003. Springer-Verlag.

[6] G. S. Hornby, M. Fujita, S. Takamura, T. Yamamoto, and O. Hanagata. Autonomous evolution of gaits with the sony quadruped robot. In *Proceedings of the Genetic and Evolutionary Computation Conference*, pages 1297–1304. Morgan Kaufmann, 1999.

[7] G. S. Hornby, S. Takamura, O. Hanagata, M. Fujita, and J. Pollack. Evolution of controllers from a high-level simulator to a high dof robot. In J. Miller, editor, *Evolvable Systems: from biology to hardware; Proc. of the Third Intl. Conf.*, Lecture Notes in Computer Science; Vol. 1801, pages 80–89. Springer, 2000.

[8] C. C. Huang and A. Kusiak. Modularity in design of products and systems. *IEEE Transactions on Systems, Man, and Cybernetics, Part A*, **28**(1):66–77, 1998.

[9] N. Jakobi. *Minimal Simulations for Evolutionary Robotics*. PhD thesis, School of Cognitive and Computing Sciences, University of Sussex, May 1998.

[10] M. Komosinski. The world of framsticks: Simulation, evolution, interaction. In *Virtual Worlds 2*, Lecture Notes in Artificial Intelligence 1834, pages 214–224. Springer-Verlag, 2000.

[11] D. S. Linden. Innovative antenna design using genetic algorithms. In P. J. Bentley and D. W. Corne, editors, *Creative Evolutionary Systems*, chapter 20, pages 487–510. Morgan Kaufmann, San Francisco, 2001.

[12] H. Lipson and J. B. Pollack. Automatic design and manufacture of robotic lifeforms. *Nature*, **406**:974–978, 2000.

[13] B. Meyer. *Object-oriented Software Construction*. Prentice Hall, New York, 1988.

[14] Z. Michalewicz, D. Dasgupta, R. G. Le Riche, and M. Schoenauer. Evolutionary algorithms for constrained engineering problems. *Computers and Industrial Engineering Journal*, **30**(2):851–870, 1996.

[15] J. T. Ngo and J. Marks. Spacetime constraints revisited. In *SIGGRAPH 93 Conference Proceedings*, pages 343–350, 1993. Annual Conference Series.

[16] G. Robinson, M. El-Beltagy, and A. Keane. Optimization in mechanical design. In P. J. Bentley, editor, *Evolutionary Design by Computers*, chapter 6, pages 147–165. Morgan Kaufmann, San Francisco, 1999.

[17] K. Sims. Evolving 3d morphology and behavior by competition. In R. Brooks and P. Maes, editors, *Proceedings of the Fourth Workshop on Artificial Life*, pages 28–39, Boston, MA, 1994. MIT Press.

[18] N. P. Suh. *The Principles of Design*. Oxford University Press, 1990.

[19] K. Ulrich and K. Tung. Fundamentals of product modularity. *Issues in Design/Manufacture Integration - 1991 American Society of Mechanical Engineers, Design Engineering Division (Publication) DE*, **39**:73–79, 1991.

[20] M. van de Panne and E. Fiume. Sensor-actuator Networks. In *SIGGRAPH 93 Conference Proceedings*, Annual Conference Series, pages 335–342, 1993.

[21] J. Ventrella. Explorations in the emergence of morphology and locomotion behavior in animated characters. In R. Brooks and P. Maes, editors, *Proceedings of the Fourth Workshop on Artificial Life*, Boston, MA, 1994. MIT Press.

In: Evolutionary Machine Design: Methodology & Applications ISBN 1-59454-405-0
Editors: N. Nedjah & L. Mourelle, pp:59-80

Chapter 3

INTRINSIC EVOLUTIONARY DESIGN OF ANALOG BUILDING BLOCKS FOR FUZZY LOGIC CONTROLLERS

José Franco M. do Amaral, Jorge Luís M. do Amaral,
Ricardo Tanscheit[†]*, Marco A. C. Pacheco*[†]*, Marley M. B. R. Vellasco*[†]

Department of Electronics Engineering, Rio de Janeiro State University,
R. S. Fco. Xavier 524, Maracana, Rio de Janeiro, CEP 20550-013, Brazil,
(franco | jamaral)@uerj.br

[†]Department of Electrical Engineering, Catholic University of Rio de Janeiro,
R. Marques S. Vicente, 225, Gavea, Rio de Janeiro, CEP 22453-900, Brazil,
(ricardo | marco | marley)@ele.puc-rio.br

This work discusses the use of an Evolvable Hardware platform in the synthesis of analog electronic circuits for Fuzzy Logic Controllers. Fuzzy Logic has proved to be a very powerful technique in the discipline of system control. A Fuzzy Logic Controller is defined by a collection of fuzzy if-then rules and a set of membership functions characterizing the linguistic terms associated with its inputs and output. The Evolvable Hardware analog platform, named PAMA-NG (Programmable Analog Multiplexer Array - Next Generation), is a reconfigurable platform that consists of integrated circuits whose internal connections can be programmed by Evolutionary Computation techniques to synthesize circuits. PAMA-NG is classified as a Field Programmable Analog Array, which constitute the state of the art in the technology of reconfigurable platforms. This work deals with the implementation of analog building blocks for modular Fuzzy Logic Controllers and presents four case studies: a type Z membership function, a type S membership function, a fuzzy logic operator and an output circuit (defuzzifier).

3.1 INTRODUCTION

A typical control system can be represented by the block diagram shown in Figure 3.1.

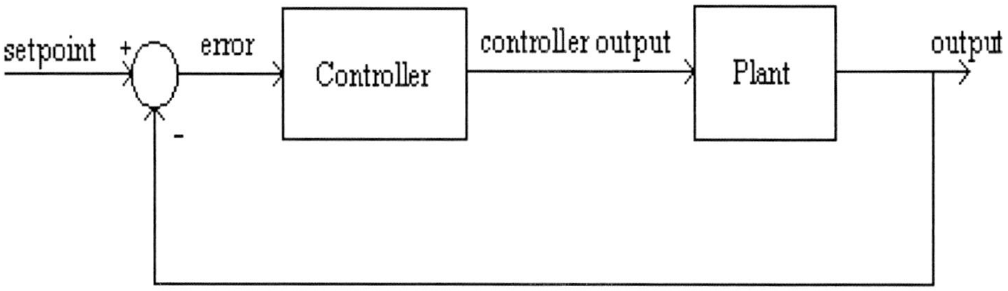

Figure 3.1. Control system block diagram

The *setpoint* expresses the desired plant output. The controller generates a signal at its output that drives the plant so that the *error* between the setpoint and the actual plant output is minimized. More sophisticated block diagrams can be used and controllers can be designed through various techniques (in the time and frequency domains) by using different representations and models [1] [2] [3].

The use of so-called intelligent techniques - fuzzy logic, artificial neural networks, evolutionary computation - in control is well established nowadays. Fuzzy controllers usually implement a control strategy derived from linguistic rules, which are translated into mathematical terms through the concepts of fuzzy sets and fuzzy logic [4] [5] [6] [7]. Neural controllers are capable of learning the system's behavior based on information about its input and output [8]. Evolutionary computation techniques, such as Genetic Algorithms [9] and Genetic Programming [10] [11], are inspired in natural evolution and genetic recombination mechanisms and have also been used for synthesizing controllers [12] [13] [14] [15] [16] [17] [18].

This work presents the main steps of the evolutionary design of analog building blocks for Fuzzy Logic Controllers. Fuzzy Controllers are defined by a collection of if-then rules and a set of membership functions that define the fuzzy sets associated to the linguistic values assigned to the fuzzy variables that constitute its inputs and output. They have been used successfully in numerous control systems applications and their most common implementations rely on microprocessors. However, they admit a high degree of parallelism and, therefore, an analog implementation could be preferable. Since the design of analog circuits is not an easy task, Evolvable Hardware techniques have been of great help in programming reconfigurable platforms in order to carry out circuit design [19] [20] [21] [22] [23].

Reconfigurable platforms, which consist of integrated circuits where internal connections can be programmed by the user, have been used successfully in the synthesis of analog circuits. Field Programmable Analog Arrays constitute the state of the art in the technology of reconfigurable analog platforms [24]. The reconfiguration of these devices enables self-adapting and self-repairing features, which are important in applications where circuits need to operate for long periods in harsh environments, such as in industrial applications. This is especially appealing to Fuzzy Logic Controller hardware that could be used in this type of applications.

Previous analog hardware implementations of Fuzzy Logic Controllers [25] [26] are based on designer's experience and intuition following electronic circuit design common rules. On the other hand, synthesis of unconventional electronic circuits is particularly appealing to techniques based on Evolvable Hardware [24] [27]. For example, as shown later, some building blocks of Fuzzy Logic Controllers may have many inputs. The design of circuits that implement those blocks can be rather difficult even for experienced designers.

The most notable features of circuits' evolution can be summarized as follows [19]:

- potential to find novel circuits;
- the possibility of finding new design rules from the novel circuits obtained;
- evolutionary methods can contemplate a larger set of design specifications compared to human design techniques;
- evolutionary systems have been able to achieve competitive circuits;
- evolutionary tools are more appropriate to analog design and it is expected that this will produce a new trend toward the research in analog circuits.

Although the techniques presented here could be used for the evolutionary design of any type of electronic circuit, the robustness of Fuzzy Logic Controllers with respect to membership function shapes and defuzzification methods makes that design less critical. In the case of membership functions, for example, the designer may choose a variety of similar shapes that may lead to equivalent performances [6], thus showing that a very strict choice is not necessary. As for defuzzification, the existing methods may provide different results for a given instant in time [28]. However, when dynamic processes are considered, the control strategy (rule base) takes care of undesirable deviations from the setpoint and drives the plant output to the desired value.

Evolvable Hardware techniques applied to the synthesis of analog electronic circuits that implement fuzzy inference systems have been explored recently with promising results [29] [30] [31].

This work is divided into four additional sections. The second section presents some basic architectural aspects of Fuzzy Logic Controllers and discusses analog hardware implementations. Section 3.3 focuses on the evolutionary platform and describes the PAMA (Programmable Analog Multiplexer Array) [32] and the modifications carried out to evolve fuzzy circuits with the new platform PAMA-NG (PAMA - Next Generation). Section 3.4 presents case studies that focus on the evolution of building blocks for analog Fuzzy Logic Controllers. Section 3.5 concludes the work.

3.2 Analog Fuzzy Logic Controllers

Fuzzy Logic Controllers are based on Fuzzy Inference Systems [6], which can model highly complex non-linear functions. When modeling a Multi-Input Single-Output (MISO) system, a Fuzzy Inference Systems (FIS) maps the n-dimensional input space to the single dimension output space. In control applications, inputs are usually the *error* (setpoint minus actual output) and the *change in error* (difference between the current and previous errors); the controller output is the input to the plant to be controlled. In this case, the Fuzzy Logic Controller implements the complex mapping function needed to control the plant and is a system realization of a fuzzy inference system.

Basically, a Fuzzy Logic Controller consists of three main function blocks: a fuzzification interface, a fuzzy inference engine and a defuzzification interface. In the fuzzification interface the actual inputs are mapped to fuzzy sets - represented by membership functions - that correspond to linguistic values. The inference engine holds the systems rules that define the control strategy. The actual controller output is obtained after defuzzification.

There are two basic approaches [29] to the implementation of an analog fuzzy system: monolithic and modular. The first approach considers a *monolithic block*, shown in Figure 3.2, that is able to map the inputs to the output. The design is rather difficult due to the complex non-linear multi-input single-output mapping that the controller needs to implement.

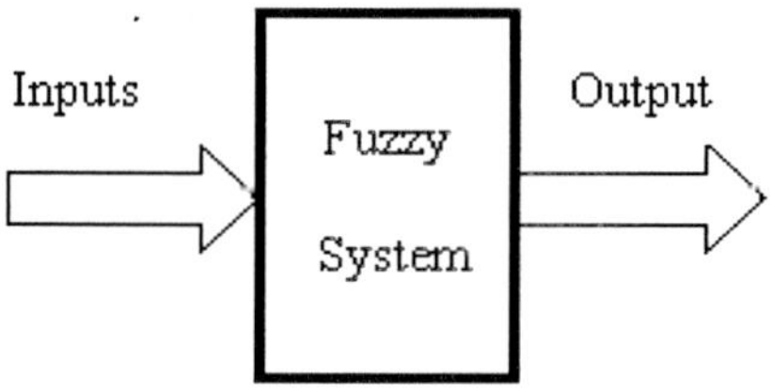

Figure 3.2. Monolithic approach to a fuzzy circuit implementation

The second approach to the implementation of an analog fuzzy system considers the three main function blocks shown in Figure 3.3: fuzzifier, fuzzy inference engine and defuzzifier.

In the modular approach, the fuzzy architecture is kept unchanged so that the analysis and understanding of each module - based on building blocks - are made easier under a fuzzy logic point of view. Many analog circuits, such as those that represent membership functions and logic operators, are needed for the implementation of a fuzzy controller. For example, a circuit that implements a given membership function is a DC mapper that has voltage levels as its input and output. Figure 3.4 illustrates the operation of a triangular membership function circuit.

Other electronic circuits are used in a similar fashion for the implementation of different blocks that constitute an analog Fuzzy Logic Controller. Figure 3.5 shows building blocks of the most important fuzzy operators: *min* and *max*.

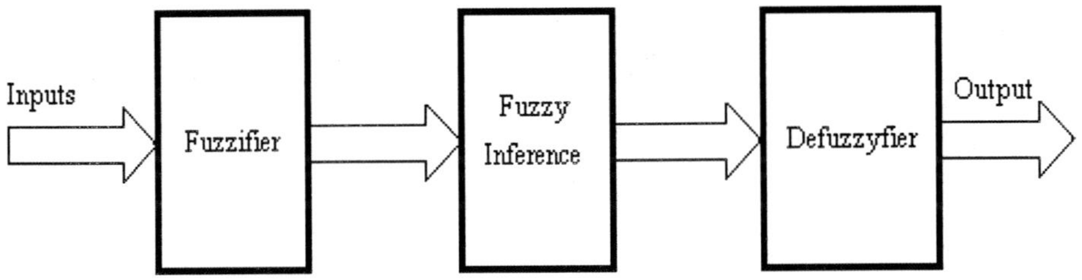

Figure 3.3. Modular approach to a fuzzy circuit implementation

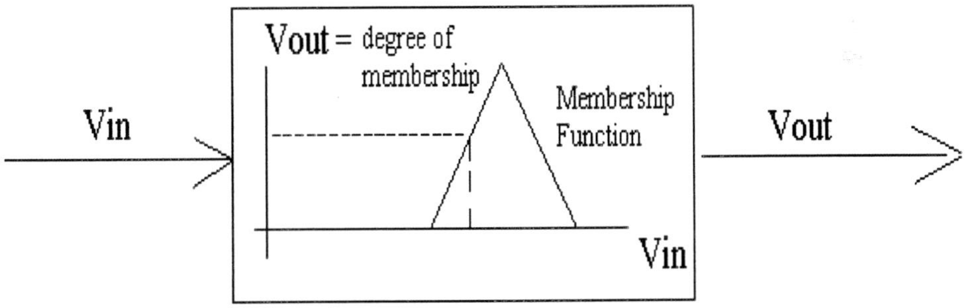

Figure 3.4. Triangular membership function

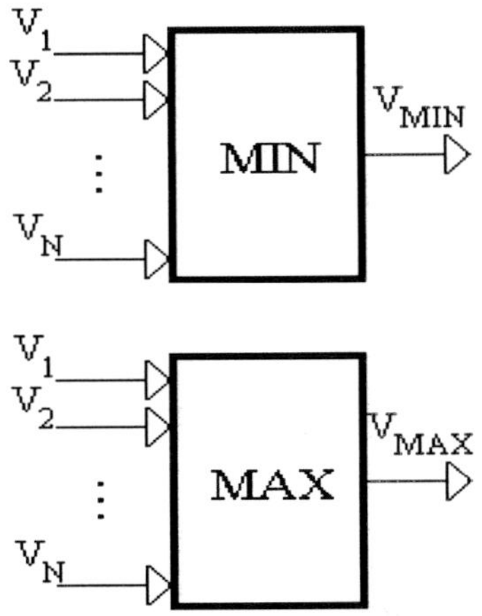

Figure 3.5. *Min* and *max* logic operators building blocks

3.3 Evolvable Hardware Platform

The Evolvable Hardware platform used is named PAMA-NG (Programmable Analog Multiplexer Array - Next Generation) and has been conceived as an environment for evolving building blocks ("fuzzy circuits") based on discrete components, without the need of electronic circuit simulators. This platform is based on the previous Programmable Analog Multiplexer Array platform [32], developed at the Department of Electrical Engineering of the Catholic University of Rio de Janeiro in 2001 as an environment to evolve generic analog circuits based on discrete components. It has been used in several projects involving intrinsic evolution ever since.

The PAMA-NG is an analog platform based on analog multiplexers/demultiplexers, as shown in Figure 3.6. These multiplexers (MUX) are fixed elements and are responsible for the interconnections of the different discrete components that can be plugged into the board. The prototype platform can interconnect 32 component terminals (leads) to up to 16 circuit connecting points (circuit nodes) or analog channels [19] [32]. Evolution on the platform takes place guided by a Genetic Algorithm (GA).

Genetic Algorithms [9] [33] [34] provide an adaptive searching mechanism inspired on Darwin's principle of reproduction and survival of the fittest. The individuals (solutions) in a population are represented by chromosomes; each of them is associated to a fitness value (problem evaluation). The chromosomes are subjected to an evolutionary process that takes several cycles. Basic operations are selection, reproduction, crossover and mutation. Parent selection gives more reproductive chances to the fittest individuals. During crossover some reproduced individuals cross and exchange their genetic characteristics. Mutations may occur in a small percentage and cause a random change in the genetic material, thus contributing to introduce variety in the population. The evolution process guides the Genetic Algorithm through more promising regions in the search space.

The so-called traditional GA [9] presents the following characteristics: binary representation, random population initialization, one-point crossover and mutation operations, elitism and linear normalization [34]. One-point crossover operation takes place when parts of two parent chromosomes are swapped after a random point selection. The parents are selected based on a parameter called crossover probability. Mutation is performed in each chromosome by replacing each bit by a randomly selected bit if a probability test is passed. This test is associated to a parameter called mutation probability. The elitism strategy copies the best individual (solution) of one generation into the next. This avoids the undesirable situation when the best individual of the population fails to produce children for the next generation. Linear normalization is a fitness technique that maps the fitness evaluation to new values. This is done by arranging chromosomes in a decreasing order in terms of evaluation and then assigning a constant value to the fittest one; the other chromosomes' fitness values are obtained by linearly decreasing that constant value. This technique helps to solve the problem where the best and worst individuals have nearly the same evaluation, for, in this situation, natural selection would not be effective.

Some of the advantages of using Genetic Algorithms are: they constitute a global search technique, can be applied to the optimization of ill-structured problems and a precise mathematical formulation for the problem is not required. Besides, Genetic Algorithms are robust, applicable to a number of problems and efficient, in the sense that either a sub-optimal or optimal solution may be found within reasonable time.

Intrinsic evolution of analog circuits is achieved through a Genetic Algorithm whose chromosomes are made up of genes (bit string). Each gene configures the select signals of a particular analog multiplexer.

The PAMA-NG block diagram shown in Figure 3.6 consists of three main blocks: Genetic Algorithm, I/O boards and the Analog Reconfigurable Circuit.

The I/O boards are connected to the PC bus responsible for analog-to-digital (A/D) and digital-to-analog (D/A) conversions and for chromosome download. Power supplies and signal conditioning circuits used to buffer the input and output signals are not shown in the diagram.

The digital output hardware is used for downloading the chromosome (128 bits) to the analog reconfigurable circuit.

Some channels of the 32 channel 12 bit analog-to-digital converter hardware sample the inputs and output nodes; others can be used to monitor the circuits nodes and perform tasks such as checking voltage sources. To evolve fuzzy circuits using the platform, an eight-channel digital-to-analog converter needs to be added to the original Programmable Analog Multiplexer Array. An eight channel 12-bit digital-to-analog converter allows the application of up to eight different input value to the fuzzy circuits being evolved, so that the desired input to output mapping specified in the *mappingfile* may be performed.

PAMA-NG presents desirable characteristics concerning other reconfigurable platforms designed to intrinsically evolve analog circuits. These platforms characteristics have been contrasted in previous work [30]. The desired characteristics are:

- Fast circuit evaluation time: the fast analog-to-digital converter used allows a short evaluation time for each circuit. This evaluation time depends on the number of inputs and output and on the sampling rate;

- Programmable granularity: PAMA-NG allows all discrete components to be selected by the user, according to the application. It's an important feature, since the optimal choice of elementary block type and granularity is task dependent;

- Transparent architecture: circuits evolved on PAMA-NG can be easily analyzed, once on-board signal acquisition can be made; it's possible to access individual circuit elements with test equipment;

- Reproduction: evolved circuits can be reproduced, just following the interconnection points and including the multiplexers on-resistance;

- Protection against damaging configurations: the parasitic resistances of the switches (Ron) provide this protection. In the case of transistors used as discrete components, the Ron helps on limiting Vbe even when the transistor's base is connected to the positive reference and the emitter to the negative reference, being the maximum Vpp allowed of 6V;

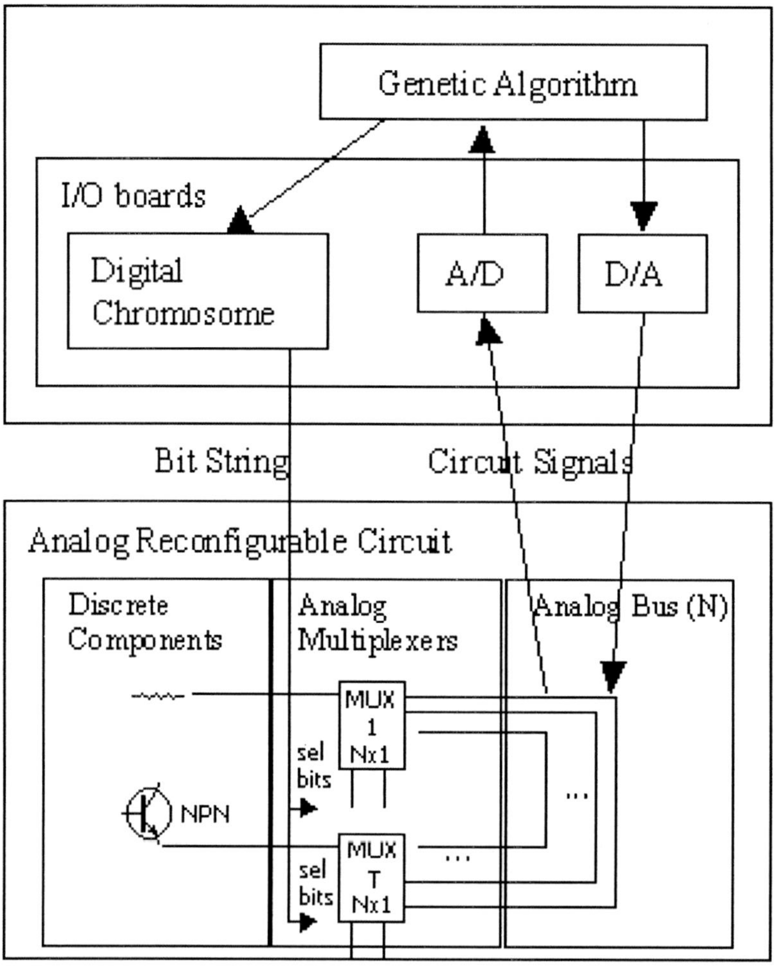

Figure 3.6. PAMA-NG block diagram

- No architecture constraints: evolution is able to exploit any interconnection pattern or architecture. There are no imposed constraints, thus producing circuits which are beyond the scope of conventional design methodologies [24];

- Input and output signals: the number of the evolved circuit's input and output signals is not fixed and can be determined according to the application;

- Scalability: the platform is scalable, allowing many Analog Reconfigurable Circuit modules to be interconnected.

Photographs of the PAMA-NG platform and of the Analog Reconfigurable Circuit are shown in Figure 3.7 and Figure 3.8, respectively.

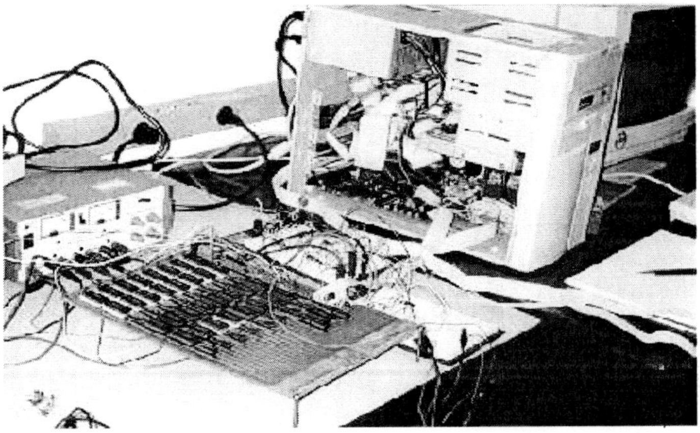

Figure 3.7. PAMA-NG platform photograph

Figure 3.8. Analog reconfigurable circuit photograph

3.3.1 Analog Reconfigurable Circuit

The Analog Reconfigurable Circuit can interconnect 32 component terminals (leads) to up to 16 circuit connecting points (circuit nodes) and is divided into three layers: discrete components, analog multiplexers and analog bus (Figure 3.6).

The circuit of Figure 3.9 corresponds to two of the 32 multiplexers of the reconfigurable circuit and one latch that holds the multiplexers' select bits. It also shows two genes of a chromosome, each of which configures one analog multiplexer used to connect one of the 16 lines of the analog bus to one of the terminals of a resistor.

The user chooses the discrete components, from low-level such as transistors, resistors and capacitors, to higher level circuits, such as operational amplifiers and comparators or even a more complex building block.

Each component terminal (lead) is plugged to a certain line of an analog bus (circuit node) through an analog multiplexer (16-to-1; 4 select bits). The chromosome bits (32 multiplexers x 4 select bits = 128 bits), which are sent by the PC, select for each analog multiplexer a specific node (line of the analog bus) to connect to the component's terminal. Each line of the analog bus corresponds to one interconnection point of the circuit; some of them can be associated with external points, such as the input signal, power supply, ground and circuit output, while others can be associated with internal points of interconnection of the circuit.

One PAMA-NG's Analog Reconfigurable Circuit module implements 32 16-to-1 analog multiplexers/demultiplexers (bi-directional) which allow the connection of up to 32 components' leads to 16 circuit nodes. The low on-resistance (Ron) - approximately 100 Ω - of the analog multiplexers prevents the reconfigurable circuit from damage during random configurations.

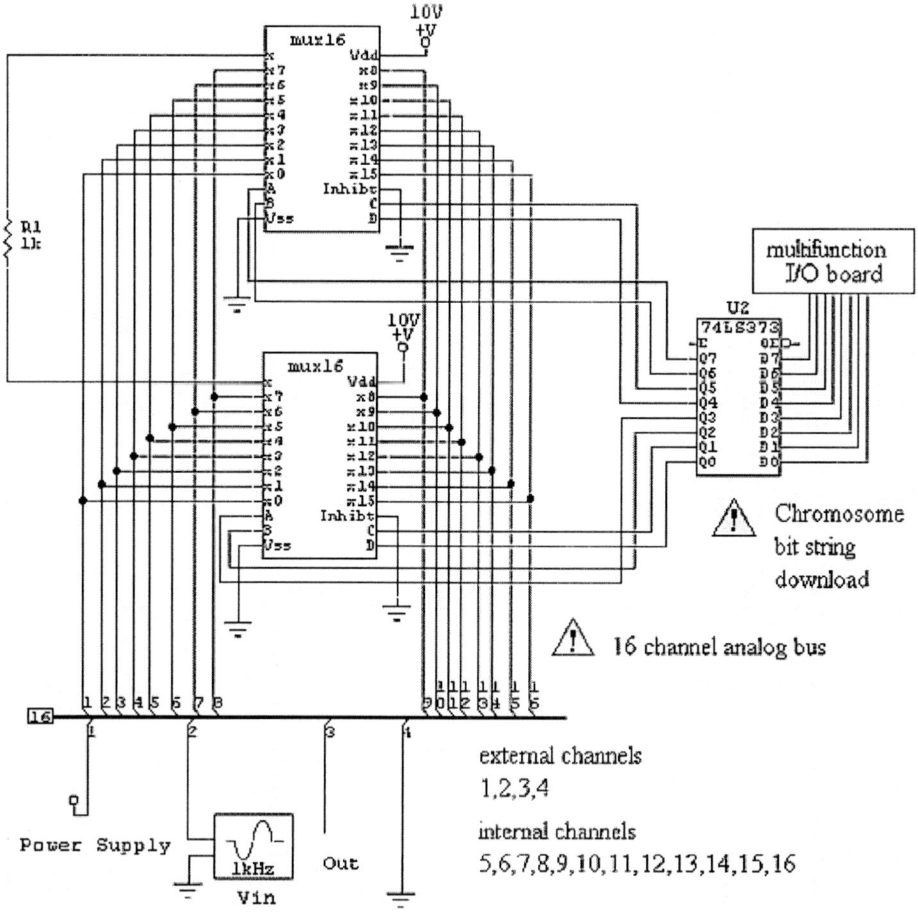

Figure 3.9. Two multiplexers of the Analog Reconfigurable Circuit

PAMA-NG is a flexible platform with respect to granularity: its building blocks can be chosen by the user, from transistors to high level analog components, such as operational amplifiers.

3.3.2 Evolution of a Fuzzy Circuit

The evolution of a fuzzy building block begins by developing a *mapping file* that defines the desired input-output mapping that the circuit shall perform. Then, the designer chooses the discrete components, from low-level - transistors and resistors - to higher level circuits - such as operational amplifiers and comparators or even a more complex circuit. Evolution takes place after specification of the Genetic Algorithm (GA) parameters.

Each chromosome is evaluated and the GA searches for the best individual (circuit topology). The GA used here has the following traditional characteristics [9] [33]:

- Binary Representation: 128 bits (32 x 4)
- Population Initialization: random
- Operators: one-point crossover and mutation
- Elitism

The techniques of steady state reproduction and exponential normalization are also employed in this work, since they improve the traditional GA performance when large search spaces are involved, as is usually the case of evolvable hardware applications [19].

In the traditional GA the entire population of individuals is replaced at each generation. This approach has a potential drawback [34], for it is possible that many of the best individuals do not reproduce at all and their genes may be lost; it is also possible that crossover or mutation operations on these best individuals destroy the good genes they have. With the steady state reproduction technique the number of individuals to replace or to keep can be chosen. In this work the steady state parameter tells the number of the best individuals to be kept in the next generation.

The exponential normalization differs from the traditional linear normalization in the sense that the selection probabilities follow, as the name implies, an exponential function. The probabilities of the ranked individuals (p_i) being selected are exponentially weighted [35] and are given by:

$$p_i = \frac{c-1}{c^n - 1} c^{n-i} \tag{3.1}$$

where n is the number of the individuals and c, which varies from 0 to 1, defines the exponential level of the method. The closer c is to 1 the lower is the function's exponential level, and, as a consequence, the selection intensity.

The techniques of steady state reproduction and exponential normalization, combined with a high mutation probability of about 0.1, help solve the problem of parent selection when many circuits have similar low scores, so that evolution occurs in a reasonable time.

Immediately after downloading the chromosome to the platform, the digital-to-analog converter applies input voltages to the circuit in accordance with the previously edited *mapping file*. The multifunction I/O board starts analog-to-digital conversions of input and output signals. These conversions do not occur in parallel. In tests, the period between two digital samples has been measured as being of 0.08ms. Since the main interest is to implement the input-output mapping, some time (0.5 ms) is allowed for the output voltage to stabilize before analog-to-digital conversion starts. For example, considering 64 samples for one circuit evaluation and 10,000 circuits evaluations, evaluation takes about 64*10,000*0.5 ms = 320 seconds.

The proper choice of the fitness evaluation function is one of the key factors to achieve a successful evolution. The chromosome fitness is evaluated by the following expression:

$$Fitness = \frac{1}{1+Error} \tag{3.2}$$

where

$$Error = \frac{1}{N}\sum_{i=1}^{N} |desired\_output(i) - real\_output(i)| \tag{3.3}$$

In the fitness function, the Error factor represents the average of the difference between the desired output from the mapping file and the real output obtained from the circuit configuration. It's worthy to mention that the fitness function is conceived to give values between 0 and 1. This helps to verify the effectiveness of the evolution because it is simple to check if the value is approaching the minimum error.

The GA searches for the best individual (circuit topology) maximizing the fitness (between 0 and 1). The desired output is read from the *mapping file*.

3.4 Tests

In preliminary tests, when PAMA-NG was still being developed, simple membership function blocks were evolved [29] [30] by using operational amplifiers and 1 KΩ resistors. Types Z and S membership functions were successfully evolved on a simplified version of the PAMA-NG (with only one channel digital-to-analog converter plugged at the PC parallel port). The First experiment presents a type Z membership function developed on the simplified version of the PAMA-NG.

Further experiments were performed [31] on the complete platform (eight-channel digital-to-analog converter): a type S membership function evolved under a different set of components, a triangular membership function, fuzzy logic operators circuits (*min* and *max*) and an output circuit (defuzzifier). Three of those experiments are presented below (the second, third and fourth experiments).

With respect to GA parameters, in all experiments described below the probability of crossover is 0.7, the probability of mutation is 0.1 and the exponential normalization c parameter is 0.9. The population and steady state parameters have been specified in accordance with each experiment. With these setups and the proper set of components, the PAMA-NG found no difficulty in evolving a working circuit.

3.4.1 The First Experiment

This experiment presents a type Z membership function developed on the simplified version of PAMA-NG (one channel digital-to-analog converter). This is a type zero membership function with 3 Volts amplitude. Figure 3.10 shows the function building block.

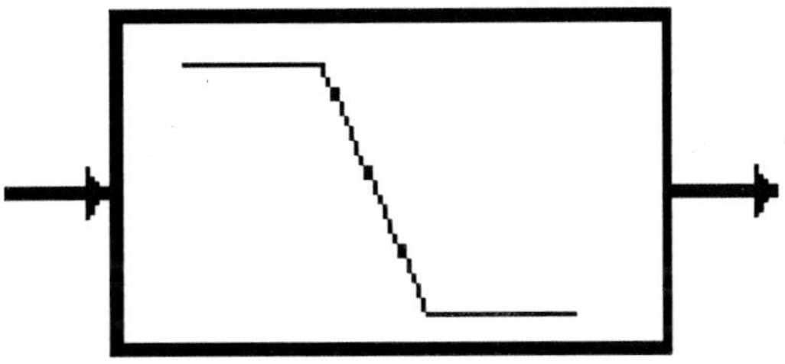

Figure 3.10. *Z* membership function building block

The fitness function used to evolve the circuit was based on the mean square error of the difference between the desired output (*Z* type membership function) and the actual output. The desired output was computed according to the membership function input-output mapping.

Recalling that the discrete electronic components can be chosen by the designer, one high level component - an operational amplifier - and some resistors have been used in this experiment. This choice of components was based on known circuit configurations for this type of input-output characteristics (one input, one output, piecewise linear function). Based on this characteristics, a population of 200 and a steady state of 10 were deemed appropriate for a successful evolution. The circuit schematic of the evolved circuit, which emerged on generation number 43, is illustrated in Figure 3.11. The multiplexer's Ron resistance (see Section 3.3) is shown as 0.1 KΩ resistors.

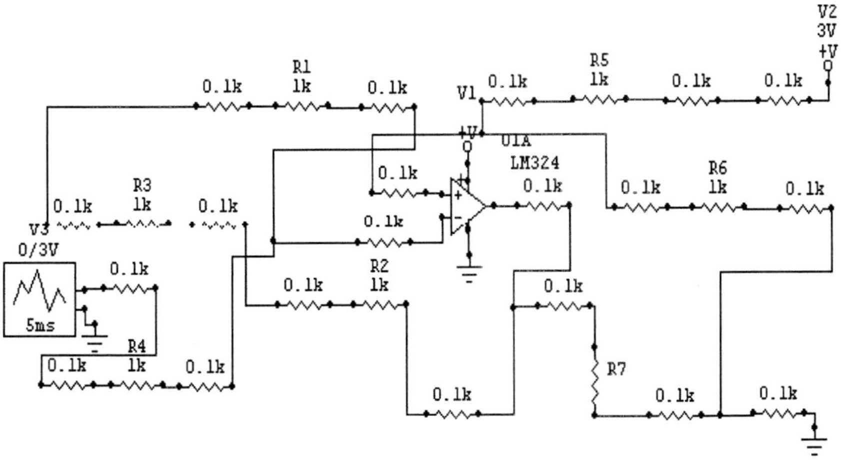

Figure 3.11. Circuit schematic of the evolved circuit for the *Z* function

Figure 3.12 presents the performance of the best evolved circuit. It shows that the real output waveform follows very closely the desired one; this attests to the suitability of the evolved circuit to the proposed task.

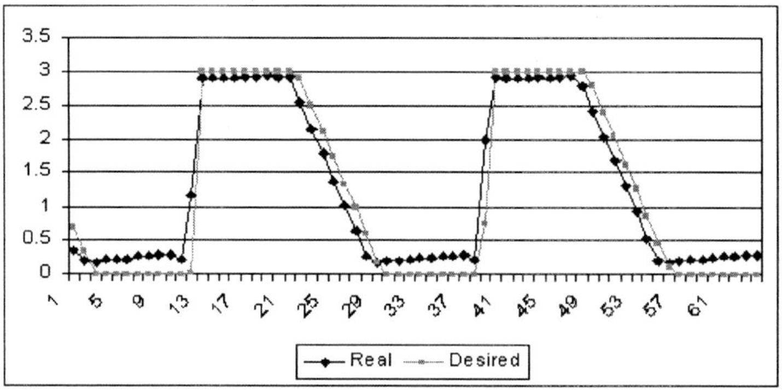

Figure 3.12. Real versus desired output for the *Z* function

3.4.2 The Second Experiment

This experiment focuses on the development of a type *S* membership function with an amplitude of 3 volts and breakpoints at 1 and 2 volts. In a previous experiment [31], a circuit for this function was successfully evolved by using the same set of components (resistors and operational amplifiers) and GA configuration employed in the first experiment above. The objective now was to check the platform's capability of evolving the circuit by using a different set of components (resistors, operational amplifiers, NPN and PNP transistors). Since this set gives rise to a larger number of possible circuit topologies, population and steady state were increased to 400 and 50, respectively. Figure 3.13 shows the evolution of the best individual (circuit) for the *S* function, which emerged on generation number 97.

The transfer function and the circuit schematic of the evolved circuit are illustrated at Figure 3.14 and Figure 3.15, respectively. The multiplexer's Ron resistance is again represented as 0.1 KΩ resistors.

The performance of the evolved circuit is shown in Figure 3.14. It can be observed that the mapping error (difference between actual and desired shapes) is negligible, with the exception of the breakpoint at 1 volt. It should be noted that this error does not affect the overall performance of the fuzzy controller due to its robustness to membership function shapes.

The circuit schematic of Figure 3.15 shows an unusual transistor configuration (Q4). Unusual configurations of analog electronic circuits occur quite often with Evolvable Hardware development tools. This enforces and demonstrates their ability to search for different circuit topologies.

3.4.3 The Third Experiment

Circuits that perform *min* and *max* operations are important building blocks in the implementation of a Fuzzy Logic Controller. This experiment consists of the evolution of a *min*

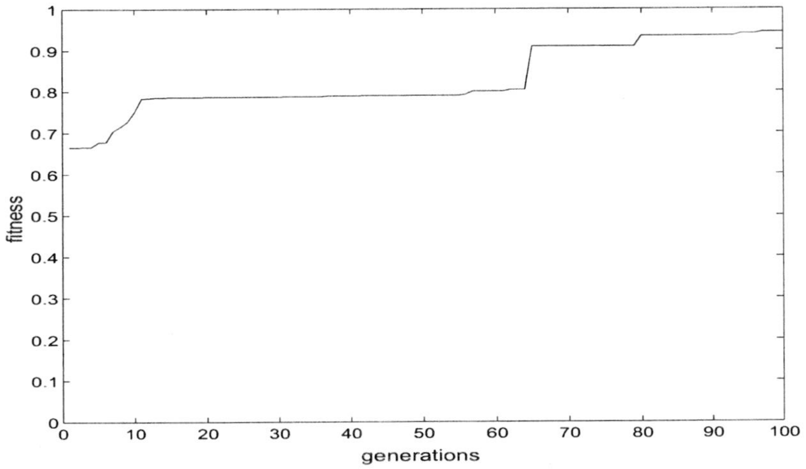

Figure 3.13. Evolution of the best circuit for the *S* function

operator (two inputs and one output) by using bipolar transistors and resistors, which are commonly used for the implementation of logic operators. A population of 400 and a steady state of 50 were used. The evolved circuit, shown in Figure 3.16, emerged on generation 278.

By applying the *mapping file* input values to the circuit, it has been observed that the maximum error is about 6%.

3.4.4 The Fourth Experiment

This experiment consists of the evolution of a three input-one output circuit that performs defuzzification (see Figure 3.3). The specification of components took inspiration on analog implementations of artificial neural networks [31] [36] that use resistors and Operational Transconductance Amplifiers (OTA). An OTA has a voltage input and a current output; it also admits a bias current, which can be used to adjust the input contribution to the output (gain). The output being a current makes the aggregation of signals an easier task. It should be noted that OTAs come as integrated circuits, enabling their connection to the platform in the same way as an operational amplifier, for example. The evolutionary process consists of the search for the proper set of connections of OTAs and of the available resistors (circuit topology).

A population of 400 and a steady state of 50 were also used in this experiment. The circuit schematic diagram of the best evolved circuit, which emerged on generation 342, is illustrated in Figure 3.17.

The maximum error between the desired and the real output voltage values for this circuit is about 12%. It should be noted that the circuit's performance is constrained by the number of components that can be connected to the platform and by the difficulty of designing a circuit that maps three inputs to one output. Besides, the performance of a fuzzy controller is not critically affected by the defuzzification procedure (see Section 3.1).

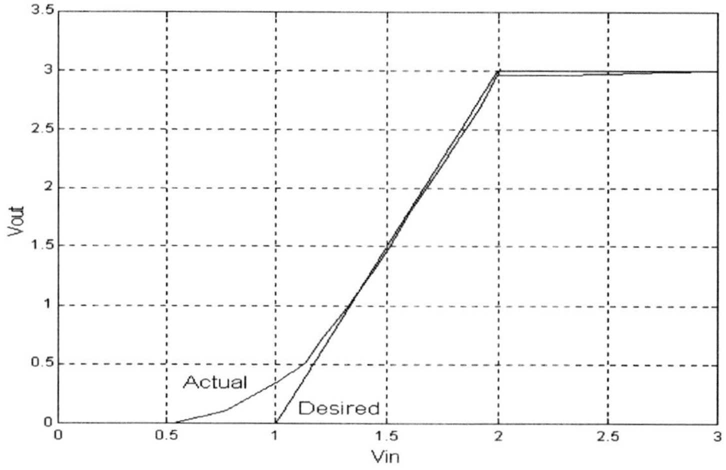

Figure 3.14. Transfer function of type *S* membership function

3.5 SUMMARY

This work has dealt with the implementation of building blocks for analog Fuzzy Logic Controllers ("fuzzy circuit") on a new Field Programmable Analog Array development platform, called PAMA-NG (Programmable Analog Multiplexer Array - Next Generation), which uses a Genetic Algorithm to achieve intrinsic circuit evolution. Membership functions and fuzzy circuits have been successfully evolved and other implementations are under way. Next steps of this study include the implementation of more complex fuzzy analog circuits.

The prototype nature of the platform does not allow the implementation of a full analog Fuzzy Logic Controller; an integrated circuit solution is crucial for the implementation of a completely evolvable controller.

Another drawback of the PAMA-NG is that the choice of adequate components to be plugged on the platform depends very much on the designer. A better alternative would be to let the components be evolved during the process, possibly exploring the unique nature of CMOS technology [37].

One important feature of the PAMA-NG platform is scalability. Ideally, in a near future, several (integrated version) platforms could be connected together, each of them with a different target, automatically defined during evolution depending on the platform's individual evolution process. Evolution would occur in parallel and the fitness value would be determined by taking into consideration the system's final output and each platform's individual output. Such a parallel system seems to be in accordance with the modular approach to developing Fuzzy Logic Controllers.

In the not too distant future, with integrated (not prototype) scalable platforms [37] [38], similar to PAMA-NG, it will be possible to build a complete intelligent analog Fuzzy Logic

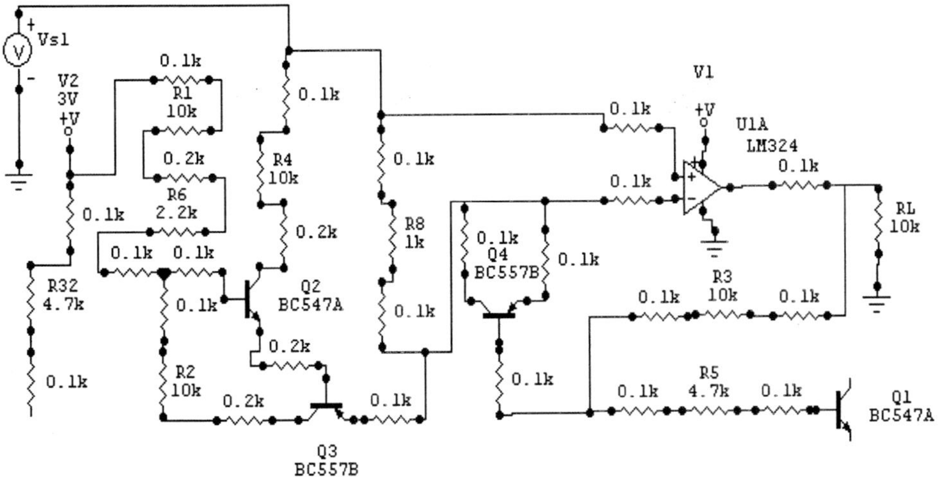

Figure 3.15. Schematic of the evolved circuit for type *S* membership function

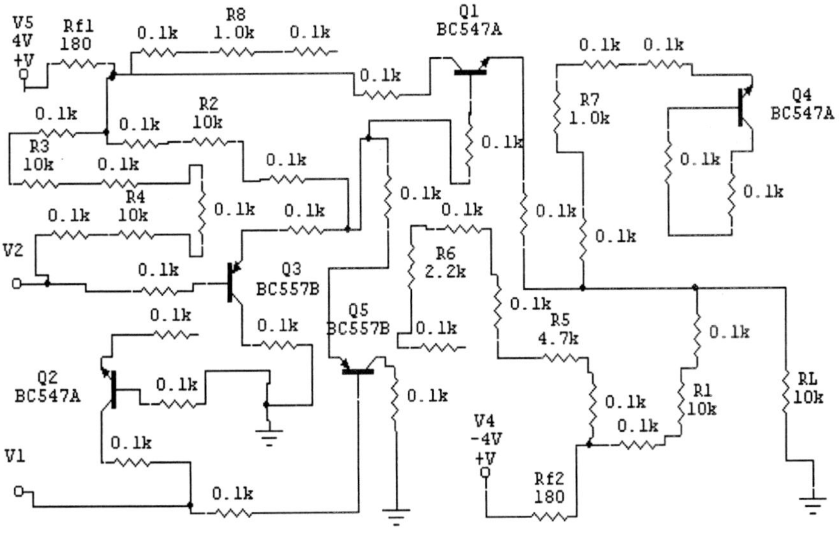

Figure 3.16. Circuit schematic of the evolved circuit for *min* fuzzy logic operator

Controller based on evolvable building blocks that shall perform useful tasks in the real world.

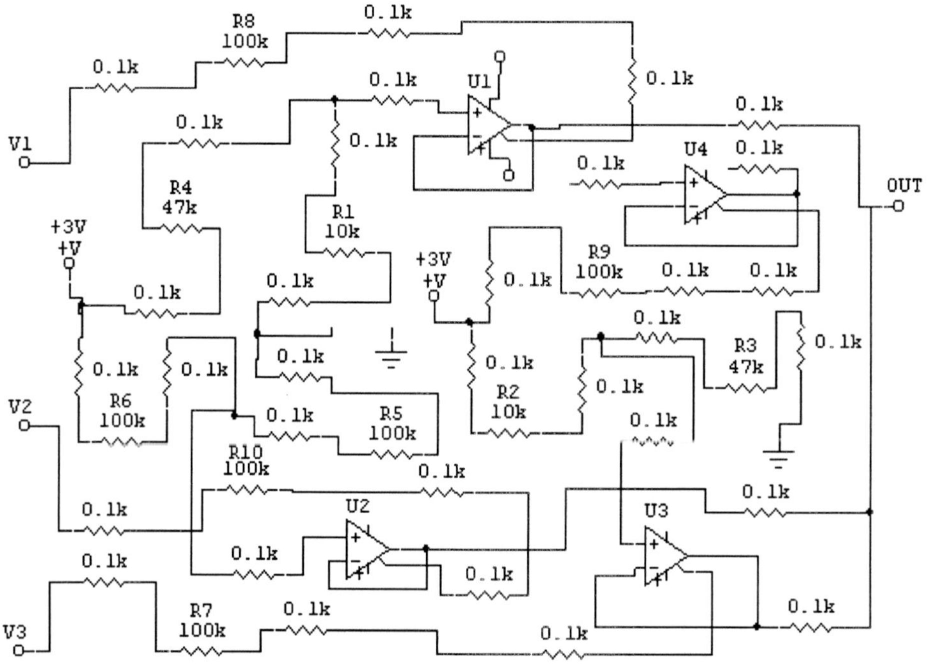

Figure 3.17. Circuit schematic of the defuzzifier circuit

Bibliography

[1] K. Ogata, *Modern Control Engineering*, 3rd Ed.,Prentice-Hall,1997.

[2] R.C. Dorf, and R.H. Bishop, *Modern Control Systems*, Addison Wesley Longman, USA, 1998.

[3] K.J. Astrm, and T. Hgglund, *PID Controller: Theory, Design and Tuning*, Instrument Society of America, North Carolina, USA, 1995.

[4] E.H. Mamdani, Application of fuzzy algorithms for control of simple dynamic plant, *Proceedings of the IEE*, Vol. 121, pp. 1585-1588, 1974.

[5] T.J. Ross, *Fuzzy Logic with Engineering Applications*, McGraw Hill, Inc., New York, USA, 1995.

[6] D. Driankov, H. Hellendoorn, and M. Reinfrank, *An Introduction to Fuzzy Control*, Springer-Verlag, 1993.

[7] W. Pedrycz, *Fuzzy Control and Fuzzy Systems*, Research Studies Press, England, 1989.

[8] P.J Werbos, *Control Handbook of Neural Computation*, Oxford University Press, UK, 1997.

[9] J.H. Holland, *Adaptation in Natural and Artificial Systems: An Introductory Analysis with Applications to Biology, Control, and Artificial Intelligence*, 2nd Edition, MIT Press, .Cambridge, MA, USA, 1992.

[10] J. R Koza,. *Genetic Programming*, MIT Press, Cambridge, MA, USA, 1992.

[11] J. R. Koza, *Genetic Programming II*, MIT Press, Cambridge, MA, USA, 1994.

[12] K. F. Man, *K.S. Tang, S. Kwong, and W.A. Halang,. Genetic Algorithms for Control and Signal Processing*, Springer-Verlag, London, 1997.

[13] K.F. Man, K.S. Tang, and S. Kwong, *Genetic Algorithms: Concepts and Designs*, Springer Verlag, London, 1999.

[14] L.S. Crawford, V. H. L. Cheng, and P. K. Menon, Synthesis of Flight Vehicle Guidance and Control Laws using Genetic Search Methods, AIAA Conference on Guidance, *Navigation and Control*, Paper 4153, Reston, VA, USA, 1999.

[15] L. D. Dewell, and P.K. Menon, Low-thrust Orbit Transfer Optimization using Genetic Search AIAA Conference on Guidance, *Navigation and Control*, Paper 4151, Reston, VA, USA, 1999.

[16] P.K. Menon, M. Yousefpor, T. Lam, and M. L. Steinberg, Nonlinear Flight Control System Synthesis using Genetic Programming, AIAA Conference on Guidance, *Navigation, and Control*, Reston, VA, USA, pp. 461-470, 1995.

[17] G.D. Sweriduk, P.K. Menon, and M.L. Steinberg, Robust Command Augmentation System Design using Genetic Search Methods,AIAA Conference on Guidance, *Navigation, and Control*, Reston, VA, USA, pp. 286 - 294, 1998.

[18] J.R. Koza, M.A. Keane, M.J. Streeter, W. Mydlowec, J.Yu, and G. Lanza, *Genetic Programming IV: Routine Human-competitive Machine Intelligence*, Kluwer Academic Publishers, 2003.

[19] R.S. Zebulum, M.A. Pacheco, and M.M. Vellasco, *Evolutionary Electronics: Automatic Design of Electronic Circuits and Systems by Genetic Algorithms* , CRC Press, Boca Raton, Florida, USA, 2001.

[20] J.D. Lohn, and S.P. Colombano, Automated Analog Circuit Synthesis Using a Linear Representation, *2nd International Conference on Evolvable Systems: From Biology to Hardware*, Lausanne, Switzerland, 1998. M. Sipper, D. Mange, and A. Prez-Uribe (Eds.), LNCS, V. 1478, Springer-Verlag, pp. 125-133, 1998.

[21] A. Thompson, On the Automatic Design of Robust Electronics Through Artificial Evolution , *2nd International Conference on Evolvable Systems: From Biology to Hardware*, Lausanne, Switzerland, 1998. M. Sipper, D. Mange, and A. Prez-Uribe (Eds.), LNCS, V. 1478, Springer-Verlag, pp. 13-24, 1998.

[22] J.R. Koza, F.H. Bennett III, D. Andre, A. Martin, and F. Dunlap, Automated Synthesis of Analog Electrical Circuits by means of Genetic Programming, *IEEE Transactions on Evolutionary Computation*, **1**(2) pp. 109-128, 1998.

[23] P. Layzell, A New Research Tool for Intrinsic Hardware Evolution, *2nd International Conference on Evolvable Systems: From Biology to Hardware, Lausanne*, Switzerland, September 1998. M. Sipper, D. Mange, and A. Prez-Uribe (Editors.), LNCS, V. 1478, Springer-Verlag, pp. 47-56, 1998.

[24] A. Stoica, D. Keymeulen, R. Zebulum, A. Thakoor, T. Daud, G. Klimeck, Y. Jin, R. Tawel, and V. Duong, *Evolution of Analog Circuits on Field Programmable Transistor Array, 2nd NASA DoD Workshop on Evolvable Hardware*, IEEE Computer Press, pp. 99-108, 2000.

[25] T. Yamakawa, A Fuzzy Inference Engine in Nonlinear Analog Mode and its Application to Fuzzy Logic Control, *IEEE Transactions on Neural Networks*, V. 4, no. 3, 1993.

[26] S. Guo, L. Peters, and H. Surmann, Design and Application of an Analog Fuzzy Logic Controller, *IEEE Transactions on Fuzzy Systems*, V. 4, no. 4, 1996.

[27] X. Yao, and T. Higuchi, Promises and Challenges of Evolvable Hardware, *1st International Conference on Evolvable Systems: From Biology to Hardware (ICES96)*, Tsukuba, Japan, LNCS 1259, pp. 55-80, 1996.

[28] E. Lembessis, and R. Tanscheit, The Influence of Implication Operators and Defuzzification Methods on the Deterministic Output of a Fuzzy Rule-based Controller. *4th IFSA Congress*, Brussels, Belgium, pp. 109-11 (Engineering), 1991.

[29] J.F.M. Amaral, J.L.M. Amaral, C. Santini, R. Tanscheit, M.M. Vellasco, and M.A. Pacheco, Towards Evolvable Analog Fuzzy Logic Controllers, *2002 NASA/DoD Conference on Evolvable Hardware (EH '02)*, Alexandria, USA, pp. 123-128, 2002.

[30] C. Santini, J.F.M. Amaral, M.A. Pacheco, M.M. Vellasco, and M. Szwarcman, Evolutionary Analog Circuit Design on a Programmable Analog Multiplexer Array, *IEEE International Conference on Field Programmable Technology (FPT'02)*, Hong Kong, pp. 189-196, 2002.

[31] J.F.M. Amaral, *Synthesis of Fuzzy Systems through Evolutionary Computation*, Ph.D. Thesis, Catholic University of Rio de Janeiro, Rio de Janeiro, Brazil, 2003.

[32] C. Santini, R. Zebulum, M.A. Pacheco, M.M. Vellasco, and M. Szwarcman, PAMA - Programmable Analog Multiplexer Array, *3rd NASA/DoD Workshop on Evolvable Hardware*, Long Beach, CA, USA, pp. 36-43, 2001.

[33] D. Goldberg, *Genetic Algorithms in Search, Optimization and Machine Learning*, Addison-Wesley Publishing Company, Reading, MA, USA, 1989.

[34] L. Davis, *Handbook of Genetic Algorithms*, VNR Comp. Library, 1990.

[35] T. Blickle, *Theory of Evolutionary Algorithms and Application to System Synthesis*, Ph.D. Thesis, Swiss Federal Institute of Technology, Zurich, Switzerland, 1996.

[36] C. Mead, *Analog VLSI and Neural Systems*, Addison-Wesley Publishing Company, Reading, MA, USA, 1989.

[37] J.P.B. Botelho, L.B. Sa, P.F. Vieira, and A. Mesquita, An Experiment on Nonlinear Synthesis Using Evolutionary Techniques based only on CMOS Transistors, *2003 NASA/DoD Conference on Evolvable Hardware*, Chicago, USA, pp. 50-58, 2003.

[38] A. Stoica, R. Zebulum, D. Keymeulen, R. Tawel, T. Daud, and A. Thakoor, Reconfigurable VLSI Architecture for Evolvable Hardware: from Experimental Field Programmable Transistor Array to Evolution Oriented Chips, *IEEE Transactions on VLSI*, V. 9, no. 1, pp. 227-232, 2001.

In: Evolutionary Machine Design: Methodology & Applications ISBN 1-59454-405-0
Editors: N. Nedjah & L. Mourelle, pp:81-107

Chapter 4

IMPROVING THE SEARCH BY ENCODING MULTIPLE SOLUTIONS IN A CHROMOSOME

Mihai Oltean

Department of Computer Science, Faculty of Mathematics and Computer Science,
Babeş Bolyai University,
Kogalniceanu 1, 3400 Cluj-Napoca, Romania,
moltean@cs.ubbcluj.ro, www.cs.ubbcluj.ro/~moltean

We investigate the possibility of encoding multiple solutions of a problem in a single chromosome. The best solution encoded in an individual will represent (will provide the fitness of) that individual. In order to obtain some benefits the chromosome decoding process must have the same complexity as in the case of a single solution in a chromosome. Three Genetic Programming techniques are analyzed for this purpose: Multi Expression Programming, Linear Genetic Programming and Infix Form Genetic Programming. Numerical experiments show that encoding multiple solutions in a chromosome greatly improves the search process.

4.1 INTRODUCTION

Evolutionary Algorithms (EAs) [9, 10] are powerful tools used for solving difficult real-world problems.

This paper describes a new paradigm called *Multi Solution Programming* (MSP) that may be used for improving the search performed by the Evolutionary Algorithms. The main idea is to encode multiple solutions (more than one) in a single chromosome. The best solution encoded in a chromosome will represent (will provide the fitness of) that individual.

This special kind of encoding is useful when the complexity of the decoding process is similar to the complexity of the decoding process of chromosomes encoding a single solution of the problem being solved.

Note that the Multi Solution Programming is not a particular technique, but a paradigm intended to be used in conjunction with an Evolutionary Algorithm. MSP refers to a new way of encoding solutions in a chromosome.

GP techniques are very suitable for the MSP paradigm because the trees offer an implicit multiple solutions representation: each sub-tree may be considered as a potential solution of the problem. Three Genetic Programming (GP) [11, 12] variants are tested with the proposed model: Multi Expression Programming (MEP) [17, 18], Linear Genetic Programming (LGP) [4–6, 16] and Infix Form Genetic Programming (IFGP) [19].

Multi Expression Programming uses a chromosome encoding similar to the way in which *C* or *Pascal* compilers translate mathematical expressions in machine code. Note that MEP was originally designed [17] to encode multiple solutions in a chromosome. A MEP variant that encodes a single solution in a chromosome is proposed and tested in this paper.

A Linear Genetic Programming chromosome is a sequence of ***C*** language instructions. Each instruction has a destination variable and several source variables. One of the variables is usually chosen to provide the output of the program. A LGP variant encoding multiple solutions in a chromosome is proposed in this paper.

Infix Form Genetic Programming chromosomes are strings of integer encoding mathematical expressions in infix form. Each IFGP chromosome encodes multiple solutions of the problem being solved [19]. A IFGP variant encoding a single solution in a chromosome is proposed and tested in this paper.

All the solutions represented in a MSP individual should be decoded by traversing the chromosome only once. Partial results are stored by using Dynamic Programming.

Several numerical experiments with the considered GP techniques are performed by using 4 symbolic regression problems. For each test problem the relationships between the success rate and the population size and the code length are analyzed.

Results show that Multi Solutions Programming significantly improves the evolutionary search. For all considered test problems the evolutionary techniques encoding multiple solutions in a chromosome are significantly better than the similar techniques encoding a single solution in a chromosome.

The paper is organized as follows. Motivation for this research is presented in section 4.2. Test problems used to asses the performance of the considered algorithms are given in section 4.3. Multi Expression Programming and its counterpart Single Expression Programming are described in section 4.4. Linear Genetic Programming and Multi-Solution Linear Genetic Programming are described in section 4.5. Infix Form Genetic Programming and Single-Solution Infix Form Genetic Programming are described in section 4.6. Conclusions and further work directions are given in section 4.6.2.

4.2 Multiple Solution Programming

This section tries to answer two fundamental questions:

- Why encoding multiple solutions in the same chromosome?
- How to efficiently encode multiple solutions in the same chromosome in order to obtain some benefits?

The answer for the first question is motivated by the No Free Lunch Theorems for Search [23]. There is neither practical nor theoretical evidence that one of the solutions encoded in a chromosome is better than the others. More than that, Wolpert and McReady [23] proved that we cannot use the search algorithm's behavior so far for a particular test function to predict its future behavior on that function.

The second question is more difficult than the first one. There is no general prescription on how to encode multiple solutions in the same chromosome. In most cases this involves creativity and imagination. However, some general suggestions can be given.

(i) In order to obtain some benefits from encoding more than one solution in a chromosome we have to spend a similar effort (computer time, memory etc) as in the case of encoding a single solution in a chromosome. For instance, if we have 10 solutions encoded in chromosome and the time needed to extract and decode these solutions is 10 times larger than the time needed to extract and process one solution we got nothing. In this case we can not talk about an useful encoding.

(ii) We have to be careful when we want to encode a multiple solutions in a variable length chromosome (for instance in a standard GP chromosome), because this kind of chromosome will tend to increase its size in order to encode more and more solutions. And this could lead to bloat [2, 15].

(iii) Usually encoding multiple solutions in a chromosome might require storing the partial results. Sometimes this can be achieved by using the Dynamic Programming [3] technique. This kind of model is employed by the techniques described in this paper.

4.3 Test Problems and Metric of Performance

For assessing the performance of the considered algorithms we use several symbolic regression problems [11]. The aim of symbolic regression is to find a mathematical expression that satisfies a set of fitness cases.

The test problems used in the numerical experiments are:

$$\begin{aligned} F_1(x) &= x^4 - x^3 + x^2 - x, \\ F_2(x) &= x^4 + x^3 + x^2 + x, \\ F_3(x) &= x^4 + 2*x^3 + 3*x^2 + 4*x, \\ F_4(x) &= x^6 - 2x^4 + x^2. \end{aligned} \tag{4.1}$$

Test problem f_2 is also known as *quartic polynomial* and f_4 is known as *sextic polynomial* [11,12].

For each function 20 fitness cases have been randomly generated with a uniform distribution over the [0, 10] interval.

For each test problem the relationships between the success rate, the population size and the code length are analyzed. The success rate is computed as:

$$Success\,rate = \frac{The\,number\,of\,successful\,runs}{The\,total\,number\,of\,runs}. \tag{4.2}$$

Roughly speaking the quality of a GP chromosome is the average distance between the expected output and the obtained output [11]. A run is considered successful if the fitness of the best individual in the last generation is less than 0.01.

4.4 Multi Expression Programming

In this section, *Multi Expression Programming* (MEP) [17] is briefly described.

4.4.1 MEP Representation

MEP genes are represented by substrings of a variable length. The number of genes per chromosome is constant. This number defines the length of the chromosome. Each gene encodes a terminal or a function symbol. A gene encoding a function includes pointers towards the function arguments. Function arguments always have indices of lower values than the position of that function in the chromosome.

This representation is similar to the way in which ***C*** and ***Pascal*** compilers translate mathematical expressions into machine code [1].

MEP representation ensures that no cycle arises while the chromosome is decoded (phenotypically transcripted). According to this representation scheme the first symbol of the chromosome must be a terminal symbol. In this way only syntactically correct programs (MEP individuals) are obtained.

Example. A representation where the numbers on the left positions stand for gene labels is employed here. Labels do not belong to the chromosome, they being provided only for explanation purposes.

For this example we use the set of functions $F = \{+, *\}$, and the set of terminals $T = \{a, b, c, d\}$. An example of chromosome using the sets F and T is given below:

$$\begin{array}{ll} 1: & a \\ 2: & b \\ 3: & +1,2 \\ 4: & c \\ 5: & d \\ 6: & +4,5 \\ 7: & *3,6 \end{array} \tag{4.3}$$

4.4.2 Decoding MEP Chromosomes and Fitness Assignment Process

In this section is described the way in which MEP individuals are translated into computer programs and the way in which the fitness of these programs is computed.

This translation is achieved by reading the chromosome top-down. A terminal symbol specifies a simple expression. A function symbol specifies a complex expression obtained by connecting the operands specified by the argument positions with the current function symbol.

For instance, genes 1, 2, 4 and 5 in the previous example encode simple expressions formed by a single terminal symbol. These expressions are:

$$\begin{aligned} E_1 &= a, \\ E_2 &= b, \\ E_4 &= c, \\ E_5 &= d, \end{aligned} \tag{4.4}$$

Gene 3 indicates the operation + on the operands located at positions 1 and 2 of the chromosome. Therefore gene 3 encodes the expression:

$$E_3 = a+b. \tag{4.5}$$

Gene 6 indicates the operation + on the operands located at positions 4 and 5. Therefore gene 6 encodes the expression:

$$E_6 = c+d. \tag{4.6}$$

Gene 7 indicates the operation * on the operands located at position 3 and 6. Therefore gene 7 encodes the expression:

$$E_7 = (a+b)*(c+d). \tag{4.7}$$

E_7 is the expression encoded by the whole chromosome.

Each MEP chromosome is allowed to encode a number of expressions equal to the chromosome length. Each of these expressions is considered as being a potential solution of the problem.

The value of these expressions may be computed by reading the chromosome top down. Partial results are computed by dynamic programming and are stored in a conventional manner.

Usually the chromosome fitness is defined as the fitness of the best expression encoded by that chromosome.

For instance, if we want to solve symbolic regression problems the fitness of each sub-expression E_i may be computed using the formula:

$$f(E_i) = \sum_{k=1}^{n} |o_{k,i} - w_k|, \tag{4.8}$$

where $o_{k,i}$ is the obtained result by the expression E_i for the fitness case k and w_k is the targeted result for the fitness case k. In this case the fitness needs to be minimized.

The fitness of an individual is set to be equal to the lowest fitness of the expressions encoded in chromosome:

$$f(C) = \min_i f(E_i). \tag{4.9}$$

When we have to deal with other problems we compute the fitness of each sub-expression encoded in the MEP chromosome and the fitness of the entire individual is given by the fitness of the best expression encoded in that chromosome.

4.4.3 Search Operators

Search operators used within MEP algorithm are crossover and mutation. Considered search operators preserve the chromosome structure. All offspring are syntactically correct expressions.

Crossover By crossover two parents are selected and are recombined. For instance, within the uniform recombination the offspring genes are taken randomly from one parent or another.

Example. Let us consider the two parents C_1 and C_2 given in Table 4.1. The two offspring O_1 and O_2 are obtained by uniform recombination as shown in Table 4.1.

Table 4.1. MEP uniform recombination.

Parents		**Offspring**	
C_1	C_2	O_1	O_2
1: ***b***	1: *a*	1: *a*	1: ***b***
2: *** 1, 1**	2: *b*	2: *** 1, 1**	2: *b*
3: **+ 2, 1**	3: + 1, 2	3: **+ 2, 1**	3: + 1, 2
4: ***a***	4: *c*	4: *c*	4: ***a***
5: *** 3, 2**	5: *d*	5: *** 3, 2**	5: *d*
6: ***a***	6: + 4, 5	6: + 4, 5	6: ***a***
7: **- 1, 4**	7: * 3, 6	7: **- 1, 4**	7: * 3, 6

Mutation Each symbol (terminal, function of function pointer) in the chromosome may be target of mutation operator. By mutation some symbols in the chromosome are changed. To preserve the consistency of the chromosome its first gene must encode a terminal symbol.

Table 4.2. MEP mutation.

C	O
1: a	1: a
2: * 1, 1	2: * 1, 1
3: ***b***	3: **+ 1, 2**
4: * 2, 2	4: * 2, 2
5: b	5: b
6: + **3**, 5	6: + **1**, 5
7: a	7: a

Example. Consider the chromosome C given in Table 4.2. If the boldfaced symbols are selected for mutation an offspring O is obtained as shown in Table 4.2.

4.4.4 MEP Algorithm

In this paper we use a steady-state [22] as underlying mechanism for Multi Expression Programming. The algorithm starts by creating a random population of individuals. The following steps are repeated until a stop condition is reached. Two parents are selected using a selection procedure. The parents are recombined in order to obtain two offspring. The offspring are considered for mutation. The best offspring replaces the worst individual in the current population if the offspring is better than the worst individual.

The algorithm returns as its answer the best expression evolved along a fixed number of generations.

4.4.5 Single Expression Programming

The MEP variant encoding a single solution in a chromosome is called Single Expression Programming (SEP). The expression encoded in a SEP chromosome is given by its last gene.

Example. Consider again the chromosome given in section 4.4.1.

$$\begin{aligned} &1: a \\ &2: b \\ &3: +1,2 \\ &4: c \\ &5: d \\ &6: +4,5 \\ &7: *3,6 \end{aligned} \tag{4.10}$$

The SEP expression encoded by this chromosome is:

$$E = (a+b)*(c+d). \tag{4.11}$$

4.4.6 Numerical Experiments with MEP and SEP

Several numerical experiments with Multi Expression Programming and Single Expression Programming are performed in this section using the test problems described in section 4.3.

The general parameters of the MEP and SEP algorithms are given in Table 4.3. The same settings are used for Multi Expression Programming and for Single Expression Programming.

Table 4.3. Parameters of the MEP and SEP algorithms for solving symbolic regression problems.

Parameter	**Value**
Number of generations	51
Crossover probability	0.9
Mutations	2 / chromosome
Function set	$F = \{+, -, *, /, \}$
Terminal set	Problem inputs
Selection	Binary Tournament

For all problems the relationship between the success rate and the chromosome length and the population size is analyzed. The success rate is computed as the number of successful runs over the total number of runs (see section 4.3).

First experiment. In this experiment the relationship between the success rate and the chromosome length is analyzed. The population size was set to 50 individuals. Other parameters of the MEP and SEP algorithms are given in Table 4.3. Results are depicted in Figure 4.1.

Figure 4.1 shows that Multi Expression Programming significantly outperforms Single Expression Programming for all the considered test problems and for all the considered parameter setting. More than that, large chromosomes are better for MEP than short chromosomes. This is due to the multi-solution ability: increasing the chromosome length leads to more solutions encoded in the same individual. The easiest problem is f_2. MEP success rate for this problem is over 90% when the number of instructions in a chromosome is larger than 10. The most difficult problem is f_3. For this problem and with the parameters given in Table 4.3, the success rate of the MEP algorithm never increases over 70%. However, these results are very good compared to those obtained by SEP (the success rate never increases over 10% for the test problem f_3).

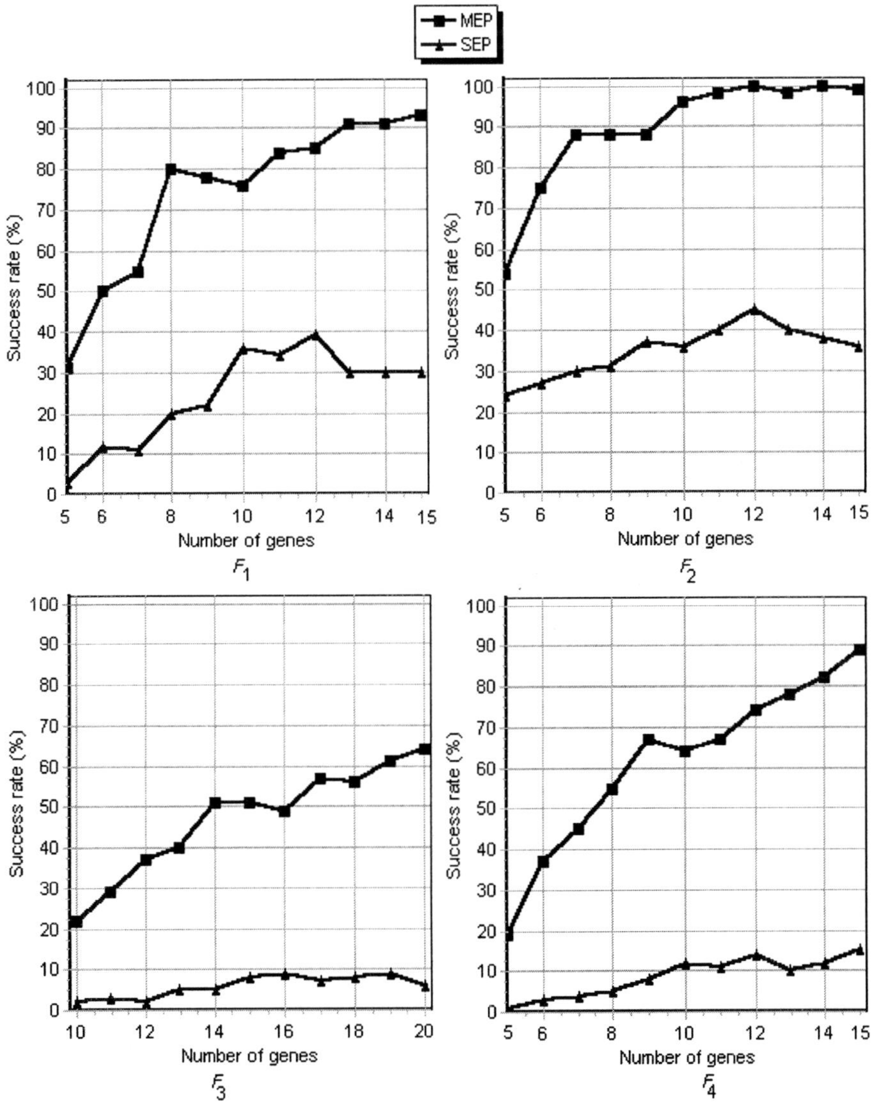

Figure 4.1. The relationship between the success rate and the number of instructions in a chromosome. Results are averaged over 100 runs.

Second experiment. In this experiment the relationship between the success rate and the population size is analyzed. The number of instructions in a MEP or SEP chromosome was set to 10. Other parameters for the MEP and SEP are given in Table 4.3. Results are depicted in Figure 4.2.

Figure 4.2 shows that MEP performs better than SEP. Problem f_2 is the easiest one and problem f_3 is the most difficult one.

4.5 Linear Genetic Programming

Linear Genetic Programming (LGP) [4, 16] uses a specific linear representation of computer programs. Instead of the tree-based GP expressions [11] of a functional programming language (like ***LISP***), programs of an imperative language (like ***C***) are evolved.

4.5.1 LGP Representation

A LGP individual is represented by a variable-length sequence of simple ***C*** language instructions. Instructions operate on one or two indexed variables (registers) r or on constants c from predefined sets. The result is assigned to a destination register, e.g. $r_i = r_j * c$. An example of the LGP program is the following one:

```
void LGP(double r[8])
{
    r[0] = r[5] + 73;
    r[7] = r[3] - 59;
    r[2] - r[5] + r[4];
    r[6] = r[7] * 25;
    r[1] = r[4] - 4;
    r[7] = r[6] * 2;
}
```

4.5.2 Decoding LGP Individuals

A linear genetic program can be turned into a functional representation by successive replacements of variables starting with the last effective instruction [4].

Usually one of the variables ($r[0]$) is chosen as the output of the program. This choice is made at the beginning of the program and is not changed during the search process. In what follows we will denote this LGP variant as Single-Solution Linear Genetic Programming (SS-LGP).

4.5.3 Genetic Operators

The variation operators used in conjunction with Linear Genetic Programming are crossover and mutation. Standard LGP crossover works by exchanging continuous sequences of instructions between parents [4].

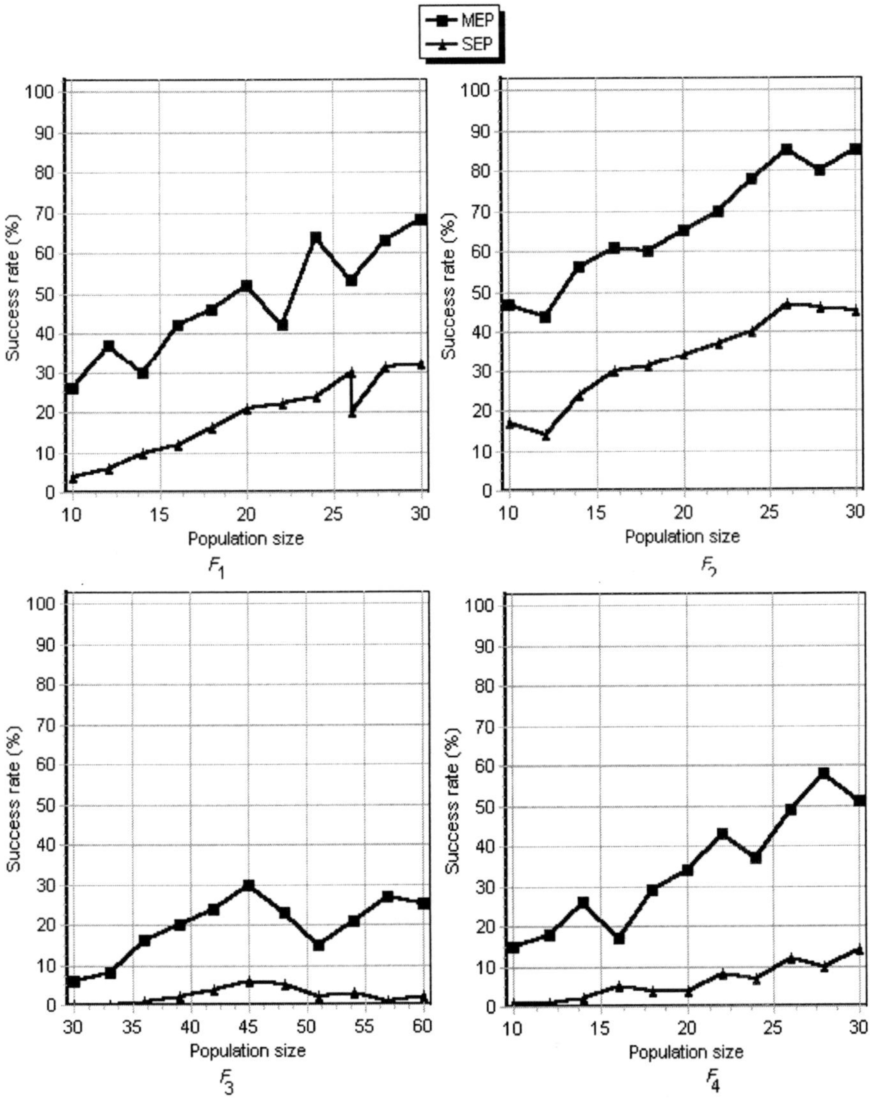

Figure 4.2. The relationship between the success rate and the population size. Results are averaged over 100 runs.

Two types of standard LGP mutations are usually used: micro mutation and macro mutation. By micro mutation an operand or an operator of an instruction is changed [4].

Macro mutation inserts or deletes a random instruction [4].

Since we are interested more in multi-solutions paradigm rather than in variable length chromosomes we will use fixed length chromosomes in all experiments performed in this paper. Genetic operators used in numerical experiments are uniform crossover and micro mutation.

LGP uniform crossover LGP uniform crossover works between instructions. The offspring's genes (instructions) are taken with a 50% probability from the parents.

Example. Let us consider the two parents C_1 and C_2 given in Table 4.4. The two offspring O_1 and O_2 are obtained by uniform recombination as shown in Table 4.4.

Table 4.4. LGP uniform recombination.

Parents		**Offspring**	
C_1	C_2	O_1	O_2
r[5]=*r*[3]**r*[2];	***r*[2]=*r*[0]+r[3];**	*r*[5]=*r*[3]**r*[2];	***r*[2]=*r*[0]+r[3];**
r[3]=*r*[1]+6;	***r*[1]=*r*[2]*r[6];**	***r*[1]=*r*[2]*r[6];**	*r*[3]=*r*[1]+6;
r[0]=*r*[4]**r*[7];	***r*[4]=*r*[6]-4;**	*r*[0]=*r*[4]**r*[7];	***r*[4]=*r*[6]-4;**
r[5]=*r*[4]-*r*[1];	***r*[6]=*r*[5]/r[2];**	*r*[5]=*r*[4]-*r*[1];	***r*[6]=*r*[5]/r[2];**
r[1]=*r*[6]*7;	***r*[2]=*r*[1]+7;**	***r*[2]=*r*[1]+7;**	*r*[1]=*r*[6]*7;
r[0]=*r*[0]+*r*[4];	***r*[1]=*r*[2]+r[4];**	***r*[1]=*r*[2]+r[4];**	*r*[0]=*r*[0]+*r*[4];
r[2]=*r*[3]/*r*[4];	***r*[0]=*r*[4]*3;**	***r*[0]=*r*[4]*3;**	*r*[2]=*r*[3]/*r*[4];

LGP mutation LGP mutation works inside of a LGP instruction. By mutation each operand (source or destination) or operator is affected with a fixed mutation probability.

Example. Consider an individual C which is affected by mutation. An offspring O is obtained as shown in Table 4.5 (modified variables are written in boldface):

4.5.4 LGP Algorithm

LGP uses a modified steady-state algorithm [4]. Initial population is randomly generated. The following steps are repeated until a termination criterion is reached: Four individuals are randomly selected from the current population. The best two of them are considered the winners of the tournament and they will act as parents. The parents are recombined and the offspring are mutated and then replace the losers of the tournament.

Table 4.5. LGP mutation.

C	*O*
$r[5] = r[3] * r[2];$	$r[5] = r[3] * r[2];$
$r[3] = r[1] + 6;$	$r[3] = \mathbf{r[6]} + \mathbf{r[0]};$
$r[0] = r[4] * r[7];$	$r[0] = r[4] + r[7];$
$r[5] = r[4] - r[1];$	$\mathbf{r[4]} = r[4] - r[1];$
$r[1] = r[6] * 7;$	$r[1] = r[6] * \mathbf{2};$
$r[0] = r[0] + r[4];$	$r[0] = r[0] + r[4];$
$r[2] = r[3] / r[4];$	$\mathbf{r[0]} = r[3] / r[4];$

4.5.5 Multi Solution Linear Genetic Programming

The LGP structure is enriched as follows:

(i) We allow as each destination variable to represent the output of the program. In the standard LGP only one variable is chosen to provide the output.

(ii) We check for the program output after each instruction in chromosome. This is again different from the standard LGP where the output was checked after the execution of all instructions in a chromosome.

After each instruction, the value stored in the destination variable is considered as a potential solution of the problem. The best value stored in one of the destination variables is considered for fitness assignment purposes.

Example. Consider the chromosome *C* given below:

```
void LGP(double r[8])
{
    r[5] = r[3] * r[2];
    r[3] = r[1] + 6;
    r[0] = r[4] * r[7];
    r[6] = r[4] - r[1];
    r[1] = r[6] * 7;
    r[2] = r[3]/r[4];
}
```

Instead of encoding the output of the problem in a single variable (as in SS-LGP) we allow that each of the destination variables ($r[5]$, $r[3]$, $r[0]$, $r[6]$, $r[1]$ or $r[2]$) to store the program output. The best output stored in these variables will provide the fitness of the chromosome.

For instance, if we want to solve symbolic regression problems, the fitness of each destination variable $r[i]$ may be computed using the formula:

$$f(r[i]) = \sum_{k=1}^{n} |o_{k,i} - w_k|, \tag{4.12}$$

where $o_{k,i}$ is the result obtained in variable $r[i]$ for the fitness case k, w_k is the targeted result for the fitness case k and n is the number of fitness cases. For this problem the fitness needs to be minimized.

The fitness of an individual is set to be equal to the lowest fitness of the destination variables encoded in the chromosome:

$$f(C) = \min_i f(r[i]). \tag{4.13}$$

Thus, we have a Multi-Solution LGP program at two levels: first level is given by the possibility that each variable to represent the output of the program and the second level is given by the possibility of checking for the output at each instruction in the chromosome.

4.5.6 Numerical Experiments with LGP and MS-LGP

In this section several experiments with SS-LGP and MS-LGP are performed. For this purpose we use several well-known symbolic regression problems described in section 4.3.

The general parameters of the LGP algorithms are given in Table 4.6. The same settings are used for Multi-Solution LGP and for Single-Solution LGP.

Table 4.6. Parameters of the LGP and MS-LGP algorithms for solving symbolic regression problems.

Parameter	**Value**
Number of generations	51
Crossover probability	0.9
Mutations	2 / chromosome
Function set	$F = \{+, -, *, /, \}$
Terminal set	Problem inputs + 4 supplementary registers
Selection	Binary Tournament

For all problems the relationship between the success rate, the chromosome length and the population size is analyzed. The success rate is computed as the number of successful runs over the total number of runs as described in section 4.3.

First experiment 1. In this experiment the relationship between the success rate and the chromosome length is analyzed. The population size was set to 50 individuals. Other parameters of the LGP are given in Table 4.6. Results are depicted in Figure 4.3.

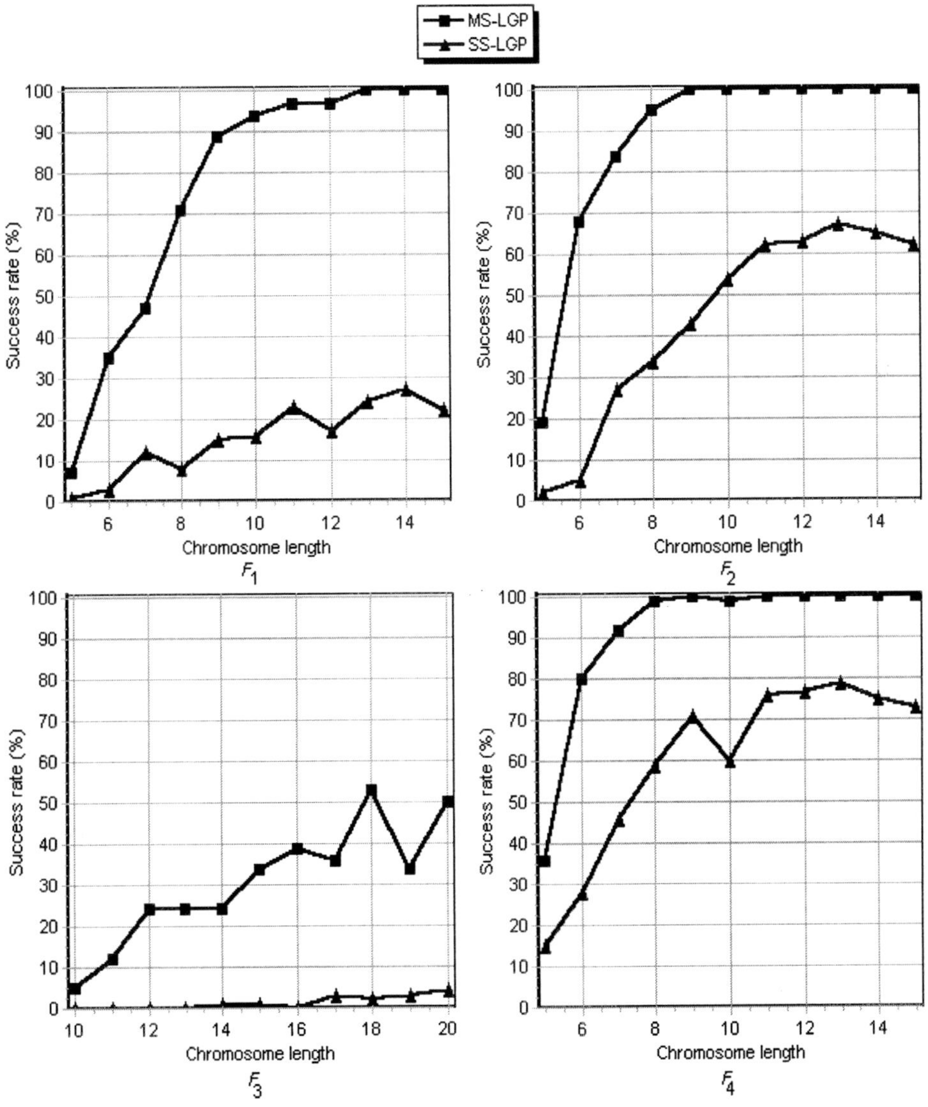

Figure 4.3. The relationship between the success rate and the number of instructions in a chromosome. Results are averaged over 100 runs.

Figure 4.3 shows that Multi-Solution LGP significantly outperforms Single-Solution LGP for all the considered test problems and for all the considered parameter setting. As in the case of MEP larger chromosomes are better for MS-LGP than shorter ones. This is due to the multi-solution ability: increasing the chromosome length leads to more solutions encoded in the same individual. The most difficult problem is f_3. For this problem the success rate of SS-LGP never increases over 5%).

Second experiment. In this experiment the relationship between the success rate and the population size is analyzed. The number of instructions in a LGP chromosome was set to 12. Other parameters for the LGP are given in Table 4.6. Results are depicted in Figure 4.4.

Figure 4.4 shows that Multi-Solution LGP performs better than Single-Solution LGP. For the test problem f_3 the success rate of SS-LGP is 0% (no run successful).

4.6 Infix Form Genetic Programming

In this section *Infix Form Genetic Programming* (IFGP) [19] technique is described. IFGP uses linear chromosomes for solution representation (i.e. a chromosome is a string of genes). An IFGP chromosome usually encodes several solutions of a problem.

In [19] IFGP was used for solving several classification problems taken from [20]. The conclusion was that IFGP performs similar and sometimes even better that Linear Genetic Programming and Neural Networks [4, 20].

4.6.1 Prerequisite

We denote by F the set of function symbols (or operators) that may appear in a mathematical expression. F usually contains the binary operators $\{+, -, *, /\}$. By *Number_of_Operators* we denote the number of elements in F. A correct mathematical expression also contains some terminal symbols. The set of terminal symbols is denoted by T. The number of terminal symbols is denoted by *Number_of_Variables*.

Thus, the symbols that may appear in a mathematical expression are $T \cup F \cup \{\text{'('}, \text{')'}\}$. The total number of symbols that may appear in a valid mathematical expression is denoted by *Number_of_Symbols*.

By C_i we denote the value on the ith gene in a IFGP chromosome and by G_i the symbol in the ith position in the mathematical expression encoded into an IFGP chromosome.

4.6.2 IFGP Individual Representation

In this section we describe how IFGP individuals are represented and how they are decoded in order to obtain a valid mathematical expression.

Each IFGP individual is a fixed size string of genes. Each gene is an integer number in the interval [0 .. *Number_Of_Symbols* - 1]. An IFGP individual can be transformed into a functional mathematical expression by replacing each gene with an effective symbol (a variable, an operator or a parenthesis).

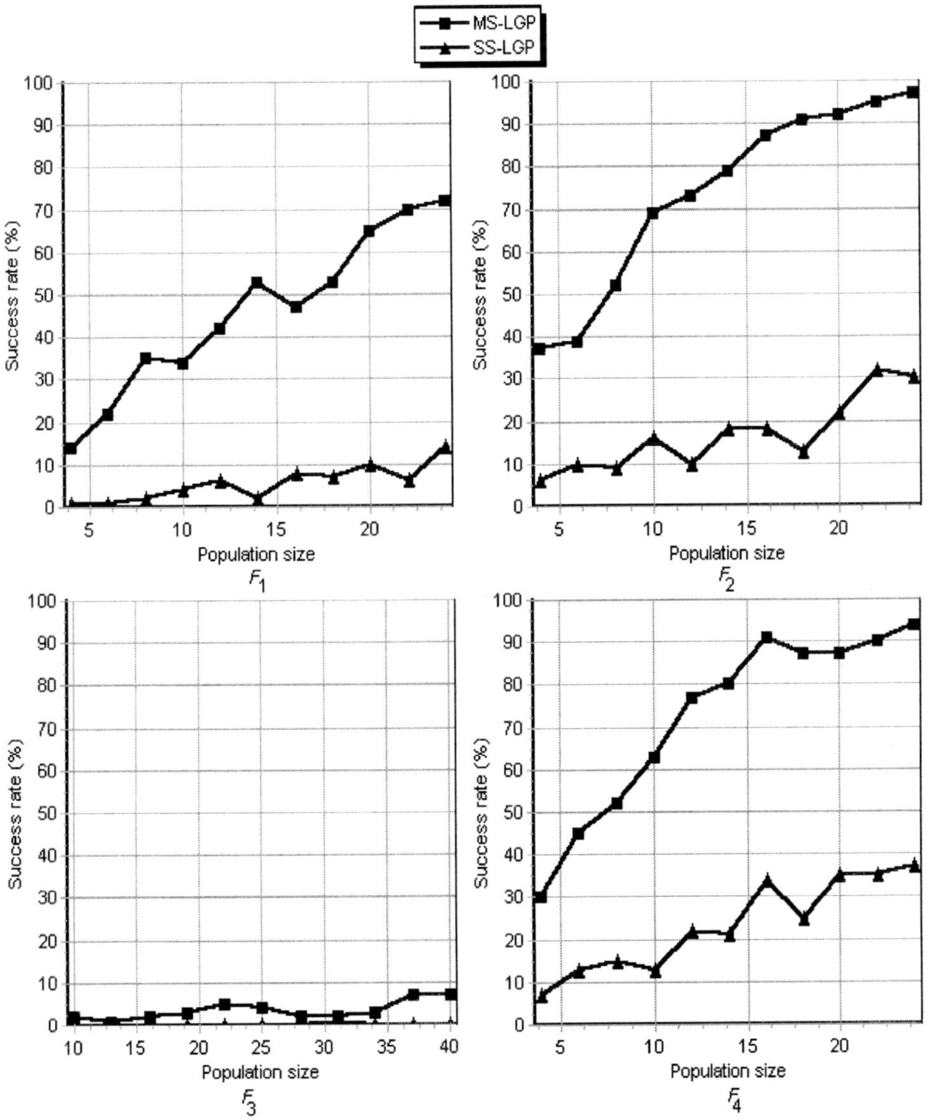

Figure 4.4. The relationship between the success rate and the population size. Results are averaged over 100 runs.

Example. If we use the set of functions symbols $F = \{+, *, -, /\}$, and the set of terminals $T = \{a, b\}$, the following chromosome is a valid chromosome in IFGP system.

$$C = 7, 3, 2, 2, 5 \tag{4.14}$$

4.6.3 IFGP Decoding Process

We begin to decode this chromosome into a valid mathematical expression. In the first position (in a valid mathematical expression) we may have either a variable, or an open parenthesis. That means that we have *Number_Of_Variables* + 1 possibilities to choose a correct symbol on the first position. We put these possibilities in order: the first possibility is to choose the variable x_1, the second possibility is to choose the variable x_2 ... the last possibility is to choose the closed parenthesis ')'. The actual value is given by the value of the first gene of the chromosome. Because the number stored in a chromosome gene may be larger than the number of possible correct symbols for the first position we take only the value of the first gene *modulo* number of possibilities for the first gene. Note that the *modulo* operator is used in a similar context by Grammatical Evolution [21].

Generally, when we compute the symbol stored in the ith position in expression we have to compute first how many symbols may be placed in that position. The number of possible symbols that may be placed in the current position depends on the symbol placed in the previous position. Thus:

(i) if the previous position contains a variable (x_i), then for the current position we may have either an operator or a closed parenthesis. The closed parenthesis is considered only if the number of open parentheses so far is larger than the number of closed parentheses so far.

(ii) if the previous position contains an operator, then for the current position we may have either a variable or an open parenthesis.

(iii) if the previous position contains an open parenthesis, then for the current position we may have either a variable or another open parenthesis.

(iv) if the previous position contains a closed parenthesis, then for the current position we may have either an operator or another closed parenthesis. The closed parenthesis is considered only if the number of open parentheses so far is larger than the number of closed parentheses.

Once we have computed the number of possibilities for the current position it is easy to determine the symbol that will be placed in that position: first we take the value of the corresponding gene modulo the number of possibilities for that position. Let p be that value ($p = C_i$ *mod Number_Of_Possibilities*). The pth symbol from the permitted symbols for the current is placed in the current position in the mathematical expression. (Symbols that may appear into a mathematical expression are ordered arbitrarily. For instance we may use the following order: $x_1, x_2, \ldots$, +, -, *, /, '(', ')'.)

All chromosome genes are translated excepting the last one. The last gene is used by the correction mechanism (see below).

The obtained expression usually is syntactically correct. However, in some situations the obtained expression needs to be repaired. There are two cases when the expression needs to be corrected:

The last symbol is an operator (+, -, *, /) or an open parenthesis. In that case a terminal symbol (a variable) is added to the end of the expression. The added symbol is given by the last gene of the chromosome.

The number of open parentheses is greater than the number of closed parentheses. In that case several closed parentheses are automatically added to the end in order to obtain a syntactically correct expression.

Remark. If the correction mechanism is not used, the last gene of the chromosome will not be used.

Example. Consider the chromosome C = 7, 3, 2, 0, 5, 2 and the set of terminal and function symbols previously defined ($T = \{a, b\}, F = \{+, -, *, /\}$).

For the first position we have 3 possible symbols (a, b and '('). Thus, the symbol in the position C_0 ***mod*** 3 = 1 in the array of possible symbols is placed in the current position in expression. The chosen symbol is b, because the index of the first symbol is considered to be 0.

For the second position we have 4 possibilities (+, -, *, /). The possibility of placing a closed parenthesis is ignored since the difference between the number of open parentheses and the number of closed parentheses is zero. Thus, the symbol '/' is placed in position 2.

For the third position we have 3 possibilities (a, b and '('). The symbol placed on that position is an open parenthesis '('.

In the fourth position we have 3 possibilities again (a, b and '('). The symbol placed on that position is the variable a.

For the last position we have 5 possibilities (+, -, *, /) and the closed parenthesis ')'. We choose the symbol on the position 5 **mod** 5 = 0 in the array of possible symbols. Thus the symbol '+' is placed in that position. The obtained expression is $E = b\,/\,(a+$.

It can be seen that the expression E it is not syntactically correct. For repairing it we add a terminal symbol to the end and then we add a closed parenthesis. Now we have obtained the following correct expression. The expression tree of E is depicted in Figure 4.5.

$$E = \quad b/(a+a). \tag{4.15}$$

4.6.4 Fitness Assignment Process

In this section we describe how IFGP may be efficiently used for solving symbolic regression problems.

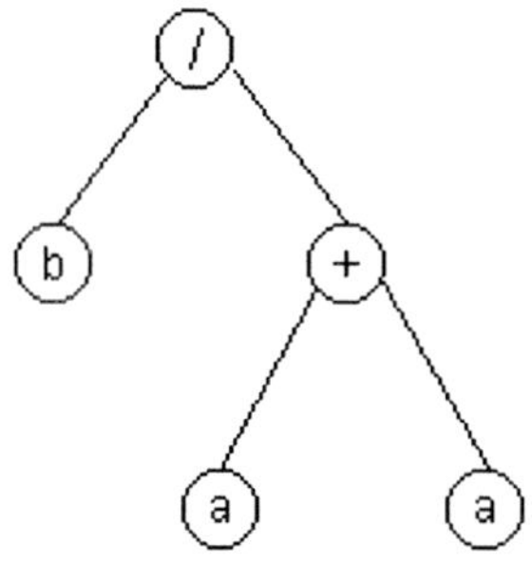

Figure 4.5. The expression tree of $E = b \,/\, (a + a)$.

A GP chromosome usually stores a single solution of a problem and the fitness is normally computed using a set of fitness cases.

Instead of encoding a single solution, an IFGP individual is allowed to store multiple solutions of a problem. The fitness of each solution is computed in a conventional manner and the solution having the best fitness is chosen to represent the chromosome.

In the IFGP representation each sub-tree (sub-expression) is considered as a potential solution of a problem. For example, the previously obtained expression (see section 4.6.2) contains 4 distinct solutions (sub-expressions):

$$\begin{aligned} E_1 &= a, \\ E_2 &= b, \\ E_3 &= a+a, \\ E_4 &= b/(a+a). \end{aligned} \tag{4.16}$$

The fitness of an IFGP individual using the same formulas used for MEP in section 4.4.2.

4.6.5 Search Operators

Search operators used within the IFGP model are recombination and mutation. These operators are similar to the genetic operators used in conjunction with binary encoding [8]. By recombination two parents exchange genetic material in order to obtain two offspring. In this paper only two-point recombination is used. Mutation operator is applied with a fixed mutation probability (p_m). By mutation a randomly generated value over the interval [0, *Number_of_Symbols*-1] is assigned to the target gene.

4.6.6 IFGP Algorithm

A steady-state [22] algorithm (similar to that used by MEP) is used as underlying mechanism for IFGP. The algorithm starts with a randomly chosen population of individuals. The following steps are repeated until a termination condition is reached. Two parents are chosen at each step using binary tournament selection [8]. The selected individuals are recombined with a fixed crossover probability p_c. By recombining two parents, two offspring are obtained. The offspring are mutated and the best of them replaces the worst individual in the current population (only if the offspring is better than the worst individual in population).

The algorithm returns as its answer the best expression evolved for a fixed number of generations.

4.6.7 Single Solution Infix Form Genetic Programming

As IFGP was originally designed to encode multiple solutions in a single chromosome [19] we modify the technique in order to encode a single solution / chromosome. The obtained variant is called Single-Solution IFGP (SS-IFGP). The expression encoded in a SS-IFGP chromosome is that representing the entire individual (the largest expression).

Example. Consider again the chromosome $C = 7, 3, 2, 2, 5$. The SS-IFGP expression is $E = b/(a+a)$.

4.6.8 Numerical Experiments with IFGP and SS-IFGP

Several numerical experiments with Infix Form Genetic Programming and Single-Solution Infix Form Genetic Programming are performed in this section using the test problems described in section 4.3.

The general parameters of the IFGP and SS-IFGP algorithms are given in Table 4.7. The same settings are used for Infix Form Genetic Programming and for Single Solution Infix Form Genetic Programming.

Table 4.7. Parameters of the IFGP and SS-IFGP algorithms for solving symbolic regression problems.

Parameter	Value
Number of generations	51
Crossover probability	0.9
Mutations	2 / chromosome
Function set	$F = \{+, -, *, /\}$
Terminal set	Problem inputs
Selection	Binary Tournament

For all problems the relationship between the success rate and the chromosome length and the population size is analyzed. The success rate is computed as the number of successful runs over the total number of runs.

First experiment. In this experiment the relationship between the success rate and the chromosome length is analyzed. The population size was set to 50 individuals. Other parameters of the IFGP and SS-IFGP algorithms are given in Table 4.7. Results are depicted in Figure 4.6.

Figure 4.6 shows that Infix Form Genetic Programming outperforms Single-Solution Infix Form Genetic Programming for the considered test problems. However the differences between MS-IFGP and SS-IFGP are not so significant as in the case of MEP and LGP.

Second experiment. In this experiment the relationship between the success rate and the population size is analyzed. The number of symbols in a IFGP or SS-IFGP chromosome was set to 30. Other parameters for the IFGP and SS-IFGP are given in Table 4.7. Results are depicted in Figure 4.7.

Figure 4.7 shows that Infix Form Genetic Programming performs better than Single-Solution Infix Form Genetic Programming. Problem f_2 is the easiest one (the IFGP success is 100 % when the population size is 20) when the chromosome length is 20 and problem f_3 is the most difficult one.

4.7 Summary

The ability of encoding multiple solutions in a single chromosome has been analyzed in this paper for 3 GP techniques: Multi Expression Programming, Linear Genetic Programming and Infix Form Genetic Programming. It has been show how to efficiently decode the considered chromosomes by traversing them only once.

Numerical experiments have shown that Multi-Solution Programming significantly improves the evolutionary search for all the considered test problems. There are several reasons for which Multi Solution Programming performs better than Single Solution Programming:

- MSP chromosomes act like variable-length chromosomes even if they are stored as fixed-length chromosomes. The variable-length chromosomes are better than fixed-length chromosomes because they can easily store expressions of various complexities,
- MSP algorithms perform more function evaluations than their SSP counterparts. However the complexity of decoding individuals is the same for both MSP and SSP techniques.

The multi-solution ability will be investigated within other evolutionary models.

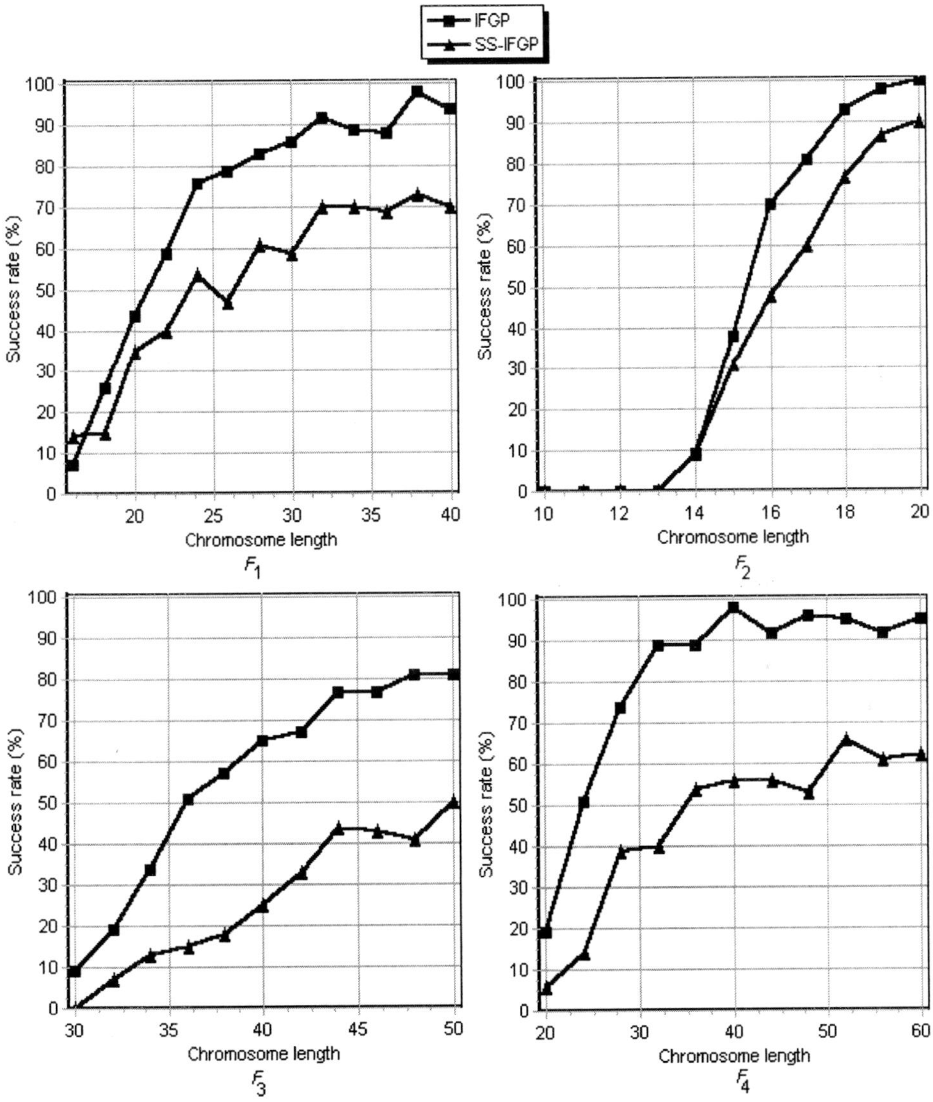

Figure 4.6. The relationship between the success rate and the number of symbols in a chromosome. Results are averaged over 100 runs.

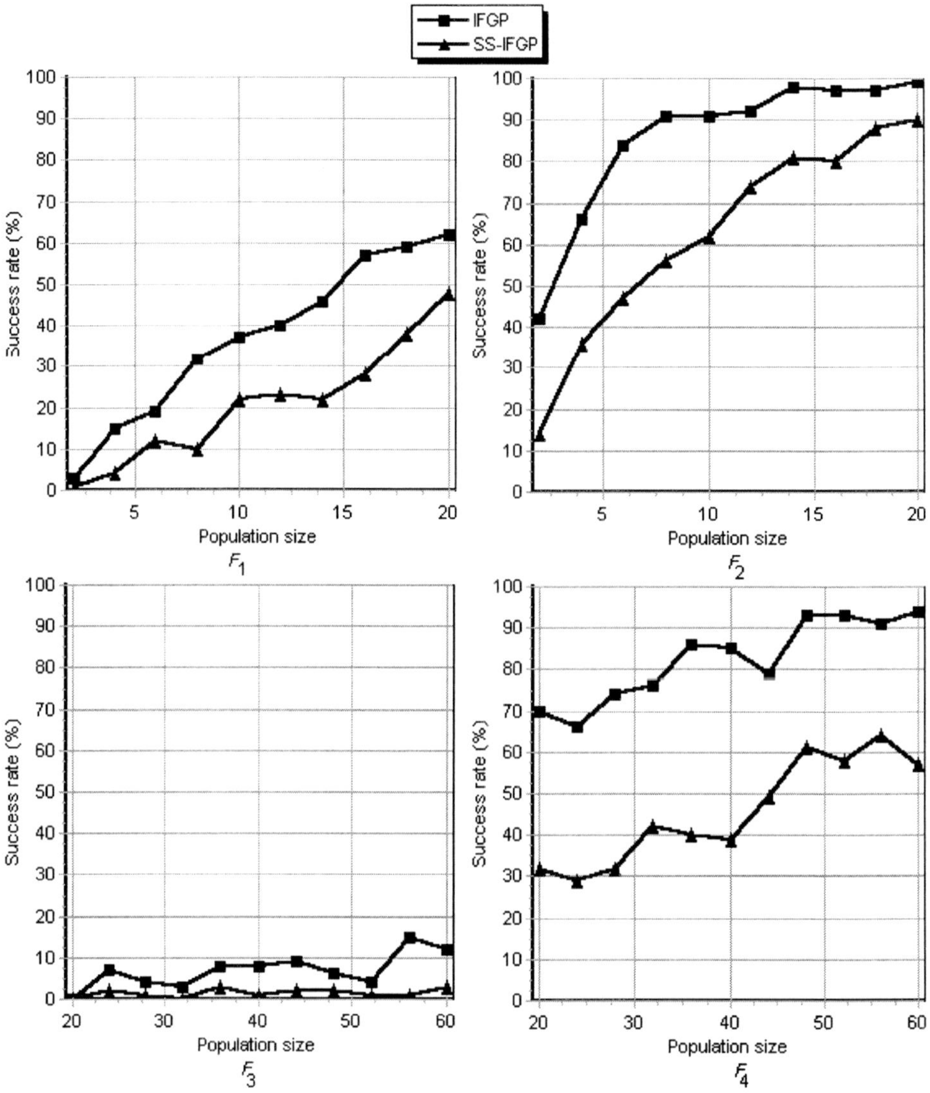

Figure 4.7. The relationship between the success rate and the population size. Results are averaged over 100 runs.

Bibliography

[1] A. Aho, R. Sethi and J. Ullman, *Compilers: Principles, Techniques, and Tools*, Addison Wesley, 1986.

[2] W. Banzhaf and W.B. Langdon, Some Considerations on the Reason for Bloat, *Genetic Programming and Evolvable Machines*, Vol. 3, pp. 81-91, 2002.

[3] R. Bellman, *Dynamic Programming, Princeton*, Princeton University Press, New Jersey, 1957.

[4] M. Brameier and W. Banzhaf, A Comparison of Linear Genetic Programming and Neural Networks in Medical Data Mining, *IEEE Transactions on Evolutionary Computation*, Vol. 5, pp. 17-26, IEEE Press, NY, 2001.

[5] M. Brameier and W. Banzhaf, Explicit Control of Diversity and Effective Variation Distance in Linear Genetic Programming, *The 4th European Conference on Genetic Programming*, E. Lutton, J. Foster, J. Miller, C. Ryan and A. Tettamanzi (Editors), pp. 38-50, Springer-Berlin, 2002.

[6] M. Brameier and W. Banzhaf, Evolving Teams of Predictors with Linear Genetic Programming, *Genetic Programming and Evolvable Machines*, Vol. 2, pp. 381-407, 2001.

[7] T.H. Cormen, C.E. Leiserson and R.R. Rivest, *Introduction to Algorithms*, MIT Press, Cambridge, MA, 1990.

[8] D. Dumitrescu, B. Lazzerini, L. Jain, A. Dumitrescu, *Evolutionary Computation*, CRC Press, Boca Raton, FL, 2000.

[9] D.E. Goldberg, *Genetic Algorithms in Search, Optimization, and Machine Learning*, Addison-Wesley, Reading, MA, 1989.

[10] J. Holland, *Adaptation in Natural and Artificial Systems*, University of Michigan Press, Ann Arbor, 1975.

[11] J.R. Koza, *Genetic Programming: On the Programming of Computers by Means of Natural Selection*, MIT Press, Cambridge, MA, 1992.

[12] J.R. Koza, *Genetic Programming II: Automatic Discovery of Reusable Subprograms*, MIT Press, Cambridge, MA, 1994.

[13] J.R. Koza, (et al.), *Genetic Programming III: Darwinian Invention and Problem Solving*, Morgan Kaufmann, San Francisco, CA, 1999.

[14] W.B. Langdon, and R. Poli, Genetic Programming Bloat with Dynamic Fitness, *First European Workshop on Genetic Programming*, W. Banzhaf, R. Poli, M. Schoenauer and T. C. Fogarty (Editors), pp. 96-112, Springer-Verlag, Berlin, 1998.

[15] S. Luke and L. Panait, Fighting Bloat with Nonparametric Parsimony Pressure, in *Proceedings of the Seventh International Conference on Parallel Problem Solving from Nature*, J. J. Merelo Guervos, P. Adamidis, H-G. Beyer, J. L. Fernandez-Villacanas Martin, and H-P. Schwefel (Editors), Springer-Verlag, Berlin, 2002.

[16] P. Nordin, A Compiling Genetic Programming System that Directly Manipulates the Machine Code, K. E. Kinnear, Jr. (Editor), *Advances in Genetic Programming*, pp. 311-331, MIT Press, 1994.

[17] M. Oltean and C. Groşan, Evolving Evolutionary Algorithms using Multi Expression Programming, *The 7th European Conference on Artificial Life*, W. Banzhaf (et. al), (Editors), LNCS 2801, pp. 651-658, Springer-Verlag, Berlin, 2003.

[18] M. Oltean, Solving Even-Parity Problems with Multi Expression Programming, *The 5th International Workshop on Frontiers in Evolutionary Algorithm*, K. Chen (et. al), (Editors), North Carolina, pp. 315-318, 2003.

[19] M. Oltean and C. Groşan, Solving Classification Problems using Infix Form Genetic Programming, *The 5th International Symposium on Intelligent Data Analysis*, M. Berthold (et al), (Editors), LNCS 2810, pp. 242-252, Springer, Berlin, 2003.

[20] L. Prechelt, PROBEN1 - A Set of Neural Network Problems and Benchmarking Rules, *Technical Report 21*, University of Karlsruhe, 1994.

[21] C. Ryan, J. J. Collins, and M. O'Neill, Grammatical Evolution: Evolving Programs for an Arbitrary Language, *First European Workshop on Genetic Programming*, W. Banzhaf, R. Poli, M. Schoenauer and T. C. Fogarty (Editors), Springer-Verlag, Berlin, 1998.

[22] G. Syswerda, Uniform Crossover in Genetic Algorithms, Schaffer, J.D., (Editor), *Proceedings of the 3rd International Conference on Genetic Algorithms*, pp. 2-9, Morgan Kaufmann Publishers, San Mateo, CA, 1989.

[23] D.H. Wolpert and W.G. McReady, No Free Lunch Theorems for Search, *technical report SFI-TR-05-010*, Santa Fe Institute, 1995.

[24] D.H. Wolpert and W.G. McReady, No Free Lunch Theorems for Optimisation, *IEEE Transaction on Evolutionary Computation*, Vol. 1, pp. 67-82, 1997.

Part II

Evolutionary Designs

In: Evolutionary Machine Design: Methodology & Applications ISBN 1-59454-405-0
Editors: N. Nedjah & L. Mourelle, pp:111-138

Chapter 5

REAL-WORLD EVOLUTIONARY DESIGNS: SECURE EVOLVABLE HARDWARE FOR PUBLIC-KEY CRYPTOSYSTEMS

Nadia Nedjah, Luiza de Macedo Mourelle

Department of System Engineering and Computation, Engineering Faculty,
State University of Rio de Janeiro,
Rua São francisco Xavier, 524, Sala 5022-D,
Maracanã, Rio de Janeiro, Brazil
(nadia | ldmm)@eng.uerj.br, www.eng.uerj.br

In this chapter, we propose a methodology based on genetic programming to automatically generate data-flow based specifications for hardware designs of combinational digital circuits. We aim at allowing automatic generation of balanced hardware specifications for a given input/output behaviour. It minimises space while maintaining reasonable response time. We show that the evolved designs are efficient and creative. We do so comparing the obtained circuits of some benchmarks against those that were produced by human designers as well as to other evolutionary ones.

To emphasize the applicability of the methodology to real-world problems, we use genetic programming as an alternative methodology to automatically generate secure and minimal hardware designs of public-key cryptosystems such as RSA encryption system. We evolve optimal hardware circuits for modular exponentiation, which a cornerstone operation in almost every cryptographic system. The evolved circuits minimize both space (i.e. required gate number) and time (i.e. encryption and decryption time). The evolved designs are shielded against side-channel leakage and hence secure. The structure of the cryptographic circuit is random and so the private key cannot be deduced using known attacks. We compare our results against existing well-known designs, which were produced by human designers based on the binary method.

5.1 INTRODUCTION

Designing a hardware that fulfills a given function consists of deriving from specific input/output behaviour, an architecture that is operational (i.e. produces all the expected outputs from the given inputs) within a specified set of constraints. Besides the input/output behaviour of the hardware, conventional designs are essentially based on knowledge and creativity. These are two human characteristics too hard to be automated.

The problem of interest consists of designing efficient and creative circuits that implement a given input/output behaviour without much designing effort. The obtained circuits are expected to be minimal both in terms of space and time requirements: The circuits must be compact i.e. use a reduced number of gates and efficient, i.e. produce the output in a short response time. The response time of a circuit depends on the number and the complexity of the gates forming the longest path in it. The complexity of a gate depends solely on the number of its inputs. Furthermore, the design should take advantage of the all the kind of gates available on reconfigurable chip of field programmable gate array (FPGAs).

The three most popular are minimisation techniques are: algebraic method, Karnaugh map [10] and Quine-McCluskey procedure [8]. The algebraic method consists of applying some known algebraic theorems and postulates. This method depends heavily on the designer ability, as it does not offer general rules to assist her/him in recognising the theorem to apply. The Karnaugh map [10] is a matrix-based representation of logical functions and allows minimisation of up to 5-input functions. McCluskey procedure [8] is a tabular method and allows one to minimise functions of any number of inputs. Both Karnaugh map and McCluskey procedure produce a minimal sum of products. A combinational circuit based on this minimal form offers the shortest response time, but not at all the smallest size. However, in some cases, the designer great concern is the minimisation of the number of gates of the circuit as well as the signal propagation delay. Moreover, the McCluskey procedure needs an execution time that grows exponentially with the number of input signals. Furthermore, Karnaugh map and McCluskey procedure produces design that only use AND, OR and NOT gates and ignores all the rest of gates. So the designer needs to perform further refinement on the circuit yield by these methods in order to introduce other kind of gates such as XOR gates [20].

Evolutionary hardware is a hardware that is yield using simulated evolution as an alternative to conventional-based electronic circuit design. Genetic evolution [7] is a process that evolves a set of individuals, which constitutes the population, producing a new population. Here, individuals are hardware designs. The more the design obeys the constraints, the more it is used in the reproduction process. The design constraints could be expressed in terms of hardware area and/or response time requirements. The freshly produced population is yield using some genetic operators such as crossover and mutation that attempt to simulate the natural breeding process in the hope of generating new design that are fitter i.e. respect more the design constraints. Genetic evolution is usually implemented using genetic algorithms.

In this work, we design innovative and efficient evolutionary digital circuits. Circuit evaluation is based on their possible implementation using CMOS technology [5], [18], [21]. The produced circuits are balanced i.e. use a reduced number of gate equivalent and propagate result signals in a reduced response time such that the factor area $\times$performance is minimised. We do so using genetic programming.

The remainder of this chapter is divided in five sections. In Section 2, we describe the principles of genetic programming. In Section 3, we describe the methodology we employ to evolve new compact and fast hardware for a given input/output behaviour. In Section 4, we compare the discovered hardware against existing most popular ones. Finally, we draw some conclusions.

5.2 Genetic Programming

Genetic programming [9] is an extension of genetic algorithms. The chromosomes are computer programs and the genes are instructions. In general, genetic programming offers a mechanism to get a computer to provide a solution of problem without being told exactly how to do it. In short, it allows one to automatically create a program. It does so based on a high level statement of the constraints the yielded program should obey to. The input/output behaviour of the expected program is generally considered as an omnipresent constraint. Furthermore, the generated program should use a minimal number of instructions and have an optimal execution time.

Starting form random set of computer programs, which is generally called initial population, genetic programming breeds a population of programs through a series of steps, called generations, using the Darwinian principle of natural selection, recombination also called crossover, and mutation. Individuals are selected based on how much they adhere to the specified constraints. Each program is assigned a value, generally called its fitness, which mirrors how good it is in solving the program. Genetic programming [9] proceeds by first, randomly creating an initial population of computer programs; then, iteratively performing a generation, which consists of going through two main steps, as far as the constraints are not met. The first step in a generation assigns for each computer program in the current population a fitness value that measures its adherence to the constraints while the second step creates a new population by applying the three genetic operators, which are reproduction, crossover and mutation to some selected individuals. Selection is done with on the basis of the individual fitness. The fitter the program is, the more probable it is selected to contribute to the formation of the new generation. Reproduction simply copies the selected individual from the current population to the new one. Crossover recombines two chosen computer programs to create two new programs using single-point crossover as shown in Figure 5.1(a) or two-points crossover as shown in Figure 5.1(b). Mutation yields a new individual by changing some randomly chosen instruction in the selected computer

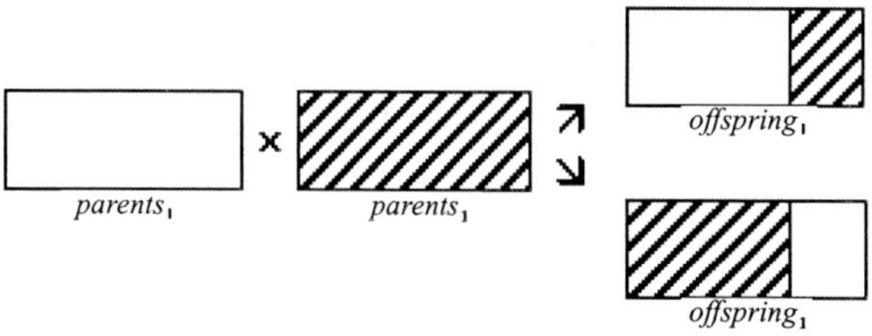

(a) single-point crossover

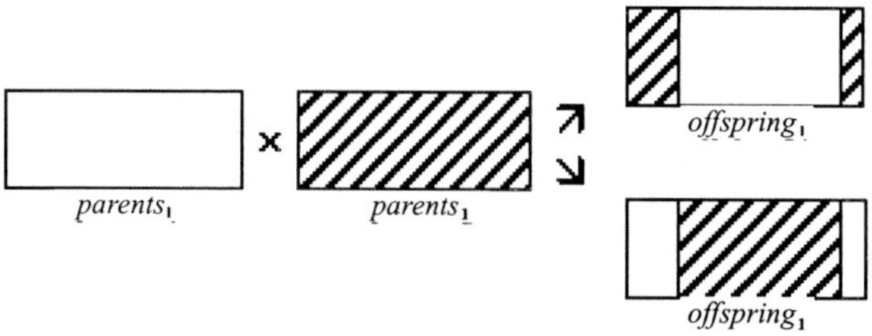

(b) double-point crossover

Figure 5.1. Types of crossover genetic operator

program. The number of genes to be mutated is called mutation degree and how many individuals should suffer mutation is called mutation rate.

5.3 Evolving Hardware for Combinational Digital Circuits

There three main aspects in implementation of genetic programming [9], [13]: *(i)* program encoding; *(ii)* crossover and mutation of programs; *(iii)* program fitness. In this section, we explain how we treat these three aspects in our implementation.

5.3.1 Circuit Specification Encoding

Encoding of individuals is one of the implementation decisions one has to take in order to use evolutionary computation. It depends highly on the nature of the problem to be solved. There are several representations that have been used with success: *binary encoding* which is the most common mainly because it was used in the first works on genetic algorithms, represents an individual as a string of bits; *permutation encoding* mainly used in ordering problem, encodes an individual as a sequence of integer; *value encoding* represents an individual as a sequence of values that are some evaluation of some aspect of the problem; and

Table 5.1. Node operators

Name	Symbol	Name	Symbol
NOT	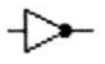	NAND	
AND	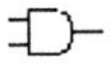	NOR	
OR	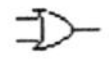	XNOR	
XOR		MUX	

tree encoding represents an individual as tree. Generally, the tree coincides with the concrete tree as opposed to abstract tree [1] of the computer program, considering the grammar of the programming language used.

Here a design is specified using register transfer level equations. Each instruction in the specification is an output signal assignment. A signal is assigned the result of an expression wherein the operators are those that represent basic gates in CMOS technology of VLSI circuit implementation and the operands are the input signals of the design. The allowed operators are shown in Table 5.1. Note that all gates introduce a minimal propagation delay as the number of input signal is minimal, which is 2.

A NOT gate inverts the input signal, an and-gate propagates a 1-signal when both input signals are 1 and 0-signal otherwise and an or-gate propagates a 0-signal when both input signals are 0 and 1-signal otherwise. An AND gate inverts the signal propagated by a NAND gate while an OR gate inverts that propagated by a NOR gate. Note that, in CMOS technology, an and-gate is a NAND gate coupled with a NOT gate and an OR gate is a NOR gate followed by a NOT gate and not the inverse [5]. The XOR gate is a CMOS basic gate that has the behaviour of sum of products $x\bar{y} + \bar{x}y$ wherein x and y are the input signals. However, a XOR gate is not implemented using 2 AND gates, 2 NOT gates and an OR gate. A 2to1-multipliexer MUX is also a CMOS basic gate and implements the sum of products $x\bar{s} + ys$ wherein x and y are the first and the second input signals and s is the control signal. It is clear that a XOR and MUX gates are of the same complexity [5], [18].

For instance, a 2-bit multiplier has 4-bit result signal so an evolved register transfer level specification is as follows, wherein the input operands are $X = \langle x_1 x_0 \rangle$ and $Y = \langle y_1 y_0 \rangle$ and the output is the product $P = \langle p_3 p_2 p_1 p_0 \rangle$. The schematic of the digital circuit implementing the above specification is given in Figure 5.2.

$$\begin{array}{lcl} p_3 & \Leftarrow & (x_0 \text{ AND } y_0) \text{ AND } (x_1 \text{ AND } y_1) \\ p_2 & \Leftarrow & (x_0 \text{ NAND } y_0) \text{ AND } (x_1 \text{ AND } y_1) \\ p_1 & \Leftarrow & (x_1 \text{ NAND } y_0) \text{ XOR } (x_0 \text{ NAND } y_1) \\ p_0 & \Leftarrow & (y_0 \text{ AND } x_0) \text{ OR } y_0 \end{array} \tag{5.1}$$

We encode specifications using an array of concrete trees corresponding to its signal assignments. The ith tree represents the evaluation tree of the expression on the left-hand side of the ith signal assignment. Leaf nodes are labelled with a literal representing a single bit of

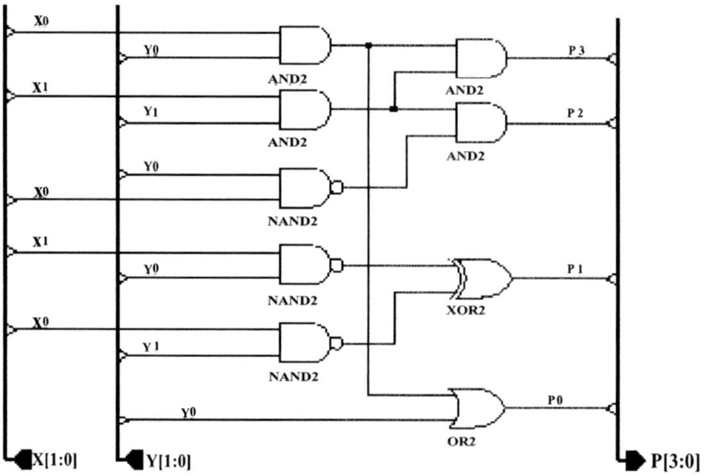

Figure 5.2. Evolved 2-bit multiplier

an input signal while the others are labelled with an operand. The individual corresponding to above specification is shown in Figure 5.3.

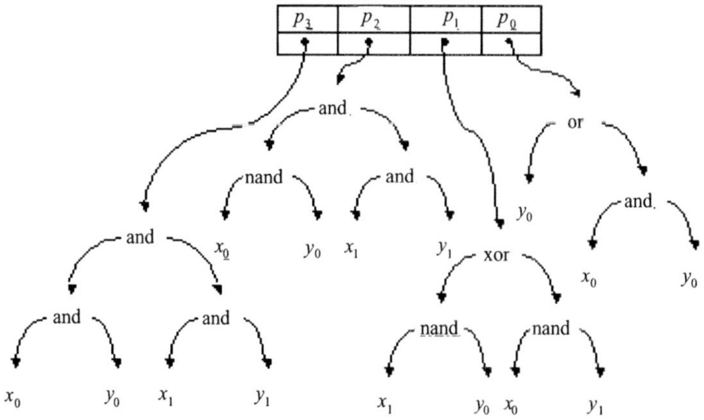

Figure 5.3. Chromosome for the evolved 2-bit multiplier

5.3.2 Circuit Specification Reproduction

Crossover of circuit specification is implemented using a double-point crossover as described in Figure 5.1. One of the important and complicated operators for genetic programming is the mutation. It consists of changing a gene of a selected individual. The number of individuals that should suffer *mutation* is defined by the *mutation rate* while how many genes should be altered within a chosen individual is given by the *mutation degree*.

Here, a gene is the tree of the expression on the left hand side of a signal assignment. Altering an expression can be done in two different ways depending the node that was randomised and so must be mutated. A node represents either an operand or operator. In the former case, the operand, which is a literal representing a bit in the input signal, is substituted with either a literal or simple expression. The decision is random. In the case in which the operand has to be changed by another operand, the literal representing the bit of lesser significance in the binary notation of the input signal or that representing its most significant bit is used. This is performed as indicated by function mutate1 below, wherein $X = \langle x_{n-1}x_{n-2}\ldots x_1x_0\rangle$ is the signal obtained by the concatenation of all input signals:

$$mutate_1(x_i) = \begin{cases} x_{n-1} & i = 0 \\ x_{i-1} & \text{otherwise} \end{cases} \tag{5.2}$$

In the case of mutating an operand node to an operator node, we proceed as follows: First let x_i be the operand being mutated. We choose randomly an operator among those available. Let OP be this operator. Its first operand is x_i. So if the chosen operator is NOT then the operand node is mutated to NOT x_i. When the selected operator is binary, a new literal is generated using $mutate_1(x_i)$. Thus, in this case, x_i is mutated to either $x_i\text{OP}mutate_1(x_i)$, wherein OP is an available binary operator. If the chosen operator is MUX, then a third operand is generated using $mutate_1(mutate_1(x_i))$. Last but not least, when the selected operator is quaternary a fourth literal is generated in the same way, i.e. using $mutate_1(mutate_1(mutate_1(x_i)))$. This mutation procedure is implemented by function $mutate_2$ below wherein the notation $mutate_1^{[i]}$ represents the i times application of $mutate_1$ and #OP represents the arity of operator OP:

$$mutate_2(x_i) = \begin{cases} \text{NOT } x_i & \#\text{OP} = 0 \\ x_i \text{ OP } mutate_1^{[1]} & \#\text{OP} = 1 \\ x_i \text{ OP } mutate_1^{[1]} mutate_1^{[2]} & \#\text{OP} = 2 \\ x_i \text{ OP } mutate_1^{[1]} mutate_1^{[2]} mutate_1^{[3]} & \#\text{OP} = 3 \end{cases} \tag{5.3}$$

So far we explained how an operand node is mutated. Now, we describe the mutation process of an operator node. Let OP be the operator being changed. An operator node can be mutated to another operator node or to an operand node. In the latter case, a literal is randomised and used to substitute the operator node. In the former case, however, things become a little more complicated depending on the relation between the arity OP and that of the operator selected to substitute it, say OP/. So we mutate OP to OP/. When #OP = #OP/ we leave the operands unchanged. Note that this case happens only for binary operators. When #OP ¿ #OP/, we use only a random subset of OPs operands. Finally, i.e. when #OP ¡ #OP/, we generate a random set of literals using function $mutate_1$repetitively as in function $mutate_2$ above.

Table 5.2. Gate equivalent and propagation delays

Name	Gate equiv.	Delay (ns)
NOT	1	0.0625
AND	2	0.209
OR	2	0.216
XOR	3	0.212
NAND	1	0.13
NOR	1	0.156
XNOR	3	0.211
MUX	3	0.212

5.3.3 Circuit Specification Evaluation

Another important aspect of genetic programming is to provide a way to evaluate the adherence of evolved computer programs to the imposed constraints. In our case, these constraints are of three kinds. First of all, the evolved specification must obey the input/output behaviour, which is given in a tabular form of expected results given the inputs. This is the truth table of the expected circuit. Second, the circuit must have a reduced size. This constraint allows us to yield compact digital circuits. Thirdly, the circuit must also reduce the signal propagation delay. This allows us to reduce the response time and so discover efficient circuits. In order to take into account both area and response time, we evaluate circuits using the $area \times performance$ factor. We evolve balanced digital circuits that implement a given behaviour that require a reduced hardware area and produce the result in a reduced time such that $area \times performance$ factor is minimal.

We estimate the necessary area for a given circuit using the concept of gate equivalent. This is the basic unit of measure for digital circuit complexity [5], [18]. It is based upon the number of logic gates that should be interconnected to perform the same input/output behaviour. This measure is more accurate that the simple number of gates [5].

When the input to an electronic gate changes, there is a finite time delay before the change in input is seen at the output terminal. This is called the propagation delay of the gate and it differs from one gate to another. Of primary concern is the path from input to output with the highest total propagation delay. We estimate the performance of a given circuit using the worst-case delay path. The number of gate equivalent and an average propagation delay for each kind of gate are given in Table 5.2. The data were taken form [5].

Let C be a digital circuit that uses a subset (or the complete set) of the gates given in Table 5.2. Let $Gates(C)$ be a function that returns the set of all gates of circuit C and $Levels(C)$ be a function that returns the set of all the gates of C grouped by level. For instance, applied to the circuit of Figure 5.2, it returns the set of sets $\{\{$AND, AND, NAND, NAND, NAND$\}$, $\{$AND, AND, XOR, OR$\}\}$. Notice that the number of levels of a circuit coincides with the cardinality of the set expected from function $Levels$. On the other hand, let $Value(T)$ be the Boolean value that the considered circuit C propagates for the input Boolean vector T assuming that the size of T coincides with the number of input signals required for circuit C. The fitness function, which allows us to determine how much an evolved circuit adheres to the specified constraints, is given as follows, wherein I represents the input values of the input signals while O represents the expected output values of the output signals of circuit C, n denotes the number of output signals that circuit C has and function *Delay* returns the propagation delay of a given gate as shown in Table 5.2. For each difference between the evolved circuit output values and the expected output signals, penalty ψ is accumulated. Note that for a correct circuit the first term in the definition of function *Fitness* is zero and so the value returned by this function is the factor $area \times performance$ of the evaluated circuit.

$$
\begin{aligned}
Fitness(C) = & \sum_{j=0}^{n} \left(\sum_{i | Value(x_i) \neq y_{i,j}} \psi \right) \\
& + \sum_{g \in Gates(C)} GateEquiv(g) \times \sum_{l \in Levels(C)} \max_{g \in l} Delay(g)
\end{aligned} \tag{5.4}
$$

For instance, consider the evolved circuit of Figure 5.4. It should propagate the output signals of Table 5.3 that appear first (i.e. before symbol /) but it actually propagates the output signals that appear last (i.e. those after symbol /). Observe that signals Z_1 and Z_2 are correct for every possible input combination of the input signals. However, signal Z_0 is correct only for the combinations 1010 and 1111 of the input signals and so for the remaining 14 combinations, Z_0 has a wrong value and so the circuit should be penalised 14 times. Applying function *Gates* to this circuit should return 5 AND gates and 3 NAND gates while function *Levels* should return {{ AND, AND, NAND, NAND, NAND }, { AND, AND, AND}}. If ψ is set to 10 then, function *Fitness* should return $140 + (5 \times 2 + 3 \times 1) + (0.209 + 0.209)$. This fitness sums up to 153.418.

In order to speed up the computation of the evolved circuit fitness, we take advantage of the parallelism of the central processing unit. This technique was first used by Poli in [16]. Instead of obtaining the output signal values one by one, one can compute them i.e. for all possible input signal combinations, in parallel. For instance, to compute the values of output signal $Z_2 \Longleftarrow (x_0 \text{ AND } y_0) \text{ AND } (x_1 \text{ AND } y_1)$ considering the circuit of Figure 5.4 and the values of Table 5.3, we proceed as follows:

1. Convert 0000111100001111, which is the content of column x_0 to integer value 3849 and 0101010101010101, which is the content of column y_0 to integer value 21849;

2. Compute the bitwise operation $3849 \ \& \ 21849 = 2569$;

3. Convert 0000000011111111, which is the content of column x_1 to integer value 255 and 0011001100110011, which is the content of column y_1 to integer value 51;

4. Compute the bitwise operation $256 \ \& \ 21849 = 51$;

Table 5.3. Truth table of the example of circuit fitness evaluation

x_1	x_0	y_1	y_0	Z_2	Z_1	Z_0
0	0	0	0	0/0	0/0	0/1
0	0	0	1	0/0	0/0	0/1
0	0	1	0	0/0	0/0	0/1
0	0	1	1	0/0	0/0	0/1
0	1	0	0	0/0	0/0	0/1
0	1	0	1	0/0	0/0	0/1
0	1	1	0	0/0	0/0	1/0
0	1	1	1	0/0	0/0	1/0
1	0	0	0	0/0	0/0	0/1
1	0	0	1	0/0	0/0	1/0
1	0	1	0	0/0	1/1	1/1
1	0	1	1	0/0	1/1	1/0
1	1	0	0	0/0	0/0	0/1
1	1	0	1	0/0	0/0	1/0
1	1	1	0	0/0	1/1	1/0
1	1	1	1	1/1	0/0	0/0

5. Compute the bitwise operation 169 & 2569 = 1;

6. Convert 1 to its 16-bit binary representation 000000000000001, which is exactly the content of column Z_2.

The use of this technique to compute the first term of fitness of an evolved circuit speeds up the process to an order of magnitude of 10. Note that for circuits of more than 6 input signals, the bitwise operations need to be split out in several 16, 32 or 64-bit operations depending on the size of the memory word.

5.4 Evolutionary vs. Conventional Designs

In this section, we compare the evolutionary circuits yield by our genetic programming based evolution to those designed by a human as well as to those evolved by Coello's genetic algorithm [4].

The truth table of the first benchmark is given in Table 5.4. It has three-bits input signal $X = \langle x_2 x_1 x_0 \rangle$ and propagates a single-bit output signal Y.

For this circuit specified in Table 5.4, a human designer came with a digital circuit that uses 2 AND gates, 1 OR gate and 2 XOR gates. The output signal is computed as in signal assignment of Equation 5.5. The Coello's genetic algorithm evolved the circuit specified in signal assignment of Equation 5.6. It uses 1 XOR gate less than the human designed circuit.

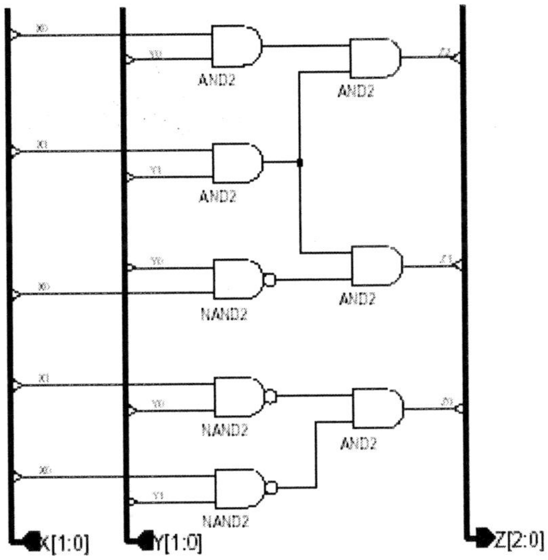

Figure 5.4. Evolved circuits for the input/output behavior of Table 5.3

$$Y \Longleftarrow x_0 \text{ AND } (x_2 \text{ XOR } x_1) \text{ OR } x_1 \text{ AND } (x_2 \text{ XOR } x_0) \tag{5.5}$$

$$Y \Longleftarrow x_0 \text{ AND } (x_2 \text{ OR } x_1) \text{ XOR } (x_2 \text{ AND } x_1) \tag{5.6}$$

Our genetic programming-based evolutionary computation yields two different circuits for the first benchmark. Both of them use 1 AND gate, 1 XOR gate and 1 MUX gate. The specifications of theses two circuits are given in signal assignment of Equation 5.7 and Equation 5.8 respectively:

$$Y \Longleftarrow \text{MUX } ((x_0 \text{ AND } x_1), (x_0 \text{ XOR } x_1), x_2) \tag{5.7}$$

$$Y \Longleftarrow \text{MUX } ((x_0 \text{ AND } x_2), (x_0 \text{ XOR } x_2), x_1) \tag{5.8}$$

Table 5.4. Truth table of the first benchmark

x_2	x_1	x_0	Y
0	0	0	0
0	0	1	0
0	1	0	0
0	1	1	1
1	0	0	0
1	0	1	1
1	1	0	1
1	1	1	0

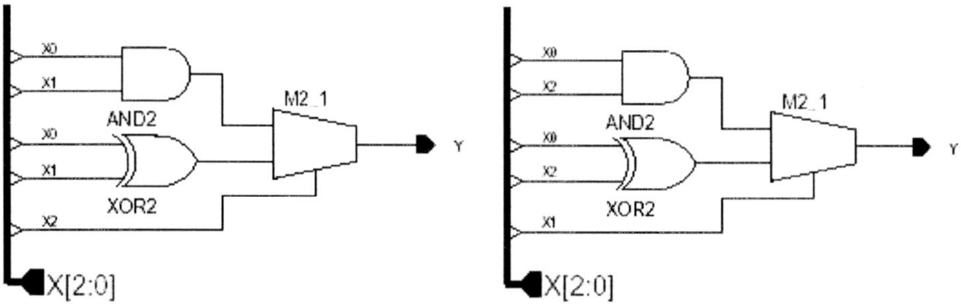

(a) First circuit (b) Second circuit

Figure 5.5. Schematics of the evolved circuits for the first benchmark

The schematics of these two circuits are given in Figure 5.5. The circuit, we evolved needs less hardware area, propagates the output signal faster and so the factor area $\times$performance is minimised. The numerical figures are given in Table 5.6 at the end of this section.

Both the second and third benchmarks need a 4-bit input signal $X = \langle x_3x_2x_1x_0\rangle$ and yield a single-bit output signal Y. The fourth and fifth benchmarks also requires a 4-bit input signal X but the respective circuits propagate a 4-bit and 3-bit output signal respectively. The truth tables of the four benchmarks are summarised in Table 5.5 below. Note that the fourth benchmark is a simple 2-bit multiplier of $X = \langle x_3x_2\rangle$ times $Y = \langle x_1x_0\rangle$. (The notation of the input signals is purely for space sake!)

For the second example, a human designer came with a circuit that requires 4 AND gates, 1 OR gate, 2 XOR gates and 4 NOT gates. The specification of the signal assignments as follows:

$$Y \Longleftarrow ((\overline{x}_3 \text{ AND } x_1) \text{ XOR } (\overline{x}_0 \text{ AND } \overline{x}_2)) \text{ OR } ((\overline{x}_2 \text{ AND } x_0) \text{ AND } (x_3 \text{ XOR } \overline{x}_2)) \tag{5.9}$$

For the second benchmark, the Coello's genetic algorithm evolved the circuit specified in signal assignment of Equation 5.10. It uses 1 AND gate, 3 OR gates, 3 XOR gates and 1 NOT gate.

$$Y \Longleftarrow ((x_3 \text{ XOR } ((x_2 \text{ XOR } x_0) \text{ OR } (x_1 \text{ AND } x_0)) \text{ XOR } (\text{ NOT } ((x_3 \text{ OR } (x_1 \text{ OR } x_0))) \tag{5.10}$$

The schematics of the circuit we evolved are given in Figure 5.6. It needs less hardware area, but propagates the output signal a little bit slower than Coello's evolved circuit. However, the factor *area* $\times$ *performance* is the smallest. Again, the numerical figures are given in Table 5.6.

Table 5.5. Truth tables of second, third, fourth and fifth benchmarks respectively

Input				2nd	3rd	4th Benchmark				5th Benchmark		
x_3	x_2	x_1	x_0	Y	Y	p_3	p_2	p_1	p_0	y_2	y_1	y_0
0	0	0	0	1	1	0	0	0	0	1	0	0
0	0	0	1	1	0	0	0	0	0	0	1	0
0	0	1	0	0	1	0	0	0	0	0	1	0
0	0	1	1	1	0	0	0	0	0	0	1	0
0	1	0	0	0	1	0	0	0	0	0	0	1
0	1	0	1	0	0	0	0	0	1	1	0	0
0	1	1	0	1	1	0	0	1	0	0	1	0
0	1	1	1	1	1	0	0	1	1	0	1	0
1	0	0	0	1	1	0	0	0	0	0	0	1
1	0	0	1	0	1	0	1	0	0	0	0	1
1	1	1	0	1	1	0	1	1	0	1	0	0
1	0	1	1	0	0	0	1	1	0	0	1	0
1	0	0	0	0	0	0	0	0	0	0	0	1
1	1	0	1	1	1	0	0	1	1	0	0	1
1	1	1	0	0	1	0	1	1	0	0	0	1
1	1	1	1	0	1	1	0	0	1	1	0	0

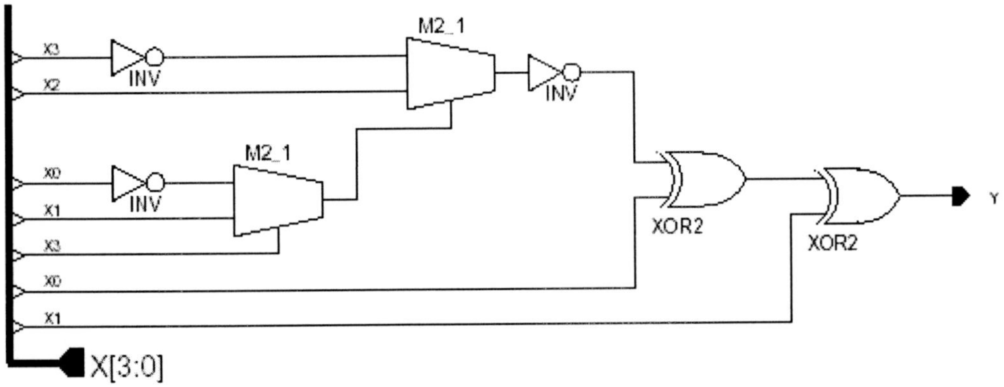

Figure 5.6. Evolved circuit for the second benchmark

For the third benchmark, a human designer obtained a circuit that requires a total of 20 gates equivalent: 5 AND gates, 3 OR gates and 4 NOT gates. The specification of the signal assignment (5.11) is as follows:

$$Y \Longleftarrow ((\overline{x}_3 \text{ AND } \overline{x}_0) \text{ OR } (\overline{x}_3 \text{ AND } \overline{x}_2)) \text{ OR } ((x_2 \text{ AND } x_1) \text{ OR } (x_3 \text{ AND } \overline{x}_1 \text{ AND } x_0)) \quad (5.11)$$

For the third benchmark, the Coello's genetic algorithm evolved the circuit specified in signal assignment of Equation 5.12. It requires 2 AND gates, 2 OR gates, 2 XOR gates and 1 NOT gate.

$$Y \Longleftarrow \text{NOT } (((x_2 \text{ AND } x_1) \text{ XOR } (x_2 \text{ OR } x_0)) \text{ AND } (x_1 \text{ OR } (x_3 \text{ XOR } x_0))) \quad (5.12)$$

The schematics of the circuit we evolved are given in Figure 5.7. The circuit, we evolved needs less hardware area, propagates the output signal faster than both circuits i.e. Coello's and the one designed by the human, and so the factor $area \times performance$ is minimised. Once more, the numerical figures about gate equivalent, delay and $area \times performance$ factor are shown in Table 5.6.

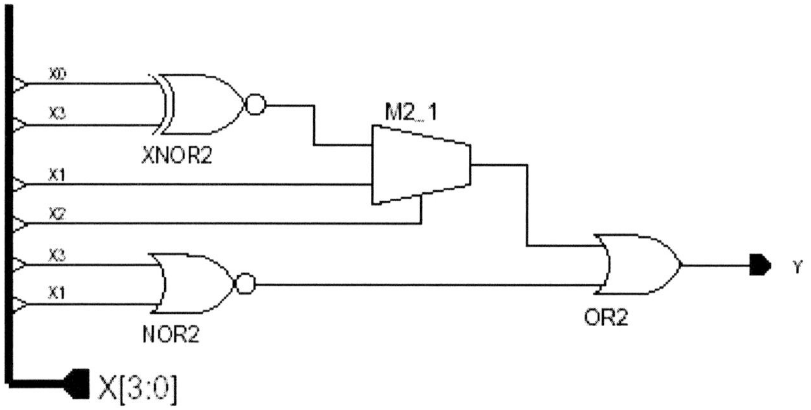

Figure 5.7. Evolved circuits for the third benchmark

Another circuit was obtained for that benchmark. Its schematics are given in Figure 5.8 below. The circuit of is less efficient than that shown in Figure 5.7. However, it is more compact that the circuits obtained by the human designer and that evolved by Coello's genetic algorithm as it requires only 11 gates equivalent compared to 20 for the circuit designed by the human and 15 for Coello's evolved circuit. Moreover, the circuit of Figure 5.8 has a smaller propagation delay of 0.853ns compared to the 0.912ns required by the human designed circuit. The circuit presents a $area \times performance$ factor of 9.383.

For the fourth benchmark, a human designer obtained a circuit that requires a total of 24 gates equivalent: 8 AND gates, 2 OR gates, 1 XOR gate and 1 NOT gate. The specification

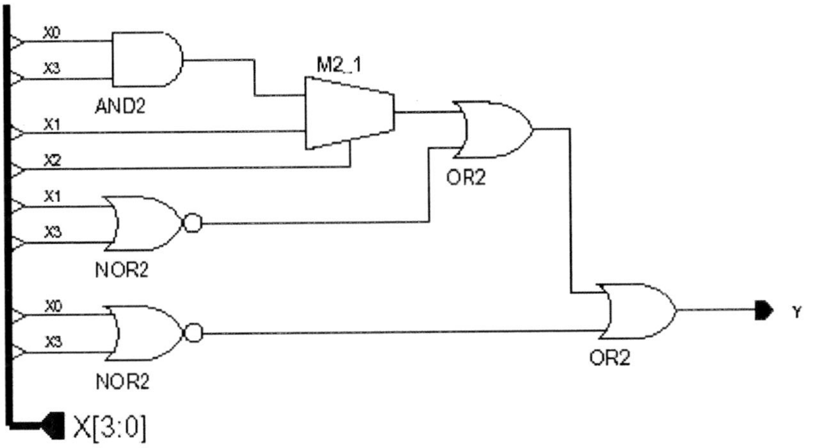

Figure 5.8. Less efficient evolved circuits for the third benchmark

of the signal assignments is as follows (Equation 5.13), wherein $y_1 = x_3$ and $y_0 = x_2$ when Table 5.5 is used.

$$\begin{aligned} p_0 &\Leftarrow (x_0 \text{ AND } y_0) \\ p_1 &\Leftarrow (x_1 \text{ OR } x_0) \text{ AND } (y_1 \text{ OR } y_0) \text{ AND } ((x_1 \text{ AND } x_0) \text{ XOR } (y_1 \text{ AND } y_0)) \\ p_2 &\Leftarrow (x_1 \text{ AND } y_1) \text{ AND NOT } ((x_0 \text{ AND } y_0)) \\ p_3 &\Leftarrow (x_1 \text{ AND } y_1) \text{ AND } (x_0 \text{ AND } y_0) \end{aligned} \tag{5.13}$$

For the fourth benchmark, the Coello's genetic algorithm evolved the circuit specified in the output signal assignments of Equation 5.14. It requires an area of 16 gates equivalent. That is 5 AND gates and 2 XOR gates.

$$\begin{aligned} p_0 &\Leftarrow (x_0 \text{ AND } y_0) \\ p_1 &\Leftarrow (x_0 \text{ AND } y_1) \text{ XOR } (x_1 \text{ AND } y_0) \\ p_2 &\Leftarrow (x_1 \text{ AND } y_1) \text{ XOR } ((x_0 \text{ AND } y_0) \text{ AND } (x_1 \text{ AND } y_1)) \\ p_3 &\Leftarrow (x_1 \text{ AND } y_1) \text{ AND } (x_0 \text{ AND } y_0) \end{aligned} \tag{5.14}$$

The schematics of the circuit we evolved are given in Figure 5.9. The circuit we evolved needs the same hardware area as Coello's evolved circuit but it propagates the output signal faster than both circuits i.e. Coello's and the one designed by the human, and so the factor $area \times performance$ is minimised. The comparison of the numerical figures such as gate equivalent numbers, propagation delays and $area \times performance$ factors is detailed in Table 5.6.

Finally for the fifth benchmark, a human designer engineered a circuit that requires a total of 34 gates equivalent, i.e. 7 AND gates, 4 OR gates, 2 XOR gate and 6 NOT gates. The specification of the signal assignments of Equation 5.15, wherein $y_1 = x_3$ and $y_0 = x_2$ when Table 5.5 is used.

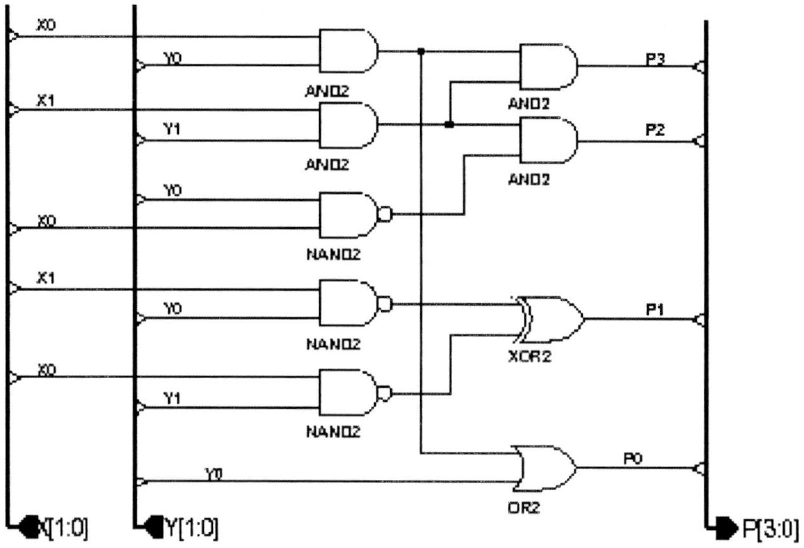

Figure 5.9. Evolved circuits for the fourth benchmark

$$
\begin{aligned}
y_0 &\Longleftarrow \text{NOT } (x_3 \text{ XOR } x_1) \text{ AND } \text{NOT } (x_2 \text{ XOR } x_0) \\
y_1 &\Longleftarrow (\overline{x}_2 \text{ AND } x_0) \text{ AND } (\overline{x}_3 \text{ OR } x_1) \text{ OR } (x_3 \text{ AND } x_1) \\
y_2 &\Longleftarrow (\overline{x}_0 \text{ AND } x_2) \text{ AND } (\overline{x}_1 \text{ OR } x_3) \text{ OR } (\overline{x}_1 \text{ AND } x_3)
\end{aligned} \tag{5.15}
$$

For the same example, the Coelho's genetic algorithm evolved the circuit specified in the output signal assignments of Equation 5.16. It requires an area of 22 gates equivalent, which consist of 2 AND gates, 3 OR gate, 3 XOR gates and 3 NOT gates.

$$
\begin{aligned}
y_0 &\Longleftarrow \text{NOT } ((x_3 \text{ XOR } x_1) \text{ AND } (x_2 \text{ XOR } x_0)) \\
y_1 &\Longleftarrow (temp \text{ AND} \\
&\quad \text{NOT } (((x_3 \text{ XOR } x_1) \text{ AND } x_3 \text{ XOR } (x_0 \text{ OR } (x_3 \text{ XOR } x_1))) \text{ OR } temp)) \\
y_2 &\Longleftarrow \text{NOT } (((x_3 \text{ XOR } x_1) \text{ AND } x_3 \text{ XOR } ((x_0 \text{ OR } (x_3 \text{ XOR } x_1)) \\
&\quad \text{OR NOT } temp) \\
temp &\Longleftarrow (x_2 \text{ XOR } x_0) \text{ OR } (x_3 \text{ XOR } x_1)
\end{aligned} \tag{5.16}
$$

The schematics of the circuit that our genetic algorithm evolved are given in Figure 5.10. This circuit requires one gate equivalent more than Coello's evolved circuit but our circuit propagates the output signal much faster. Compared with the human designed circuit, our circuit has the same response time but needs a much smaller area. Furthermore, the factor $area \times performance$ for our circuit is minimal compared with the other two. The numerical figures such as gate equivalent numbers, propagation delays and $area \times performance$ factors are given in Table 5.6.

The convergence graphs of our evolutionary process for the benchmarks are shown in

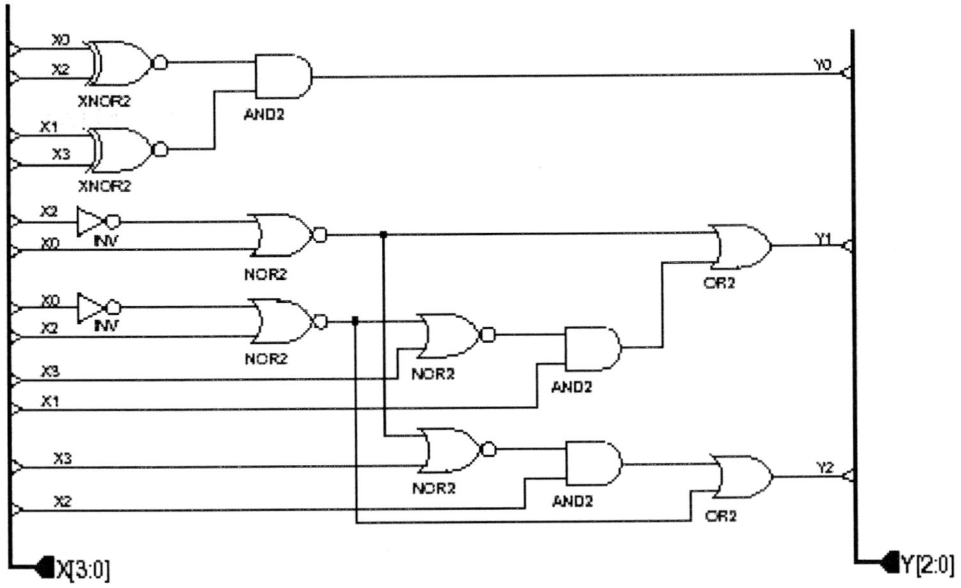

Figure 5.10. Evolved circuits for the fifth benchmark

Table 5.6. Numerical comparison of the three methods

	area			delay			factor		
	Our	Coello	Human	Our	Coello	Human	Our	Coello	Human
1st	8	9	12	0.424	0.637	0.637	3.392	5.733	7.644
2nd	15	16	20	0.973	0.918	0.702	14.595	14.696	14.050
3rd	9	15	20	0.639	0.699	0.912	5.751	10.492	18.250
4th	16	16	24	0.425	0.842	0.853	6.800	13.472	20.472
5th	22	21	34	0.799	1.065	0.703	17.589	22.365	23.919

Figure 5.11. The best circuits for the 1st, 2nd, 3rd, 4th and 5th examples were obtained in 100, 280, 320, 370 and 540 generations.

In order to evolve the circuits for the proposed behaviours (see Table 5.5) and for all of the examples we used a population of 100 individuals. The double-point crossover was used with mutation rate of 0.5 and a mutation degree of 1.

Table 5.6 shows a comparison between the fittest circuits engineered by a human designer, Coello's genetic algorithm and our genetic algorithm, which is based on genetic programming. For each benchmark, the required hardware area, the necessary propagation delay and the product $area \times performance$ are detailed. The graphical representation of these figures is shown in the chart of Figure 5.12.

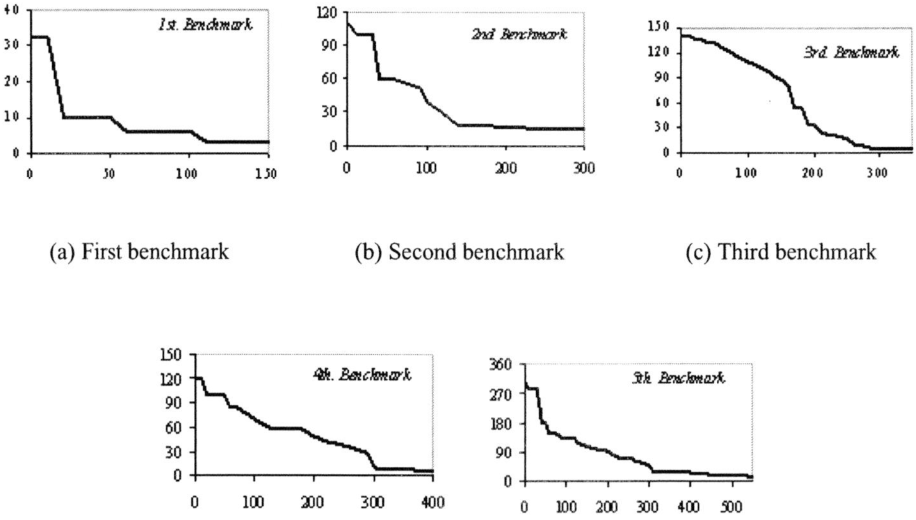

(a) First benchmark (b) Second benchmark (c) Third benchmark

(d) Fourth benchmark (e) Fifth benchmark

Figure 5.11. Convergence graphs for the evolution of the circuits of the benchmarks

5.5 RSA-Based Cryptosystems

Cryptography is the science of keeping secrets secret. Its main task is to provide confidentiality by encryption methods. The original message, which can be some text, numerical data or any other kind of information, is usually called plaintext and the encrypted plaintext is called ciphertext. Information transmission between two parties through public channels occurs after plaintext T is encrypted into ciphertext C so that an eventual adversary third party in possession of c cannot derive any information about T. Cryptosystems must provide an encryption and a decryption algorithm. Existing cryptosystems can be classified into symmetric and asymmetric systems. Both encryption and decryption processes in symmetric cryptosystems depend on the same secret key while in asymmetric ones there exist a public key on which depends the encryption algorithm and another private key used by the decryption process.

A Rivest-Shamir-Adleman or simply RSA-based cryptosystem [17] is asymmetric. It consists of triple $\langle M, e, d \rangle$, which consists of the *modulus*, *public* and *private key* respectively. The modulus and the public key of the system are made public while the private key is kept secret. To build an RSA-based cryptosystem, one needs to:

1. Create two primes p and q;

2. Compute $M = p \times q$;

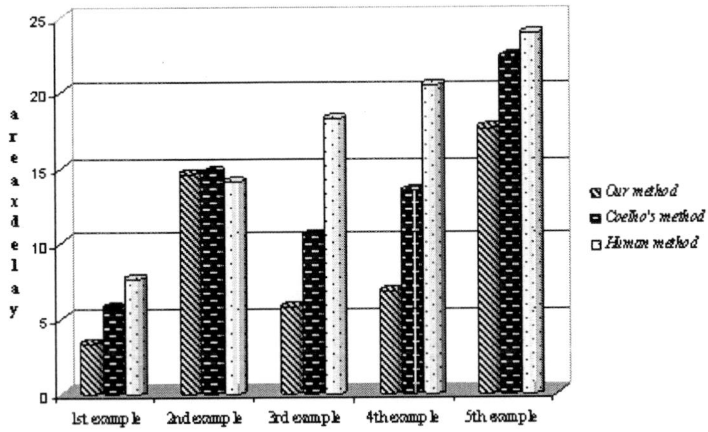

Figure 5.12. Graphical comparison of the *area* × *delay* factor for the three methods

3. Calculate the value of *Euler totient* function defined for M as $N = \Phi(M) = (p-1)(q-1)$;
4. Choose e, such that the greatest common divisor of N and e is 1—$gcd(e,N) = 1$, with $e \neq 1$ and $e \neq N$;
5. Compute d such that $e \times d \equiv 1 \bmod N$. (This can be done using the extended Euclidean algorithm [11].)

Note the public and private keys of a given cryptosystem are non-negative integer smaller than its modulus, i.e. for the system defined by $\langle M, e, d \rangle$, we have $0 \leq e, d \leq M-1$. With modulus of reasonable length, i.e. about 1024 bits, solving the factoring problem i.e. discovering p and q, which will lead to discovering the private key is impossible considering the computation power and the factoring algorithms one disposes of nowadays.

Both the encryption and decryption algorithms in RSA-based cryptosystems are implemented using the same algorithm: modular exponentiation. That is, the *ciphertext* C is obtained from *plaintext* T by $C = T^e \bmod M$ and T is obtained from C by $T = C^d \bmod M$. This characteristic is very attractive and so it increased the popularity of RSA-based cryptosystems. Note that the plaintext and its corresponding ciphertext in a given RSA-based cryptosystem are non-negative integers smaller than the modulus.

The practicality of cryptosystem depends heavily on how fast the encryption and essentially decryption process can be done. Therefore, the practicality of RSA-based cryptosystems depends essentially on how fast modular exponentiation of large integers can be performed.

Clearly, modular exponentiation is the cornerstone operation in RSA-based cryptosystem. It consists of several successive modular multiplications. Modular multiplication is time consuming for large operands. Engineering fast public-key cryptography hardware needs either optimising the time consumed by a single modular multiplication or reducing the total number of modular multiplication performed or both of them [14], [3], [2], [19]. The so far engineered hardware designs using modular exponentiation as encryption process suffer from a very serious drawback that is called *side-channel leakage*. As the designs for modular exponentiation are regular and repetitive one can trace the data transfers between operations, which usually reveal the beginning of every long integer operation very clearly [12]. This allows one with an extra little effort to discover the private key of the cryptosystem. Here, we use evolutionary computation to discover new efficient, creative and above all secure hardware for RSA-based cryptosystems.

5.6 Evolutionary vs. Conventional Cryptographic Hardware

Several efficient designs for RSA-based cryptosystems were developed [14], [3], [2]. In the following, we compare two conventional designs: one sequential and the other parallel to the evolutionary design obtained.

First of all, we describe an sequential design based on the binary exponentiation method [6] we presented in earlier research work [14], [15]. Subsequently, we present the parallel design based on the same method.

The sequential straightforward binary exponentiation algorithm is given hereafter (Algorithm 5.1, wherein m is the number of digits in exponent e. Observe that the multiplication of line 5 of the algorithm depends on the result of the squaring of line 4.

The hardware architecture of Figure 5.13 includes two Montgomery modular systolic multipliers, i.e. MULTIPLIER_1 and MULTIPLIER_2.

Algorithm 5.1 Sequential binary modular exponentiation

Input. Plaintext/ciphertext T, private/public key e and modulus M
Output. Ciphertext/palintext R

1. int $R := 1$;
2. if $e_{k-1} = 1$ then $R := T$;
3. for $i := m-2$ downto 0
4. $R := R \times R \bmod M$;
5.   if $e_i = 1$ then $R = R \times T \bmod M$;
6. return R; end.

The parallel algorithm of binary exponentiation is given in Algorithm 5.2 and the parallel architecture in Figure 5.14.

To illustrate the obtained results, we evolved a specification for two different modulus and keys, which are $M = 11$, $e = 5$ and $M = 13$, $e = 11$. The specification of the evolved RSA-based cryptographic hardware for the first case is given below, wherein the signals t_0 to t_3 are the bits constituting the plaintext from the less to most significant bit. For the sake of clarity, we use the expression prefix notation.

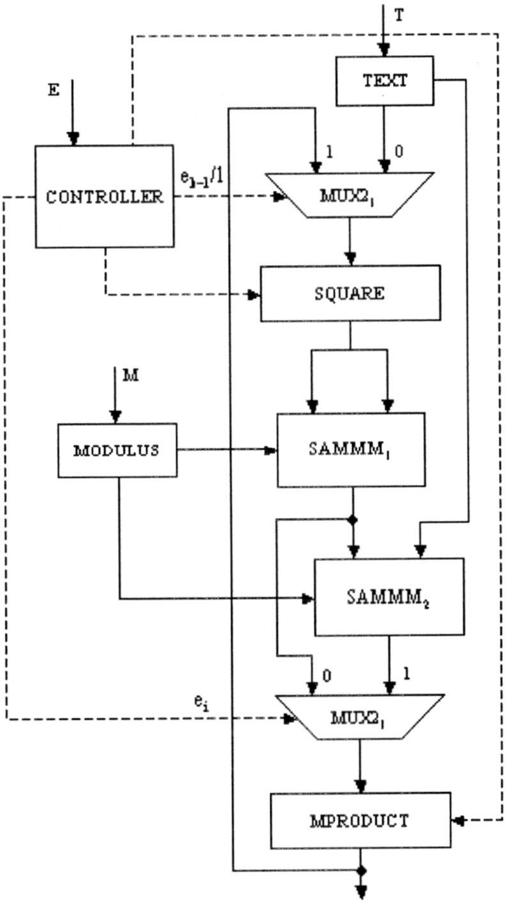

Figure 5.13. Sequential architecture for modular exponentiation

$$
\begin{aligned}
c_3 &\Longleftarrow \text{AND}\left(\text{OR}\left(t_3, \text{NOR}\left(\text{NOR}\left(\bar{t}_0, t_2\right), \bar{t}_1\right)\right), \text{NAND}\left(\text{NOR}\left(\bar{t}_0, t_2\right), \bar{t}_2\right)\right) \\
c_2 &\Longleftarrow \text{NOR}\left(\bar{t}_0, t_0\right) \\
c_1 &\Longleftarrow \text{AND}\left(\text{NAND}\left(\text{NOR}\left(\bar{t}_0, t_2\right), \bar{t}_2\right), \text{OR}\left(t_3, \text{NOR}\left(\text{NOR}\left(\bar{t}_0, t_2\right), \bar{t}_1\right)\right)\right) \\
c_0 &\Longleftarrow \text{MUX}\left(\bar{t}_1, \text{NOR}\left(\bar{t}_0, t_2\right), \bar{t}_2\right)
\end{aligned}
\tag{5.17}
$$

The specification of the evolved RSA-based cryptographic hardware for the second case, i.e. $M = 13$, $e = 11$ is given below, wherein NUX stands for NOT MUX.

Algorithm 5.2 Parallel binary modular exponentiation

Input. Plaintext/ciphertext T, private/public key e and modulus M

Output. Ciphertext/palintext R

```
int R^(0) := 1, P^(0) := T;
for i := 0 to m − 1
    P^(i+1) = P^(i) × P^(i) mod M;
    if e_i = 1 then R^(i+1) := R^(i) × P^(i) mod M
    else R^(i+1) := R^(i)
return R;
end.
```

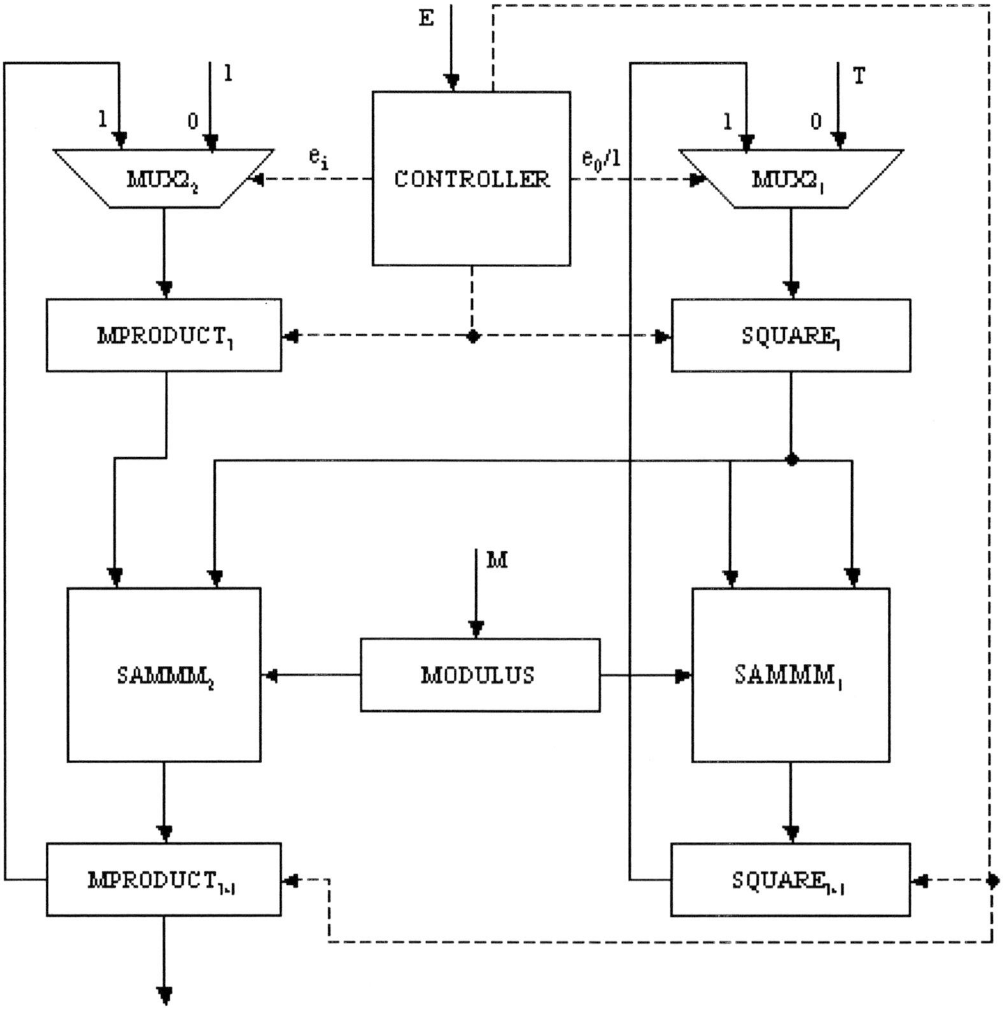

Figure 5.14. Parallel architecture for modular exponentiation

$$
\begin{aligned}
c_3 &\Longleftarrow \text{NUX} \left(\text{AND} \left(\text{NAND} \left(t_2,\bar{t}_0\right), \text{NAND} \left(\bar{t}_1,t_2\right)\right), \right. \\
&\quad \text{NOR} \left(\text{NOR} \left(\text{NOR} \left(\bar{t}_0,\bar{t}_2\right),\bar{t}_0\right), \text{AND} \left(\text{NAND} \left(t_2,\bar{t}_0\right),\bar{t}_1\right)\right), \\
&\quad \left. \text{NOR} \left(\text{MUX} \left(\bar{t}_3,\bar{t}_1, \text{NOR} \left(\text{NOR} \left(\bar{t}_0,\bar{t}_2\right),\bar{t}_0\right)\right),t_3\right)\right) \\
c_2 &\Longleftarrow \text{NUX} \left(\text{NOR} \left(\text{MUX}\left(\bar{t}_3,6, \text{NOR} \left(\text{NOR} \left(\bar{t}_0,\bar{t}_2\right),\bar{t}_0\right)\right),t_3\right), \right. \\
&\quad \left. \text{MUX} \left(\bar{t}_3,\bar{t}_1, \text{NOR} \left(\text{NOR} \left(\bar{t}_0,\bar{t}_2\right),\bar{t}_0\right)\right), \text{NAND} \left(\bar{t}_2,t_1\right)\right) \qquad (5.18) \\
c_1 &\Longleftarrow \text{MUX} \left(\text{NOR} \left(\text{NOR} \left(\bar{t}_0,\bar{t}_2\right),\bar{t}_0\right), \text{NOR} \left(\text{NOR} \left(\text{NOR} \left(\bar{t}_0,\bar{t}_2\right),\bar{t}_0\right), \right.\right. \\
&\quad \left.\left. \text{AND} \left(\text{NAND} \left(t_2,\bar{t}_0\right),\bar{t}_1\right)\right),\bar{t}_3\right) \\
c_0 &\Longleftarrow \text{AND} \left(\text{NAND} \left(\bar{t}_1,t_2\right), \text{MUX} \left(\text{NOR} \left(\text{NOR} \left(\bar{t}_3,\bar{t}_1\right), \right.\right.\right. \\
&\quad \left.\left.\left. \text{NOR} \left(\bar{t}_0,\bar{t}_2\right)\right),t_3, \text{NOR} \left(t_0,t_1\right)\right)\right)
\end{aligned}
$$

The schematics of the evolved circuit with the above given specification were generated automatically using the XILINX^{TM} Project Manager [22] and are shown in Figure 5.16. The simulation waveform of the yielded circuit is depicted in Figure 5.15. The ciphertext for all possible values of the plaintext are considered.

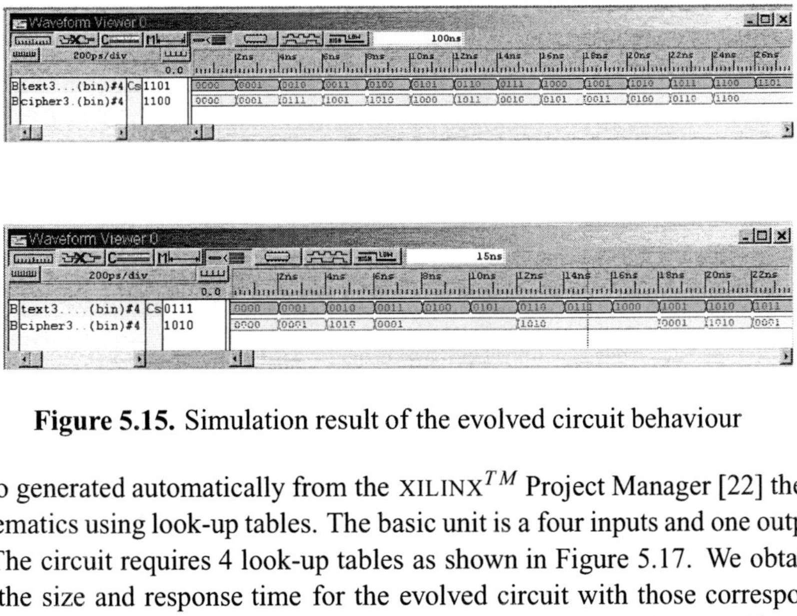

Figure 5.15. Simulation result of the evolved circuit behaviour

We also generated automatically from the XILINX^{TM} Project Manager [22] the evolved circuit schematics using look-up tables. The basic unit is a four inputs and one output look-up table. The circuit requires 4 look-up tables as shown in Figure 5.17. We obtained and compared the size and response time for the evolved circuit with those corresponding to the sequential and parallel binary exponentiation implementations whose architectures are depicted in Figure 5.6 and Figure 5.14. Table 5.7 lists the collected data for $M = 13$ and $e = 11$.

The size of the circuits is expressed in terms of gate equivalent and the response time is nano-seconds. The data provide in this table show clearly that the evolved circuit is far better than the conventional designs: It requires much less hardware area and encrypts/decrypts much faster. Furthermore, it is shielded against side-channel leakage as it has no repetitive behaviour, as it is the case for conventional designs. However, the evolved circuit is not scalable. When a new cryptosystem with new modulus and/or key, a new design need be evolved from scratch.

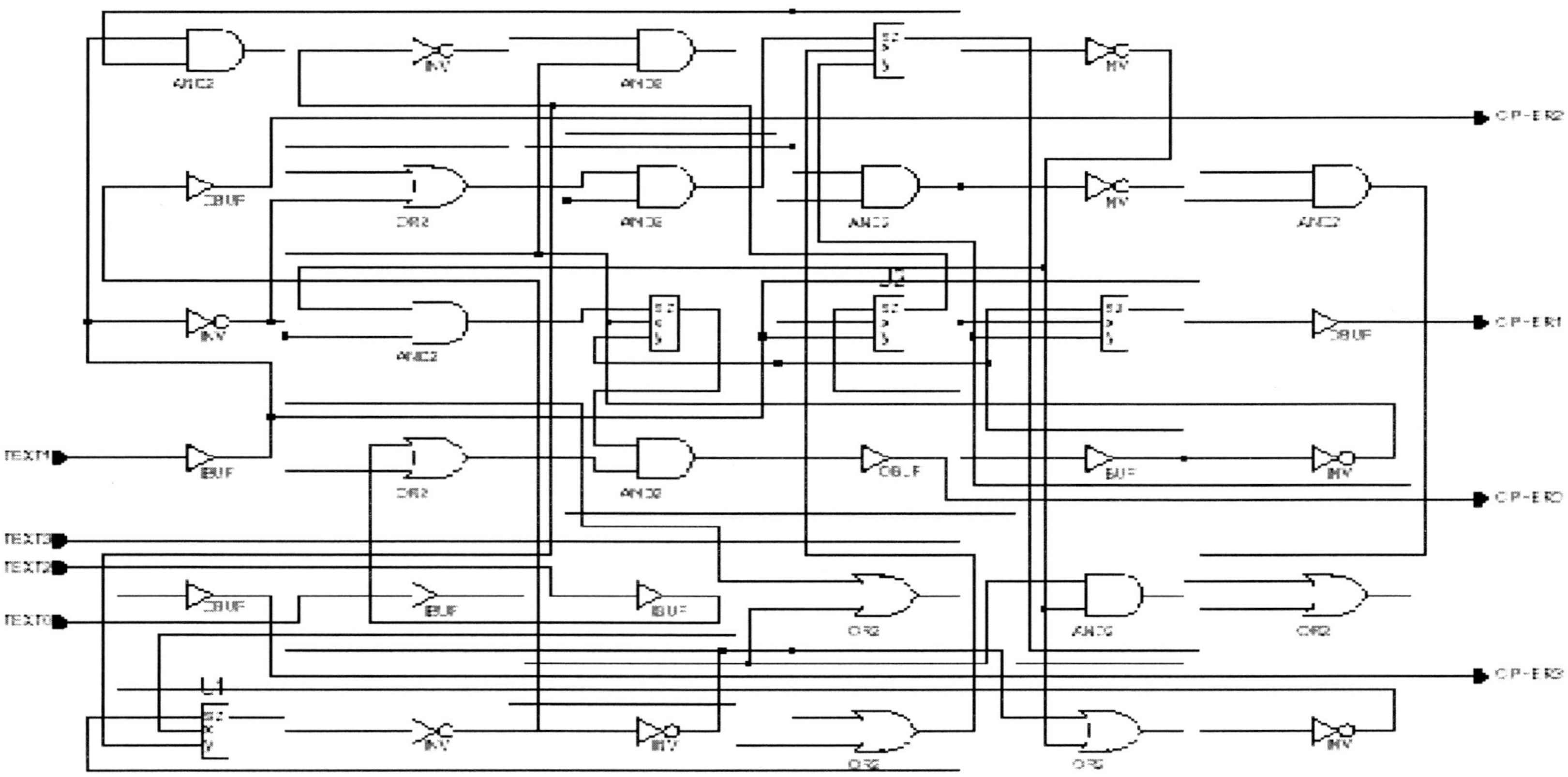

Figure 5.16. Schematics of the evolved RSA-based cryptographic hardware for M=13 and E=11

Table 5.7. Conventional vs. evolutionary designs for the RSA-based cryptosystems

Design	Size	Time (ns)
Sequential Binary	524	7.321
Parallel Binary	992	4.992
Evolved circuit	24	1.313

5.7 SUMMARY

In this chapter, we described an evolutionary technique to engineer compact, efficient and creative digital combinational circuit given the expected input/output behaviour. We explored the use of genetic programming and changing from the binary representation of circuits to a tree representation. We showed how to improve the evolution process by taking advantage of the central processing unit parallelism. An advantage of using genetic programming consists of the readability of the evolved circuit for synthesis using one of the available synthesis tools [15].

Our evolutionary process is multi-objective as it allows one to yield balanced i.e. compact and efficient digital circuits. The proposed fitness function evaluates a given circuit with respect to correctness, required hardware area and necessary propagation delay of output signals. It does so using the well-agreed-upon factor $area \times performance$ as a measure to appreciate the complexity of a digital circuit.

We evolved a better circuit for every example used by Coello et al. [12] compared to both human designs and evolved circuit that only consider the number of required gates to evaluate an evolved solution. On one hand, this proves that the fitness function we engineered is far more realistic than that of used by Coello et al. On the other hand, it also proves that evolutionary hardware can offer an alternative way to human design techniques to design efficient digital circuit. We showed how the evaluation of circuit fitness can be computed efficiently taking advantage of the inherent parallelism of the central processing units of the computers.

Using the evolutionary process described earlier, we automatically generate data-flow based specifications for hardware designs of public-key cryptosystems such as RSA-based encryption system. We focussed on evolving minimal hardware specifications, i.e. hardware that minimises both space (i.e. required gate number) and time (i.e. encryption and decryption time), for modular exponentiation. Modular exponentiation is the cornerstone operation of most public-key cryptosystems. The advantage of such evolved cryptosystems are shielded against side-channel leakage. However, the designs are not scalable, i.e. for new modulus or keys, one needs to evolve a new design. We compared our results against existing and well-known designs, which are based on the binary modular exponentiation method. The evolved is far more efficient in both required hardware area and encryption/decryption throughput.

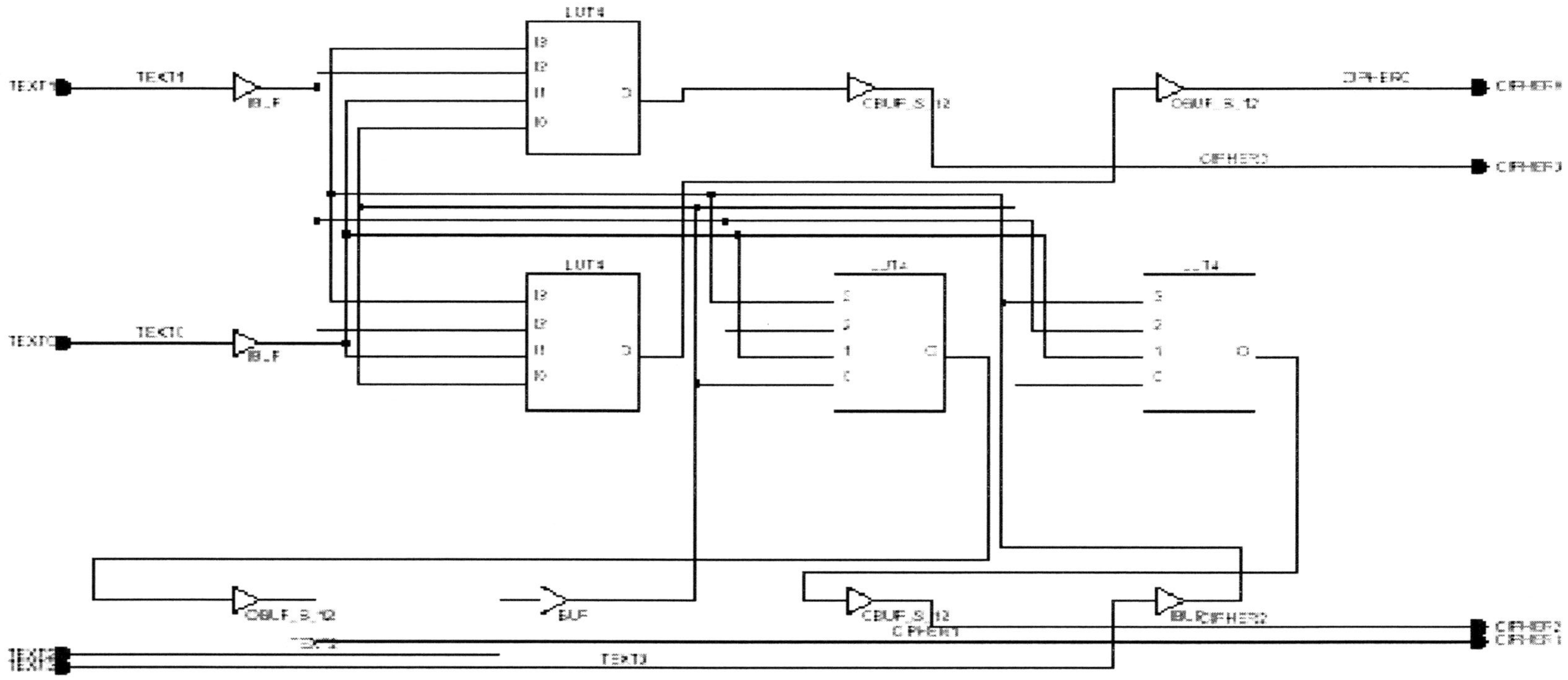

Figure 5.17. Circuit schematics using look-up tables generated by the Xilinx^{TM} project manager for the evolved circuit

Bibliography

[1] Aho, A.V., Ravi, S. and Ullman, J.D., *Compilers: principles, techniques and tools*, Addison-Wesley, 1986.

[2] Blum, T. and Paar, C. Montgomery modular exponentiation on reconfigurable hardware, *Proceedings of the 14th. IEEE Symposium on Computer Arithmetic*, Australia, 1999.

[3] Brickell, E.F., A survey of hardware implementation of RSA, In G. Brassard, ed., Advances in Cryptology, *Proceedings of CRYPTO'98*, Lecture Notes in Computer Science 435:368-370, Springer-Verlag, 1989.13:39 3/6/2004

[4] Coello, C.A.C., Christiansen, A.D. and Aguirre, A.H., Towards Automated Evolutionary Design of Combinational Circuits, *Comput. Electr. Eng.*, **27**, pp. 1-28, 2001

[5] Ercegovac, M.D., Lang, T. and Moreno, J.H., *Introduction to digital systems*, John Wiley, 1999.

[6] Gordon, D.M., A survey of Fast exponentiation methods, *Journal of Algorithms* **27**, pp. 129-146, 1998.

[7] Haupt, R.L. and Haupt, S.E., *Practical genetic algorithms*, John Wiley and Sons, 1998.

[8] Karnaugh, M., A map method for synthesis of combinational logic circuits, Transactions of the AIEE, *Communications and Electronics*, **72**(I):593-599, November 1953.

[9] Koza, J.R., *Genetic Programming*. MIT Press, 1992.

[10] McCluskey, E.J., Minimisation of Boolean functions, *Bell Systems Technical Journal*, **35**(5):1417-1444, November 1956.

[11] Menezes, A.J., Van Oorschot, P.C., and Scott A. Vanstone. *Handbook of Applied Cryptography*. CRC Press, 1996.

[12] Dabbish, E.A. and Sloan, R.H., Power analysis attacks of modular exponentiation in smartcards, Proc. Cryptographic Hardware and Embedded Systems, *Lecture Notes in Computer Science*, vol. 1717, pp. 144-157, 1999.

[13] Miller, J.F. and Job, D., *Principles in the evolutionary design of digital circuits*

[14] Nedjah, N., Mourelle, L.M., Two hardware implementations for the Montgomery multiplication: sequential vs. parallel, *Proceedings of the 15th. Symposium on Integrated Circuits and Systems Design*, Porto Alegre, RS, Brazil, R. Reis and Calazans, N. (Eds.), IEEE Computer Society Press, pp. 3-8, 2002.

[15] Nedjah, N., Mourelle, L.M., Reconfigurable hardware implementation of Montgomery modular multiplication and parallel binary exponentiation, *Proceedings of the Euromicro Symposium on Digital System Design*, Dortmund, Germany, IEEE Computer Society Press, pp. 226-235, 2002.

[16] Poli, R., Efficient evolution of parallel binary multipliers and continuous symbolic regression expressions with sub-machine code GP, *Technical Report CSRP-9819*, University of Birmingham, School of Computer Science, December 1998.

[17] Rivest, R., Shamir, A. and Adleman, L., A method for obtaining digital signature and public-key cryptosystems, *Communications of the ACM*, **21**:120-126, 1978.

[18] Rhyne, V.T., *Fundamentals of digital systems design*, F.F. Kuo Ed. Prentice-Hall Electrical Engineering Series, 1973.

[19] Tiountchik, A., Systolic modular exponentiation via Montgomery algorithm, *Electronic Letters*, **34**(9):874-875, 1998.

[20] Turton, B.C.H., Extending Quine-McCluskey for exclusive-or logic synthesis, *IEEE Transactions on Education*, **39**(1):81-85, February 1996.

[21] Thompson, A., Layzel, P. and Zebelum, R.S., Explorations in design space: unconventional design through artificial evolution, *IEEE Transactions on Evolutionary Computations*, **3**(3):81-85, February 1996.

[22] XILINX^{TM}, Inc., Foundation Series Software, http://www.xilinx.com, 2002.

In: Evolutionary Machine Design: Methodology & Applications ISBN 1-59454-405-0
Editors: N. Nedjah & L. Mourelle, pp:139-164

Chapter 6

Automated Discovery of Innovative Designs of Mechanical Components Using Evolutionary Multi-objective Algorithms

Kalyanmoy Deb and Shamik Chaudhuri

Department of Mechanical Engineering, Indian Institute of Technology Kanpur, PIN 208016, India, (deb | shamik)@iitk.ac.in, http://www.iitk.ac.in/kangal/deb.htm

Automated design of different mechanical components, particularly in terms of their shapes and sizes, has been an important task in engineering design. In this chapter, we consider the design task as a simultaneous optimization of two or more conflicting objectives and use an evolutionary algorithm (EA) for finding multiple trade-off optimal solutions. An analysis of the optimized solutions reveals innovative design principles for solutions to become optimum, a task which is otherwise difficult to achieve by other means. The proposed methodology is generic, and its usefulness is demonstrated by applying it to a number of mechanical component shape design problems.

6.1 Introduction

Design of mechanical components, particularly for their shapes and sizes, has received plenty of attention in the past. Various methods have been used for this purpose. However, due to the advancement of genetic algorithms (GAs) – search and optimization algorithms motivated by the principles of natural evolution and genetics, the shape optimization of mechanical components have been dealt by discretizing the design domain in a number of finite sized elements and by forming a shape by deciding whether to keep or not keep each element [5, 11]. In this chapter, we use this strategy as a mode of developing optimal shapes for different applications.

Although most earlier studies on automated shape design seem to have concentrated in finding a shape which will minimize or maximize a particular objective (or a goal) of design, here we look beyond and attempt to unveil important properties related to the design which any optimum solution may possess. In this chapter, we restrict our computations for two conflicting objectives, although the proposed methods can also be extended to more than two conflicting objectives. We treat a design problem as a simultaneous optimization of two conflicting objectives and use an evolutionary multi-objective optimization (EMO) procedure to find the resulting Pareto-optimal (or non-inferior) solutions [2,13]. The reason for using an evolutionary algorithm for the task is straightforward. A pair of conflicting objectives will give rise to a multitude of optimum solutions (known as Pareto-optimal solutions) and an evolutionary algorithm (including a GA) is an optimization algorithm which deals with more than one solution in an iteration. Thus, a GA is an ideal candidate for the task of finding more than one solution in one single simulation. After a set of trade-off optimal solutions are obtained, they will be analyzed to decipher useful design principles which all or most of the optimized solutions may possess. Such information, if known are useful to designers.

In the remainder of this chapter, we describe the EMO-based procedure and demonstrate the working principles by applying on four different mechanical engineering design problems. The suggested procedure is generic and can also be applied to similar other engineering design activities.

6.2 Evolutionary Multi-objective Optimization (EMO)

The practice of evolutionary algorithms (EAs) in engineering applications, although a recent phenomenon, has been well demonstrated. In most applications, EAs are applied in finding an optimum or a near-optimum solution of a single-objective optimal design problem. For the past five years or so, EAs are increasingly being used in solving multi-objective optimization problems, involving more than one objective of design, such as minimization of cost, maximization of reliability, and others. It is intuitive that a low-cost solution is less-reliable and vice versa. Therefore, while optimizing both cost and reliability, a designer faces with a dilemma: Which of the two objectives is to be optimized? Theoretically, such multi-objective optimization problems give rise to a set of optimal solutions, each trading off the two objectives in a different manner. It then becomes a task on the designer to choose one such solution by using some other *higher-level* information. Although the literature on multi-objective optimization using classical methods is comparatively old and growing, the research and application of evolutionary multi-objective optimization (EMO) introduces a completely different way of solving such problems. By first finding a well-distributed set of Pareto-optimal solutions, EMO provides useful information about the working range of each objective, which in turn should help a designer to choose a particular solution at the end of optimization process.

Based on the above principle of evolutionary multi-objective optimization, there now exist a number of efficient algorithms, such as non-dominated sorting GA (or NSGA-II) [4], strength Pareto EA (or SPEA) [6], Pareto-envelope evolution strategy (or PESA) [1] and others. Interested readers may refer to a recent introductory text [2] by the first author on these algorithms and the working principles of EMO methodologies. In this chapter, we use NSGA-II [4] as a representative EMO methodology, a brief discussion of which is given in the next section.

6.3 An Evolutionary Multi-objective Optimizer: NSGA-II

Contrary to the classical approaches, evolutionary multi-objective optimization (EMO) procedures aim at finding a finite, representative set of Pareto-optimal solutions of a problem. Figure 6.1 illustrates this aspect on a hypothetical three-objective minimization problem. The task of an EMO procedure is to *identify* the Pareto-optimal front (shown separately as a

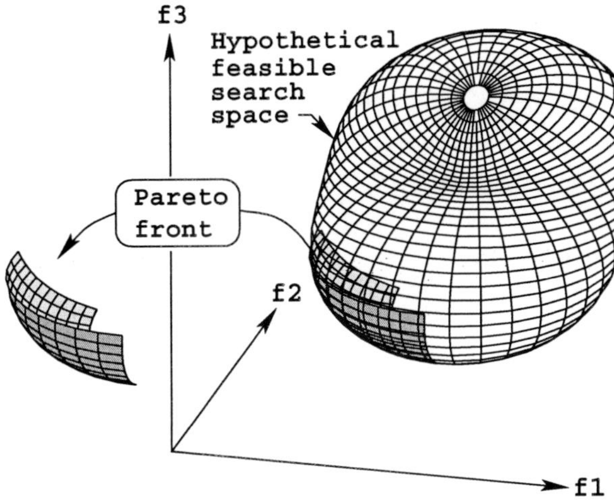

Figure 6.1. A three-objective feasible region and the corresponding Pareto-optimal front are shown.

surface) out of the entire feasible search space. This is, by no means, an easy task. Various optimization concepts must have to be used to clearly identify the true Pareto-optimal front. In the next section, we shall demonstrate how different optimization concepts can be used to discover the Pareto-optimal front for a number of mechanical component design problems.

Although one optimal solution would be chosen at the end of the optimization task, a knowledge of the entire range of Pareto-optimal solutions is helpful in (i) choosing a particular optimal solution and (ii) getting useful insights about trade-off among objectives of the problem [3]. Thus, the task of an EMO is to (i) converge to the true Pareto-optimal front and (ii) maintain a good distribution of solutions on the entire front. Here we describe the elitist non-dominated sorting GA or NSGA-II procedure [4] for achieving both the above tasks in a multi-objective optimization problem.

Like in a genetic algorithm (GA), NSGA-II starts with a population of N_{pop} random solutions. In the N-th iteration of NSGA-II, the offspring population Q_N is first created by using the parent population P_N and the usual genetic operators – reproduction, recombination, and mutation [8]. Thereafter, both populations are combined together to form R_N of size $2N_{\text{pop}}$. Then, a non-dominated sorting procedure [2] is applied to classify the entire population R_N into a number of hierarchical non-dominated fronts. Figure 6.2 shows a schematic of one iteration of NSGA-II. Fronts are marked as 1,2,... in the decreasing level of non-domination of solutions. A property of such fronts is that a solution lying on a better non-dominated front (say $\mathcal{F}$) does not get dominated by any solution of a front worse than $\mathcal{F}$. For M objectives, there exists an algorithm requiring $O(N \log^{M-1} N)$ computations to make such a non-dominated sorting of the entire population of size N [12].

Once the non-dominated sorting of the set R_N is over, the new population is filled with solutions of different non-dominated fronts, one at a time. The filling starts with the best non-dominated front (marked as front 1) and continues with solutions of the second non-dominated front, followed by the third non-dominated front, and so on. Since the overall population size of R_N is $2N_{\text{pop}}$, not all fronts may be accommodated in N slots available in the new population. This scenario is shown in Figure 6.2. All fronts which could not be accommodated (such as, fronts 4, 5 and 6 in the figure) are simply deleted. When the last allowed front (front 3 in the figure)is being considered, there may exist more solutions in the front than the remaining slots in the new population. Instead of arbitrarily discarding some members from the last front, the solutions which will make the *diversity* of the selected solutions the largest are chosen. In this step, a *crowded-sorting* of the solutions of front i

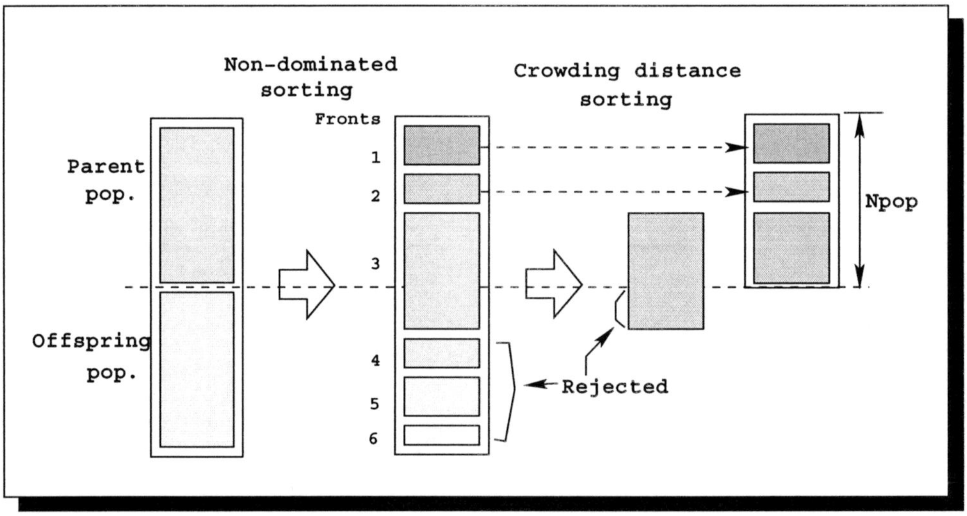

Figure 6.2. Schematic of the NSGA-II procedure.

(the last front which could not be accommodated fully) is performed by using a *crowding distance metric* and the adequate number of solutions are picked from the top of the list.

The crowding distance of a solution in a non-dominated front is a measure of crowding by other members of the front. In the NSGA-II implementation, a metric totalling the objective-wise distances between neighboring solutions is used. For details, readers are encouraged to refer to the original NSGA-II study [4]. The reproduction operator uses a *crowded tournament* selection method in which two solutions are compared and the winner is declared as the one residing on a better non-dominated front, or the one having a larger crowding distance value. The computational complexity of one iteration of NSGA-II is dictated by the non-dominated sorting complexity mentioned above.

6.3.1 Constraint-Handling in NSGA-II

The constraint handling method modifies the crowded tournament selection operator of NSGA-II by checking the feasibility of two participating solutions [2]. In the presence of constraints, each solution can be either feasible or infeasible. Thus, there may exist at most three situations: (i) both solutions are feasible, (ii) one is feasible and other is not, and (iii) both are infeasible. We consider each case by simply redefining the domination principle as follows for any two solutions $x^{(i)}$ and $x^{(j)}$).

A solution $x^{(i)}$ is said to 'constrain-dominate' a solution $x^{(j)}$, if any of the following conditions are true:

1. Solution $x^{(i)}$ is feasible and solution $x^{(j)}$ is not.

2. Solutions $x^{(i)}$ and $x^{(j)}$ are both infeasible, but solution $x^{(i)}$ has a smaller constraint violation.

3. Solutions $x^{(i)}$ and $x^{(j)}$ are feasible and solution $x^{(i)}$ dominates solution $x^{(j)}$ in the usual sense.

The highlight of this procedure is that it makes a simple adjustment on the definition of the domination and does not require any additional parameter, such as the penalty parameter. This is because feasible solutions are always better than infeasible solutions and are sorted into different non-dominated levels in the usual way. However, the infeasible solutions get sorted depending on their aggregate normalized constraint violation values – an infeasible solution having a larger constraint violation lies on a worse non-dominated front.

6.4 EMO for Discovering Useful Design Variants

In this section, we describe how the EMO methodology discussed above is used for the task of finding useful design variants for engineering shape design problems. We divide the task into two phases: (i) finding a set of trade-off optimal solutions using an EMO and (ii) analyzing the obtained solutions for useful insights.

6.4.1 Phase I: Finding a Set of Pareto-Optimal Solutions

In principle we can simply use an existing EMO, such as NSGA-II described in the previous section, for achieving the first task mentioned above. Here, we employ a hybrid search strategy of using an EMO with a *local-search* method to make sure that the obtained solutions are indeed very close to the real optima of the problem. Such a hybrid strategy was first suggested elsewhere [2, 5] and is also a quick and reliable procedure to reach near optima. However, a number of other hybrid EMO approaches are also suggested elsewhere [9, 10].

In this approach, first, an EMO is applied without the use of any preference information, such as a weight-vector often used to scalarize multiple objectives. Here, we have used NSGA-II [4] for this purpose. After some generations are elapsed (thereby allowing the EMO procedure to reach near to the true Pareto-optimal front), a local-search algorithm is applied from each of the obtained EMO solutions. This local-search algorithm can be a variant of classical hill-climbing procedures [14, 15]. However, since a single-objective function is required for the hill-climbing procedure, the multi-objective problem is reduced to a single-objective problem by using a weighted-sum of different objectives. The scaled single-objective function is given below:

$$F(x) = \sum_{j=1}^{M} \bar{w}_j^x f_j^{(x)}, \tag{6.1}$$

where, $f_j(x)$ is the jth objective function and $\bar{w}_j^x$ is the weight to the jth objective function. In this approach, the weight vector decides the importance of different objectives. In other words, the weight-vector provides a direction of the local-search procedure in the objective space. In the original study, the weights were assigned with the knowledge of a solution's location on the Pareto-optimal front [5]. When a solution is near the minimum value of a objective function, the weight of that function will get a large value. The weight calculation can be performed as follows [5]:

$$\bar{w}_j = \frac{(f_j^{max} - f_j^{(x)})/(f_j^{max} - f_j^{min})}{\sum_{k=1}^{N}(f_k^{max} - f_k(x))/(f_k^{max} - f_k^{min})}, \tag{6.2}$$

where, $\bar{w}_j$ is the weight for the jth objective, f_j^{max} is the scaled maximum value of the jth function in a EMO population, $f_j(x)$ is the scaled value of the jth function, and f_j^{min} is the scaled minimum value of the jth function in the population.

It is noteworthy that the use of above weighted approach may not be useful in problems having non-convex Pareto-optimal front and other difficult problems. In such problems, the methodology suggested for a local-search technique can be replaced by using a Tchebycheff metric [2, 13] or by using Benson's method [7]. The essential idea is to employ a local-search method from each optimized solution obtained using the EMO procedure and obtain the corresponding optimum solution. Thus, at the end of the first phase, we are expected to obtain a set of near Pareto-optimal or Pareto-optimal solutions.

6.4.2 Phase II: Analyzing Optimized Solutions for Useful Properties

The obtained set of Pareto-optimal solutions can then be analyzed for finding possible *commonality* principles among all such solutions. Although not intuitive, such commonality principles are expected to be present in most engineering design problems. Qualitatively, since all these solutions are optimal (and are definitely not arbitrary solutions in the search space), they may follow certain properties for being optimal. Quantitatively, for any multi-objective optimization problem, all Pareto-optimal solutions must satisfy the Fritz-John optimality conditions given below [13]:

Fritz–John necessary condition Theorem. A necessary condition for x^* to be Pareto-optimal is that there exist vectors $\lambda \geq 0$ and $u \geq 0$ (where $\lambda \in \mathbb{R}^M$, $u \in \mathbb{R}^J$ and $\lambda, u \neq 0$) such that the following conditions are true:

1. $\sum_{m=1}^{M} \lambda_m \nabla f_m(x^*) - \sum_{j=1}^{J} u_j \nabla g_j(x^*) = 0$, and

2. $u_j g_j(x^*) = 0$ for all $j = 1, 2, \ldots, J$.

Although the above set of conditions require that the objective functions and constraints are required to be differentiable, they collectively indicate that for a solution to be Pareto-optimal, it must satisfy certain optimality conditions. Now, it is very well be true that for every Pareto-optimal solution such conditions give rise to a different set of properties and when all Pareto-optimal solutions are considered together there is no commonality principle among all Pareto-optimal solutions. Although this is a possibility theoretically, it is unlikely for most engineering problems due to the underlying scientific laws which the engineering systems abide by. In any case, for a particular problem of interest, it is worth investigating whether there exist such commonality principles among all Pareto-optimal solutions.

If in a problem there exists some commonality principles, they are undoubtedly important to the decision-maker or the user. Once such principles are known, the user can easily change the existing operating optimal solution to another by maintaining the commonality principles identical between them but simply changing the properties which must vary among them. Moreover, the knowledge of such commonality principles will provide important insights about the engineering system under consideration.

In short, after a set of Pareto-optimal solutions are found in Phase I, their decision variable vectors can be investigated for the existence of any *common* principles and *principles* which make them lie on different parts of the Pareto-optimal front. In all problems here, we make a visual investigation for finding such principles (and in most cases such a visual inspection may be enough); a more systematic investigation can also be used. We are currently devising an automatic method of deciphering such common principles from the obtained Pareto-optimal set by using machine learning principles, results of which will be communicated at a later date.

We now suggest a systematic multi-objective optimization procedure used in this study for solving engineering design problems having multiple objectives.

6.5 Proposed Multi-objective Optimization Procedure

The methodology described in Phase I is extended to develop an efficient optimization procedure:

1. **Varying the grid size:** Here, we suggest varying the grid (or mesh) size from coarse to fine. We recognize that at the start of an optimization process, it is not necessary to evaluate a solution very precisely. However, as iterations progress, more precise evaluations are necessary. Many researchers implement this aspect in many different ways so as to reduce the overall computational efficiency, but without sacrificing the solution quality. Here, we simply use a coarse grid to start with and as iterations proceed, we make the grid finer and finer by simply reducing the grid size in each dimension to half.

2. **Improved crossover operator:** The standard row or column-wise crossover operator may be used for a crude mesh. But for a fine mesh, swapping rows or columns is too generic to mix the properties of two parents to come up with a good offspring solution. Not only that, the operator is also discrete in nature, that is, the rows or columns, which are interchanged may not be contiguous. For this reason, here we swap a contiguous rectangular region (not necessarily spanning to a complete row or a column) of and between two parents to create two offsprings.

3. **A fast local-search operator:** The local-search algorithm used in a past study [5] was not a particularly efficient one. It starts searching the domain by mutating each and every bit of the string under consideration. If the element (representing a void) under mutation is far away from the main body of the design, application of the mutation operator will turn it into a material element from a void element. This newly-formed material element will not be a part of the main cluster and will not alter the mesh used in the FEM analysis. Thus, there will not be any improvement in the scaled objective function. Due to the above reason, the search effort will be wasted. Here, we only restrict the mutation operator (or the local-search operator) to boundary elements dictated by the shape. Figure 6.3 shows the domain for mutation operator (shaded elements). For element A, only eight elements around it will be attempted to mutate. Elements, such as B, will not be mutated because of non-existence of any material member around it.

4. **Distributed computing:** The EMO algorithm used in the earlier study [5] was a serial one. The time required to complete one simulation of the optimization procedure on a Pentium II, 350 MHz serial computer was around 2 days. To reduce the computing time, we use a distributed computing machine and population members are computed in a parallel fashion, thereby reducing the overall computational time within a few hours.

   After the EMO run, the non-dominated solutions are clustered and representatives are sent for further improvement using the local-search procedure. At this stage,

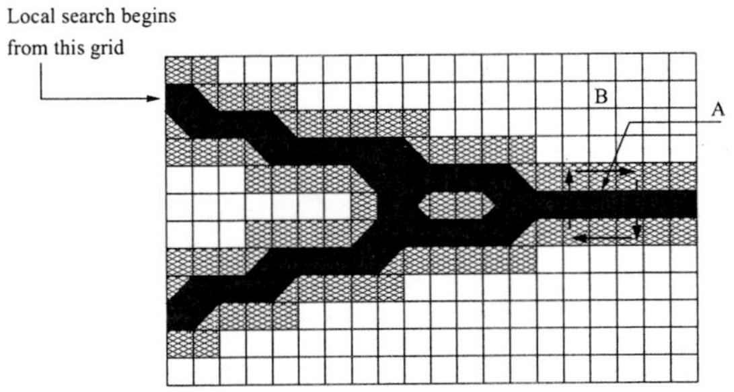

Figure 6.3. The fast local-search procedure.

processing of different solutions are independent of each other. So parallelization can also be applied in this stage. The maximum speed up that can be available is $T_{\text{local-search}}/N$ (assuming that each solution takes an identical processing time). Here, N is the number of solutions in local-search and $T_{\text{local-search}}$ is the time required for a single processor to process N solutions. In this module, a parallelization is implemented in a different way. Here, all the individuals are queued up. If there are N processors, then processing starts with the first N solutions. Whenever processing on a particular processor is over, a queued solution is sent for processing to that processor.

6.5.1 Iterative local-search based EMO

Initially, the grid size (that is, the size of the square elements) of the search domain is large, so the NSGA-II procedure can remove large chunks of material from the initial random shape within a few generations, if needed. If the grid size is large, the required computation time will be small. The non-dominated front after the NSGA-II run is clustered and the representative solutions are taken for further refinement. To make the solutions smoother, the mesh is refined by dividing each square of the crude mesh into four equal squares. Thereafter, a fast local-search algorithm is applied to a non-dominated solution with a composite objective function, formed by the location of the solution on the non-dominated front [5]. Using this level of refined mesh, the search moves further and ultimately until no further improvement in the combined objective value is obtained. At this stage, the mesh is refined again in the same way. The local-search is applied again and the shapes are made smoother. The step-by-step procedure is illustrated in Figure 6.4.

6.6 Simulation Results

In this section, we present simulation results for a number of mechanical component design problems.

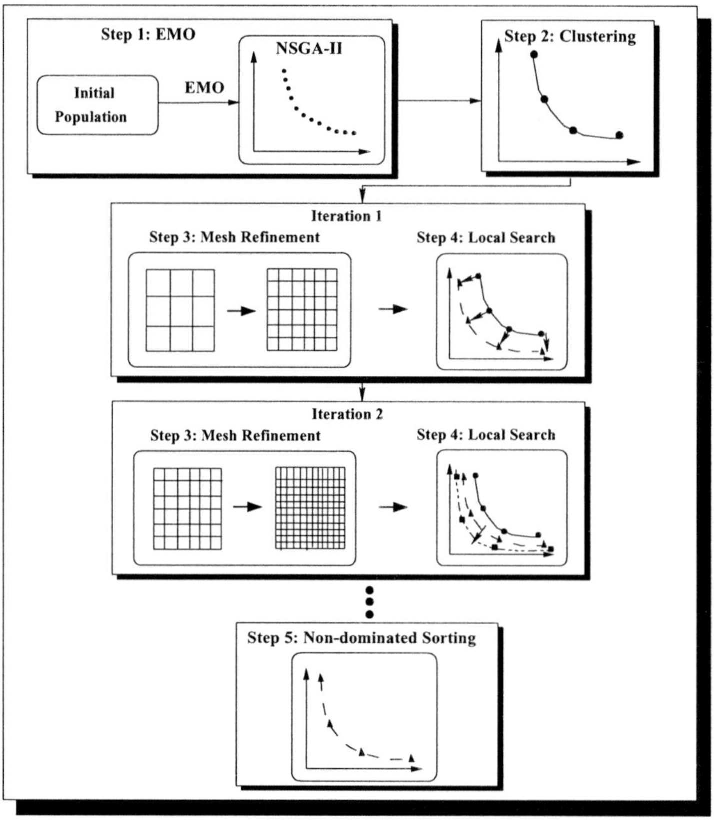

Figure 6.4. A flowchart of the proposed local-search based EMO procedure (Phase I).

6.6.1 A Cantilever Plate

The cantilever plate is designed with an end load of P = 100 kN as shown in Figure 6.5. The thickness of the plate is 20 mm. For the NSGA-II simulation in the first phase, the grid size taken is chosen to be (6×10), such that a solution is represented by a 60 bit binary string. Thereafter, the grids are increased to 12×20 for the first local-search. Grids are again increased to 24×40 before the second local-search is begun. Geometry constraint is implemented by keeping at least one material element at the left-most column of the grid and also at the elements adjacent to the node where the force is applied. The different parameters used in the analysis are given below:

Material Data :

Density of Material	: 7800 kg/m^3
Yield strength	: 150 MPa
Young's Modulus	: 200 GPa
Poisson's ratio	: 0.25

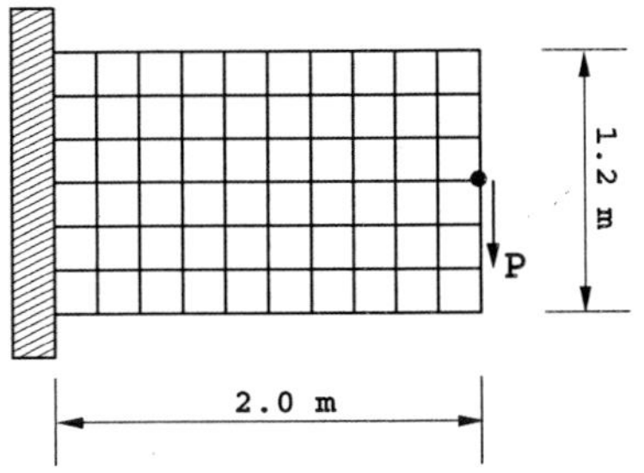

Figure 6.5. Loading and support of the cantilever plate.

NSGA-II Parameters :

Population Size	: 54
Number of Generations	: 100
Crossover Probability	: 0.95
Mutation Probability	: 1/(string length)

The solutions on the non-dominated front after the NSGA-II run (after Step 1) is shown in the Figure 6.6. The non-dominated solutions (marked using diamonds) are plotted along with the initial population (marked using '+'). Nine well-distributed solutions are picked up from the entire non-dominated front for further refinement. These representative solutions are shown in Figure 6.7. The actual geometrical shapes of these solutions after the NSGA-II run are shown in Figure 6.8. The solutions are numbered in a matrix notation. The top left figure shows the minimum-weight structure having a large displacement and the same at the bottom right is the minimum-deflection solution having a large weight. It is clear from the figure that NSGA-II is capable of developing crude structures in only 100 generations using a coarse mesh. These representative shapes are further processed by the local search procedure. Figure 6.7 showed the position of these solutions after the first local-search (Step 4 of the first iteration). The movements of the solutions in the objective space from NSGA-II solutions to local-search solutions are marked with the help of arrows. It is evident that remarkable improvements have taken place by the local-search operation.

Figure 6.9 shows the new topology of the structures. At this stage, the grid size is refined from 6×10 to 12×20. The minimum-weight solution for this problem is likely to have a reducing width towards the end load. To have the widest base, at the support, the obtained minimum-weight solution spreads two arms to the maximum extent possible. It is interesting to note that without any such information hard-coded, the optimization procedure adopted here arrives at such a solution in successive iterations of the local-search procedure. Figure 6.10 represents the plot of the non-dominated fronts after the second local-search procedure (Step 4 of iteration 2). Here also the movements of the solutions are marked by arrows. The minimum-weight solution of first local-search shown at the top left position in Figure 6.9 becomes a dominated solution after the second local-search. This is because of the zigzag shape of the two arms of the parabola. As the local-search process tries to remove material from the arms, the stress generated inside the structure exceeds the

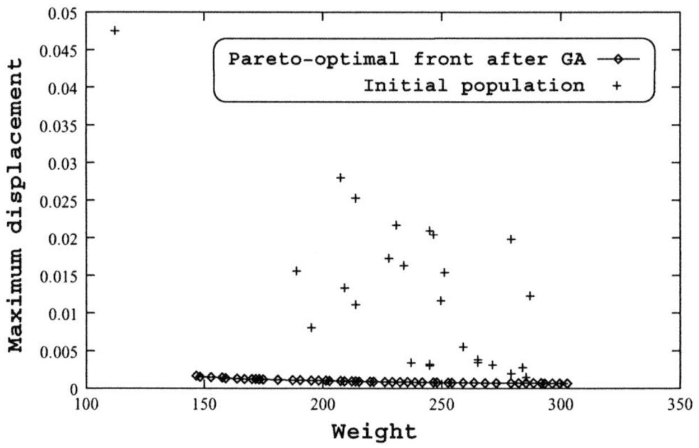

Figure 6.6. Non-dominated solutions after NSGA-II simulation on the coarse grid.

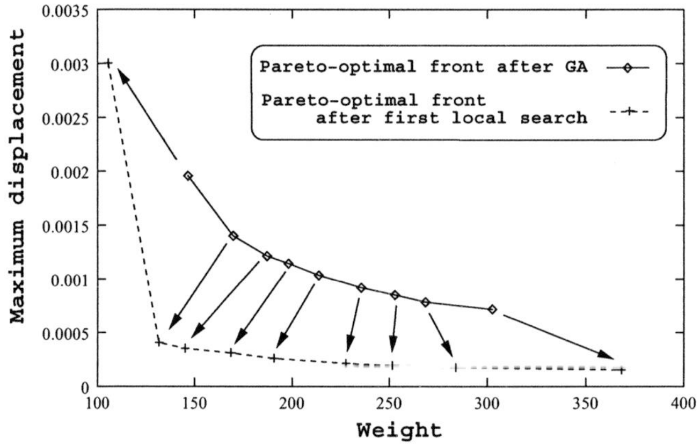

Figure 6.7. The non-dominated solutions move during the first local-search.

allowable load. The shape at the next position moving horizontally from the top left corner, is much smoother and symmetric and after second local-search the solution placed at (1,2) dominates the solution placed at (1,1). At the end, the final non-dominated front consists of eight non-dominated solutions. Figure 6.11 shows the final optimized configurations (after Step 5) of the cantilever plate problem. The shapes are presented in the same fashion, that is, in order of minimum-weight to minimum-deflection solutions. The minimum-weight solution at position (1,1) closely resembles the intuitively smallest weight solution. The next solution at (1,2) has a vertical stiffener joining the two long arms of the minimum-weight solution. Moreover, due to the stiffener the arm thickness is also reduced at the tip. The shape at (1,3) is the next stiffened solution having no stiffener. Here, the arms are made thicker providing a larger strength than that of solution (1,2). Solutions at (2,1), (2,2), (2,3) and (3,1) rediscover the stiffener and are of the same kind. The arm and the stiffener

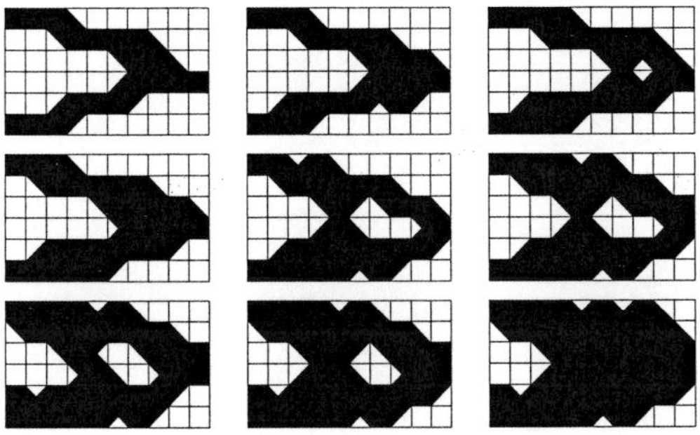

Figure 6.8. Non-dominated solutions after NSGA-II run.

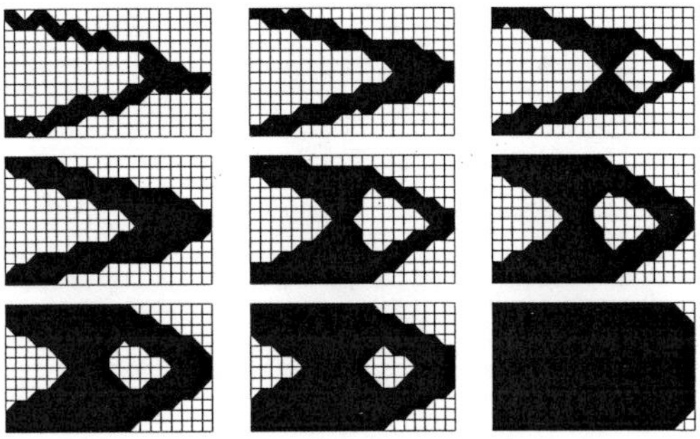

Figure 6.9. Non-dominated solutions after the first local-search procedure.

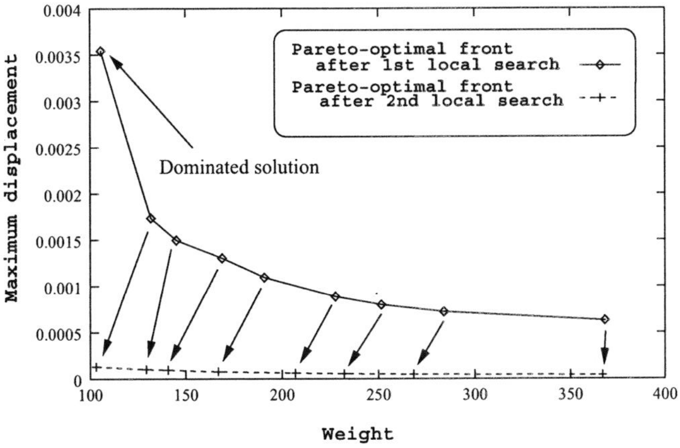

Figure 6.10. Non-dominated solutions move after the second local-search.

thickness increase gradually and hence the corresponding deflection is reduced. Finally the complete plate with right-most top and bottom ends chopped off as shown at (3,2), is the minimum-deflection solution. The achievement of an intuitive, thin, two-armed shape to the innovation of adding stiffeners to the complete covering of almost the entire plate and importantly the symmetry about the horizontal plane in the middle of the plate in all obtained solutions are not explicitly coded or programmed. The procedure adopted here has the adequate power to discover interesting and important design variants adaptively through an efficient optimization procedure.

Overall function evaluations: The number of function evaluations required to form the above shapes from random shapes is given in the Table 6.1.

It is interesting to note that the second local-search requires more evaluations than the

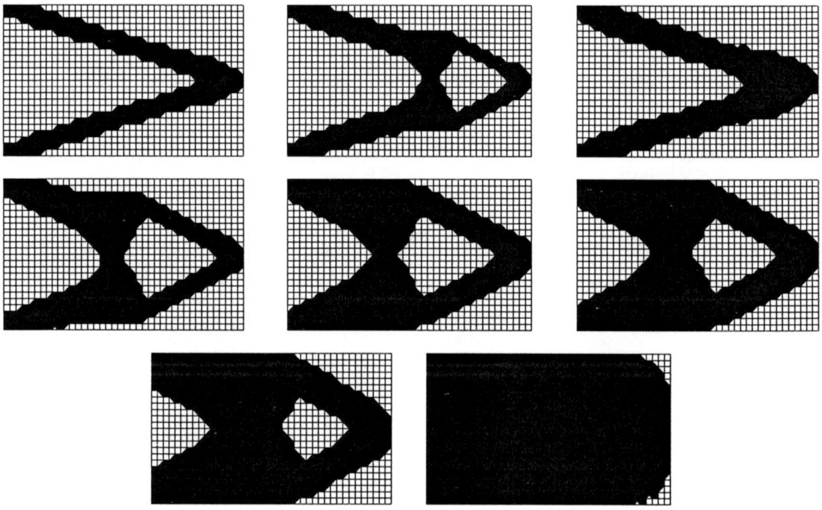

Figure 6.11. Non-dominated solutions after the second local-search procedure (at the end of Step 5).

Table 6.1. Function evaluation for the design of the cantilever plate. The 'Dom. Sol.' represents a dominated solution, shown in Figure 6.10.

Shape No.	1	2	3	4	5	6	7	8	Dom Sol.
1st local-search	696	755	672	740	411	653	358	198	410
2nd local-search	2,187	2,423	1,480	2,003	1,804	1,424	1,013	324	330
Total	2,883	3,178	2,152	2,743	2,215	2,077	1,371	522	740

first local-search. With successive local-searches, the mesh gets more refined, meaning that there are more elements involved in the decision-making. With more variables, it takes more iterations of the local-search procedure to arrive at an optimum solution. The total function evaluations required by the NSGA-II procedure are 5,400. Thus, the total number of function evaluations for the design of the cantilever plate including the local-searches are 23,281. The processing time is 57.06 hours on a 18-processor Pentium-III (1 GHz) PC cluster.

6.6.2 Comparison with NSGA-II Alone

A comparative study with NSGA-II is done on the basis of the above data. To do so, the shape optimization problem is run only using NSGA-II for the same number of function evaluations. The final non-dominated front obtained using NSGA-II is compared with the same obtained using the local-search based NSGA-II procedure described above. Figure 6.12 shows the non-dominated front of the two runs. It is clear from Figure 6.12 that only NSGA-II could not reach the obtained non-dominated front after the same number of

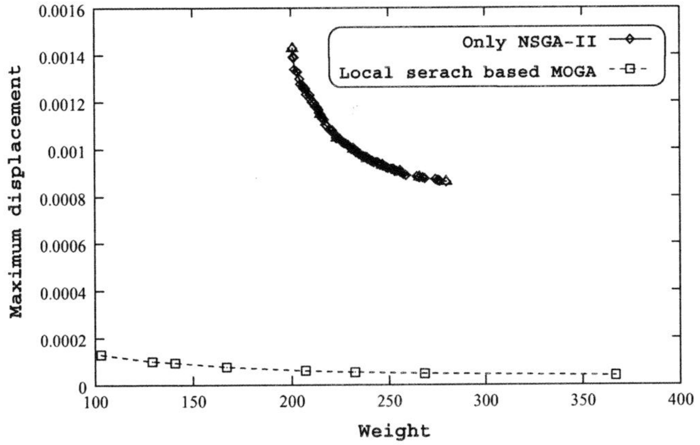

Figure 6.12. Non-dominated front obtained by the NSGA-II run alone.

function evaluations. The extent of prematurity in obtained solutions can by found by investigating the shapes generated using only NSGA-II, shown in Figure 6.13. The solutions

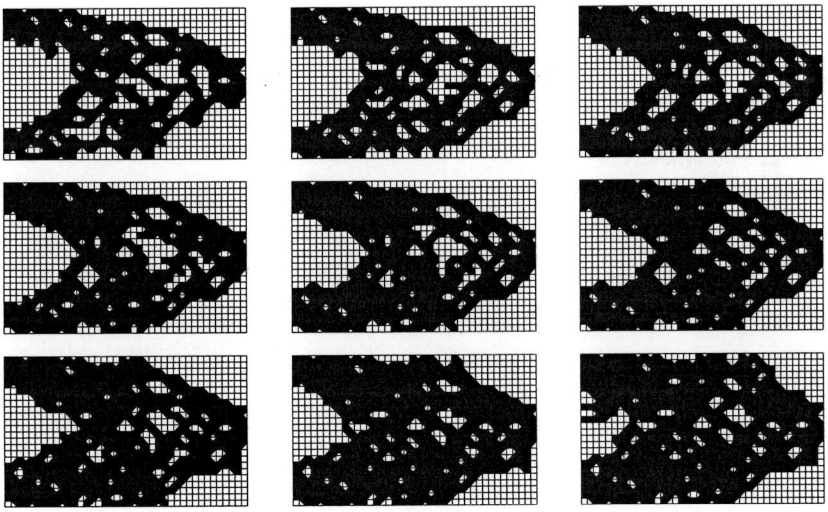

Figure 6.13. Nine trade-off shapes from NSGA-II run alone.

are certainly inferior to the solutions developed by the local search based NSGA-II (shown in Figure 6.11). Here, all solutions seem to show a similar shape with internal voids. The NSGA-II makes a decision of removing a material element from the topology on the basis of minimizing the maximum deflection and the weight of the structure. Since the mesh size is small, the contribution of one element to the overall deflection is also small. So it is difficult for NSGA-II to generate practically viable structures. The local-search based method makes a balance between a population-based EMO procedure and the point-based local-search method. The overall procedure is capable of arriving at multiple optimal shapes (shown in Figure 6.11) in a systematic manner.

6.6.3 A Simply-Supported Plate

The next problem is the design of a simply-supported plate, with a load applied on the top middle part on the plate, as shown in Figure 6.14. In this case, the plate thickness is

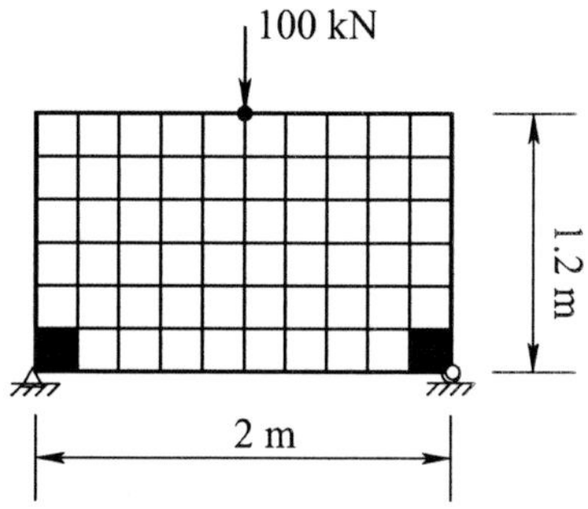

Figure 6.14. Boundary and loading conditions for simply-supported plate.

20 mm. The bottom left corner of the plate is pinned and the bottom right has a roller support. To create a valid shape, material elements are imposed at the extreme left and right elements of the bottom row as shown in the figure. The material properties and NSGA-II parameters used here remain the same as those in the previous case. The non-dominated front after the NSGA-II run is presented with the initial population in Figure 6.15. It is

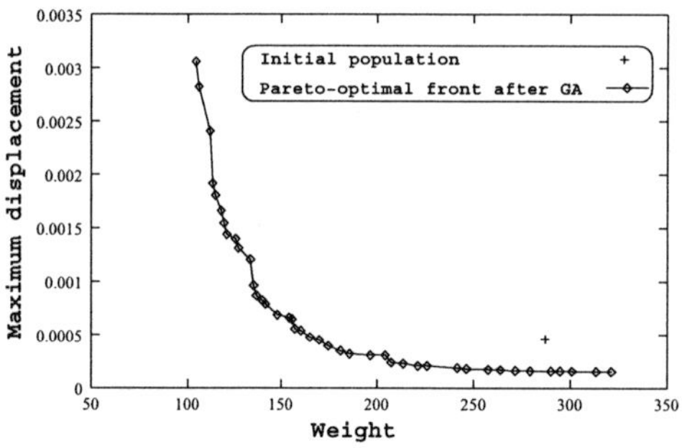

Figure 6.15. Non-dominated front after the NSGA-II run.

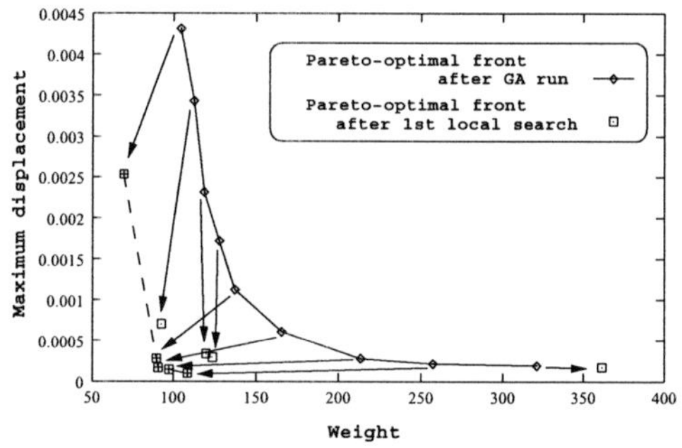

Figure 6.16. Non-dominated front after the first local-search.

interesting to note that the initial generation had only one feasible solution (shown by a '+') on the window used to plot the figure. The constraint-handling method used with NSGA-II [2] drifts infeasible solutions towards the feasible region in a systematic fashion.

Figure 6.16 presents the representative non-dominated front obtained after the first local-search procedure. It is clear from the figure that the movements of the solutions are not as regular as in the case of the cantilever plate design application. The direction of movement of the solutions depends on the weight vector associated with the solutions and also with the complexity of the problem. Besides the non-linearity in the objectives and constraints, the arbitrary location of the material elements introduces further complexity. If material is added near the support locations, maximum deflection of the structure decreases. But if material is added near the load point, due to the self-weight of the added material, the maximum deflection increases. Due to the above reason, zigzag movements of the solutions in the objective space may take place. Figure 6.17 plots the non-dominated front after the first and second local-searches. In this case also the movements of the solutions are erratic

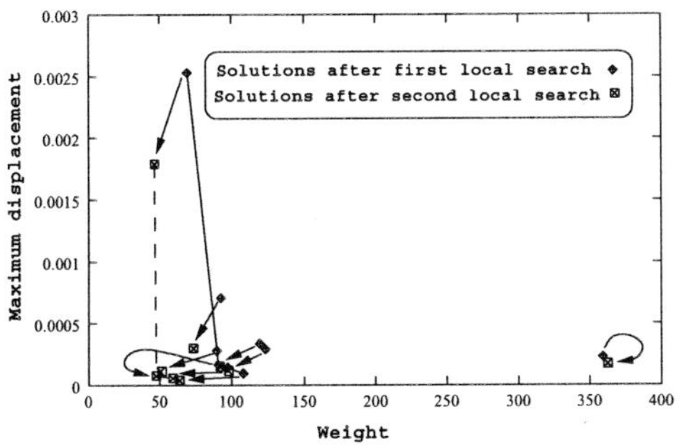

Figure 6.17. Non-dominated front after the second local-search.

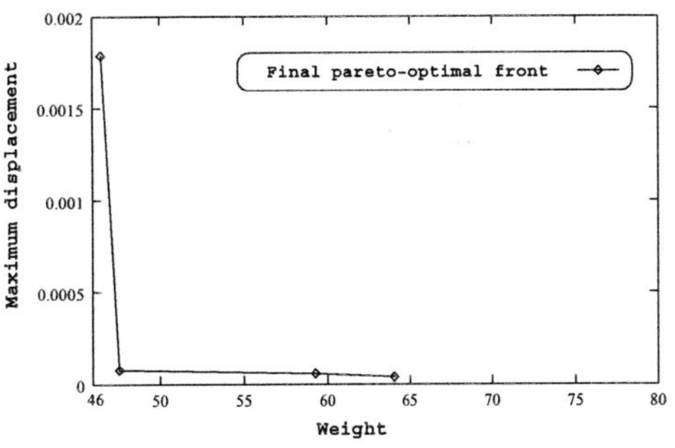

Figure 6.18. Non-dominated front at the end of local-search based EMO procedure.

in nature. All nine solutions obtained by the complete local-search based EMO procedure (that is, at the end of Step 4 of Figure 6.4) are presented in Figure 6.19. However, all of them are not non-dominated solutions, as evident from Figure 6.17. The completely-filled solution (shown in position (3,3) in Figure 6.19) is a dominated solution. Though it possess a large weight, the self-weight deflection of this solution is more than the deflection of a lesser-weight solution shown at (2,2), thereby making the completely-filled solution dominated. It is intuitive that the optimal shape for this type of a problem would be a truss-like structure. The general tendency of the obtained solutions are truss-like (although the joints of the bars are not pinned). The final four non-dominated solutions are presented in Figure 6.20. The plot of final non-dominated front showing four solutions in the objective space is given in Figure 6.18. Only truss-like shapes emerge at the end of the local-search based EMO procedure. The minimum weight solution (1,1) is a convex structure with a connection from the main body to the load point. The convex shape of the main body gives more strength than a straight horizontal connection between the supports. The second solution (1,2) is a triangle with a vertical connection between the top vertex and the load point. This shape looks like a truss (only from the view point of the shape). This is a symmetric structure, which has evolved without any prior information about symmetry.

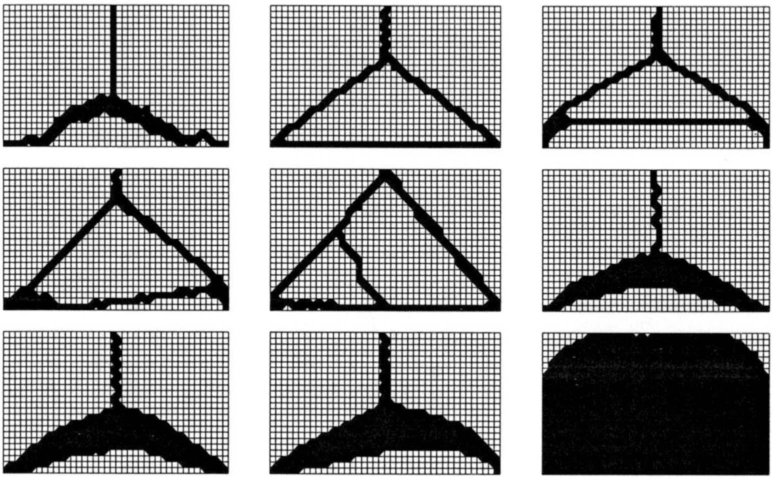

Figure 6.19. Nine trade-off shapes for the design of the simply-supported plate after Step 4.

The next solution (at (1,3)) is a variant of the previous solution, having more material at the support position. The minimum-deflection shape is also a triangle with a connection from the base to the left inclined link. This extra link provides more rigidity and hence this is the minimum-deflection solution obtained by the proposed EMO procedure.

Figure 6.18 suggests that the second-best weight solution ((1,2) in Figure 6.20) which is a truss-like symmetric structure is a 'knee' solution, meaning that a small improvement in an objective requires a large sacrifice in the other objective. Thus, there is not much motivation of choosing solutions other than the one in position (1,2). It is interesting that the proposed local-search based EMO procedure is able to discover such a well-engineered solution without any engineering knowledge and purely from an optimization process applied to a set of random shapes.

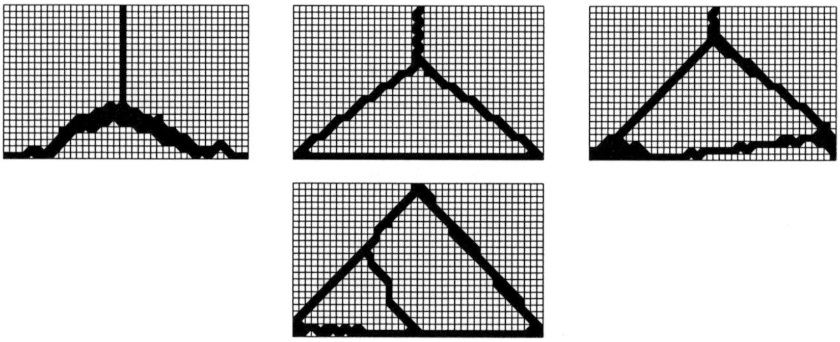

Figure 6.20. Final non-dominated shapes (after Step 5).

Function evaluations: The number of function evaluations required to develop the above shapes are given in Table 6.2. A similar trend requiring an increasing number of evaluations

Table 6.2. Function evaluations needed for the simply-supported plate design.

Shape No. →	1	2	3	4	5	6	7	8	9
First local-search	197	944	1,119	1,444	754	405	309	421	293
Second local-search	663	1,392	3,310	1,854	1,747	666	1,799	1,137	448
Total	860	2,336	4,429	3,298	2,501	1,071	2,108	1,558	741

for later local-searches is observed here as well. The total function evaluations needed for the design of simply-supported plate are 24,302, of which 5,400 evaluations are taken by the NSGA-II procedure. The total processing time is 74.25 hours on the same 18-node PC cluster.

6.6.4 A Tower Plate

The schematic diagram of the tower design problem is given in Figure 6.21. In the two-

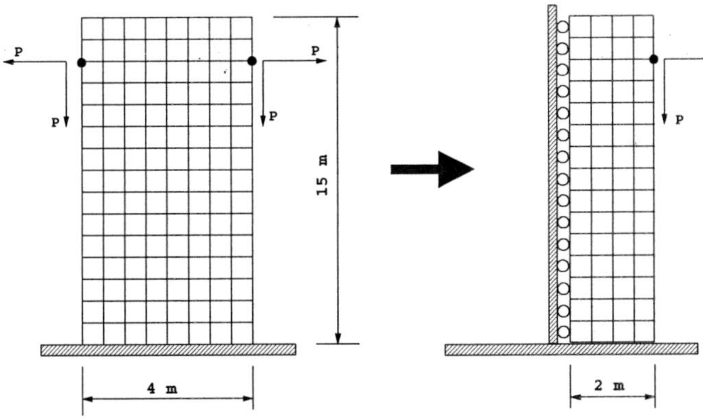

Figure 6.21. Boundary and loading conditions for the tower design problem.

dimensional model, the ground nodes are fixed and cable load is applied in the two nodes at the top. Loads are applied both in horizontal and vertical directions, as shown in the figure. It is clear from the above diagram that we have treated the problem to be symmetric about the vertical mid-plane of the structure. To keep symmetry forcibly, one half of the structure is taken for analysis. To impose appropriate boundary conditions for the half problem, the nodes at the left side of the domain is not allowed to move in the horizontal direction. However, they are allowed to move in the vertical direction. The nodes at the bottom are fixed in both horizontal and vertical directions.

Figure 6.22 plots the non-dominated front obtained using NSGA-II procedure (at the end of Step 1) with a randomly-created initial population. Also in this case, the number of

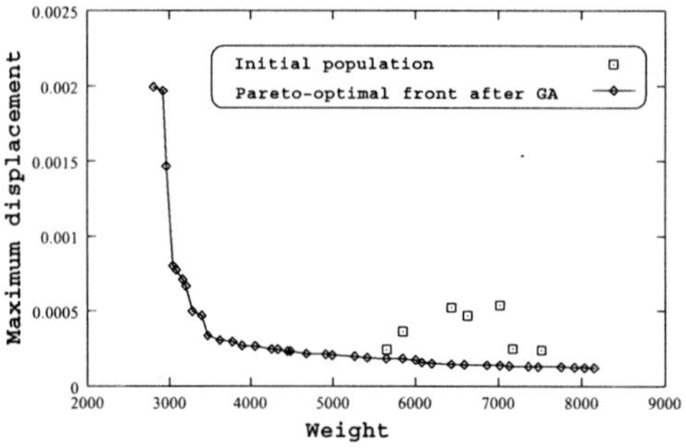

Figure 6.22. Non-dominated front after the NSGA-II run.

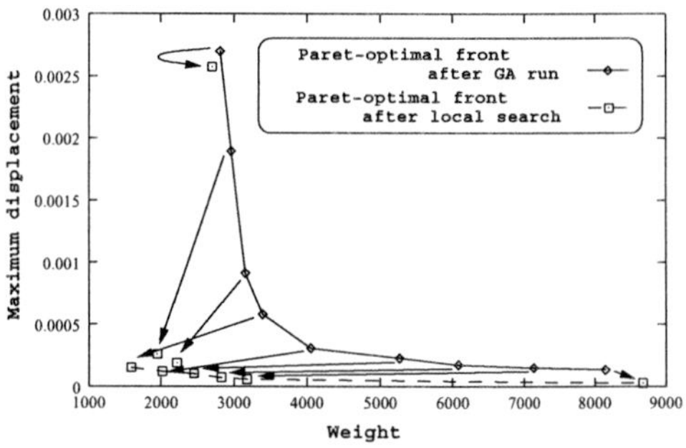

Figure 6.23. Non-dominated front after the local-search.

feasible solutions in the initial population is small. Figure 6.23 presents the non-dominated front after the first local-search. The non-dominated front after the NSGA-II run is also presented on the same plot to show the movements of the solutions. The first three small-weight solutions become dominated after the local-search procedure. In this case, the movements of solutions is not that erratic during the local-search operation. The final non-dominated front for the tower design problem is again plotted in Figure 6.24 which shows the objective values of the final solutions obtained after Step 5. The shapes of these six solutions are

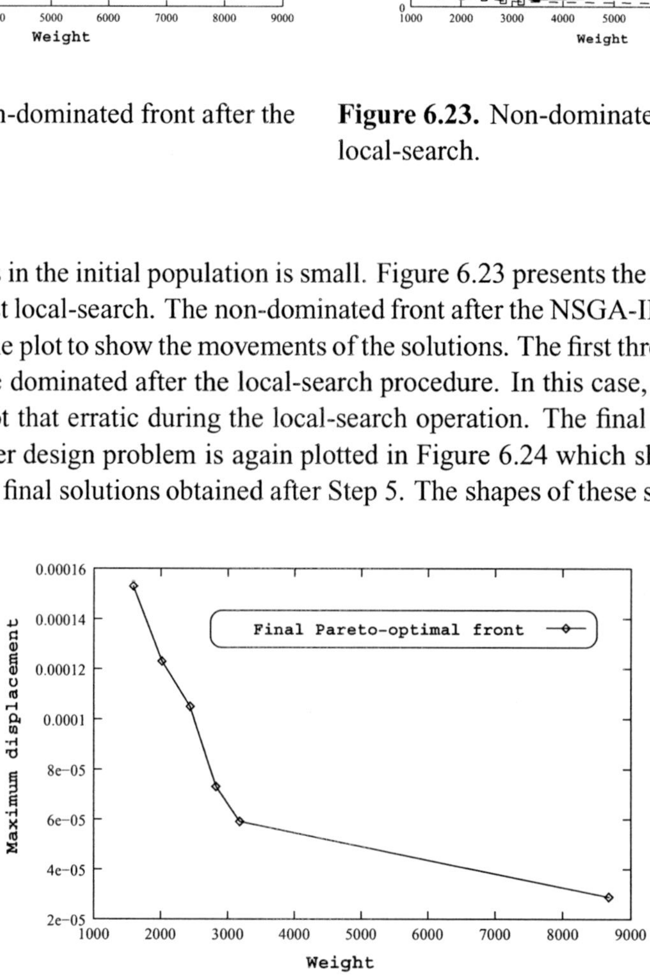

Figure 6.24. Final non-dominated front at the end of the local-search based EMO procedure.

shown in Figure 6.25. The minimum-weight solution connects the ground support and the load point by slender plates. Such shapes are often observed in optimally-designed transmission towers. To increase strength in the horizontal direction, a horizontal connection is formed in between the two vertical plates. This fix-up is common in structure design

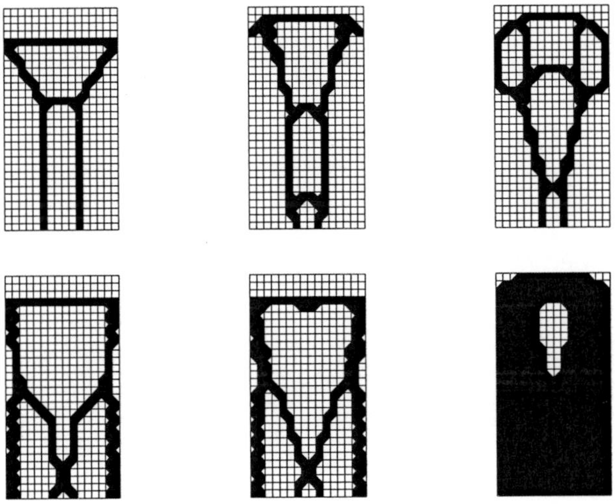

Figure 6.25. Six trade-off shapes for the design of the tower plate.

activities. The next solution has more horizontal stiffeners than the first solution. In the next solution, the thickness of the arms increases to provide more strength. Next two solutions are of similar type. They are rectangular in nature with cross-links extending from the ground to the vertical members. More connections to the ground increases the rigidity. The minimum-deflection solution is a fully solid plate with a hole at the center. The small hole does not reduce the deflection property of the plate too much, but helps reduce the weight of the plate.

The total function evaluations required for the design of the tower plate were 10,457, of which NSGA-II took 5,400 evaluations. Both local-search operations for each of the nine solutions (obtained after Step 2) took on an average 562 evaluations. The total processing time was 31 minutes on the same 18-node PC cluster.

6.6.5 A Connecting Plate

The final problem considered in this study is the shape design of a connecting plate, shown in Figure 6.26. The size of the holes at the big end and small end are known beforehand. The square elements at the hole positions are forcibly made material-free to create holes. To make a well-defined boundary around the holes, the elements surrounding the holes are always turned into material elements. This problem information helps the evolutionary algorithm to create realistic designs. The task of the search algorithm is to find the optimal link between the big and small ends. In this problem, a symmetry is imposed forcibly. To do so, the domain is divided into two equal parts about the horizontal mid-plane. Void or material elements are placed on one half of the domain. Then mirror image is taken about the horizontal mid-plane to create the entire shape. The complete structure generated by the above process is sent for the FEM analysis. Crossover and mutation operators of the

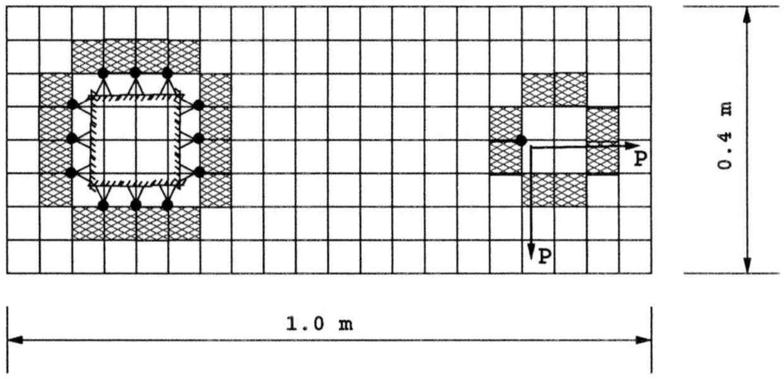

Figure 6.26. Geometric and loading conditions for the connecting plate.

NSGA-II procedure are also applied only on one half of the structure. Figure 6.27 shows the procedure of creating symmetric shapes. The connecting plate is designed on the basis

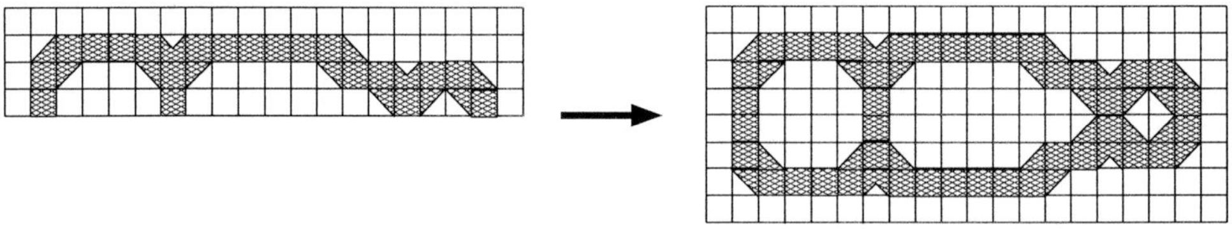

Figure 6.27. Consideration of the half of the connecting plate for optimization.

of tensile and bending stresses. Figure 6.26 schematically shows the boundary conditions as well as geometric conditions. In the analysis, the properties of the material and NSGA-II parameters are kept the same as those in the previous cases. Geometric parameters used for the analysis are shown in the Figure 6.26.

Figure 6.28 plots the non-dominated front after the NSGA-II run (Step 1) and the initial population. In Figure 6.29, plots of non-dominated front after both local-searches (Step 5) are presented. The extreme right solution (that is, the minimum-deflection solution) becomes dominated after the local-search. Due to the self-weight of the structure, the deflection of this solution is much more and hence the solution gets dominated by another solution. All eight non-dominated shapes are presented in Figure 6.30. The minimum-weight solution simply connects the two holes with thin plates to provide just enough strength. Although the complete rectangular region was available, the minimum-weight solution uses a smaller region to save weight. Thereafter, the near-support region gets thicker to provide adequate stiffness to the structure. Then on, the thickness of the arms get thicker and thicker and finally almost the whole plate becomes the minimum-deflection solution. It is interesting to note that the thickness of the connectors increases near the hole region (which acts as a support) to give more strength. These well-engineered phenomena evolve automatically without any prior information.

The overall function evaluations needed for the design of the connecting plate are 15,650, of which the NSGA-II procedure took 10,800 evaluations. Eight non-dominated

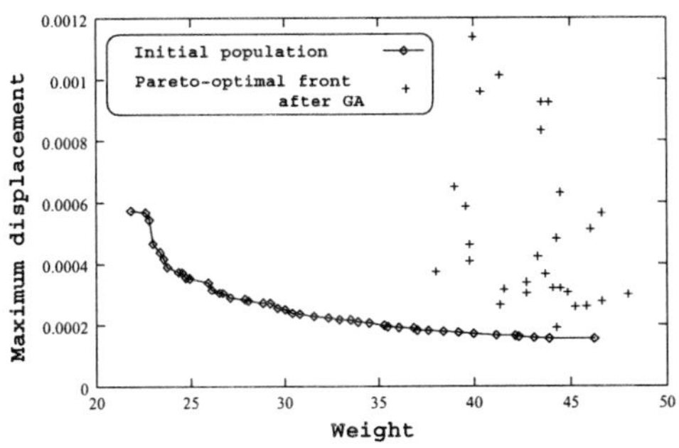

Figure 6.28. Non-dominated front after the NSGA-II run.

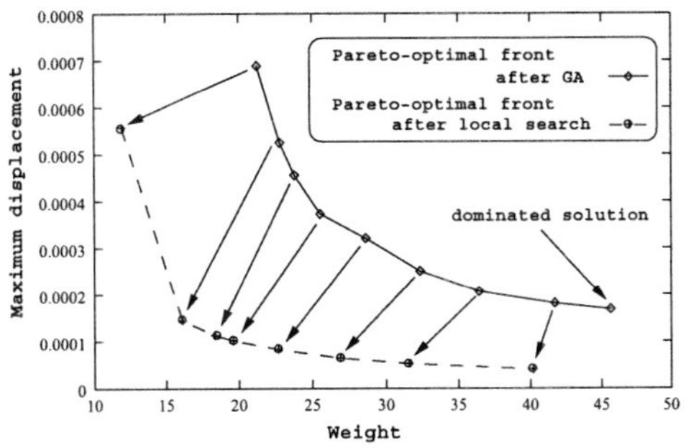

Figure 6.29. Non-dominated front after the final local-search.

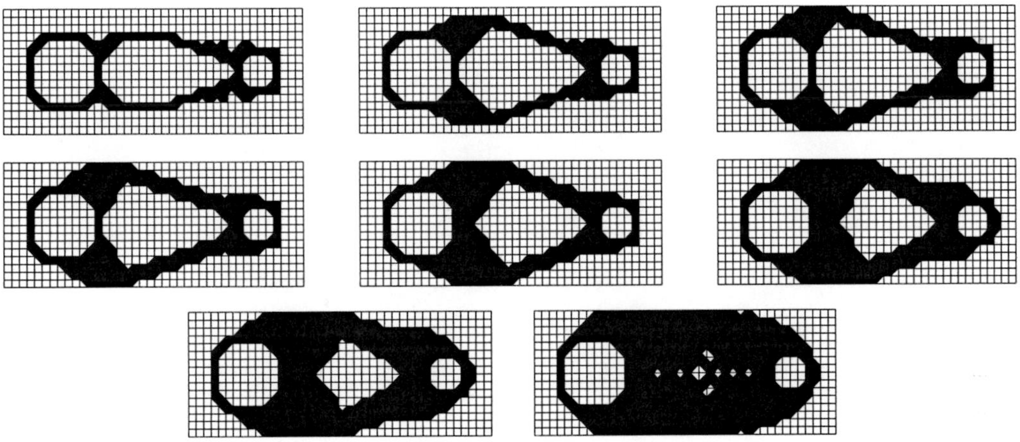

Figure 6.30. Eight trade-off shapes for the design of the connecting plate.

solutions took, on an average, 606 evaluations each for the local-search procedure. The total processing time was seven hours on the 18-node PC cluster.

6.7 SUMMARY

In this chapter, we have suggested the use of two or more conflicting objectives in engineering design activities for two reasons: (i) find a set of trade-off Pareto-optimal solutions and (ii) to decipher salient properties associated with optimal designs. We have suggested a systematic, two-phase procedure for this purpose. The use of meta-models (coarse-to-fine-grained modeling approach), a parallel computer, and efficient genetic operators has also been suggested. On a number of structural shape optimal design of mechanical engineering components, the proposed technique has discovered important properties, such as symmetry in shape, use of stiffeners to improve stiffness of designs, creation of internal voids for weight reduction, discovery of truss-like structures from plates, etc., which are found to be common among multiple design solutions corresponding to different trade-offs between two conflicting objectives of design. The procedure suggested here is generic and can be applied to other more complex engineering design problems.

Bibliography

[1] D. Corne, J. Knowles, and M. Oates. The Pareto envelope-based selection algorithm for multiobjective optimization. In *Proceedings of the Sixth International Conference on Parallel Problem Solving from Nature VI (PPSN-VI)*, pages 839–848, 2000.

[2] K. Deb. *Multi-objective optimization using evolutionary algorithms*. Chichester, UK: Wiley, 2001.

[3] K. Deb. Unveiling innovative design principles by means of multiple conflicting objectives. *Engineering Optimization*, **35**(5):445–470, 2003.

[4] K. Deb, S. Agrawal, A. Pratap, and T. Meyarivan. A fast and elitist multi-objective genetic algorithm: NSGA-II. *IEEE Transactions on Evolutionary Computation*, **6**(2):182–197, 2002.

[5] K. Deb and T. Goel. A hybrid multi-objective evolutionary approach to engineering shape design. In *Proceedings of the First International Conference on Evolutionary Multi-Criterion Optimization (EMO-01)*, pages 385–399, 2001.

[6] Zitzler E. and Thiele L. An evolutionary algorithm for multiobjective optimization: The strength pareto approach. *Technical Report 43*, Computer Engineering and Networks Laboratory, Switzerland, 1998.

[7] M. Ehrgott. *Multicriteria Optimization*. Berlin: Springer, 2000.

[8] D. E. Goldberg. *Genetic Algorithms for Search, Optimization, and Machine Learning*. Reading, MA: Addison-Wesley, 1989.

[9] H. Ishibuchi and T. Murata. A multi-objective genetic local search algorithm and its application to flowshop scheduling. *IEEE Transactions on Systems, Man and Cybernetics – Part C: Applications and reviews*, **28**(3):392–403, 1998.

[10] H. Ishibuchi and T. Murata. Multi-objective genetic local search for minimizing the number of fuzzy rules for pattern classification problems. In *Proceedings of the Sixth IEEE International Conference on Fuzzy Systems*, pages 1100–1105, 1998.

[11] M. J. Jakiela, C. Chapman, J. Duda, A. Adewuya, and K. Saitou. Continuum structural topology design with genetic algorithms. *Computer Methods in Applied Mechanics and Engineering*, **186**(2–4):339–356, 2000.

[12] M. T. Jensen. Reducing the run-time complexity of multiobjective EAs. *IEEE Transactions to Evolutionary Computation*, **7**(5):503–515, 2003.

[13] K. Miettinen. *Nonlinear Multiobjective Optimization*. Kluwer, Boston, 1999.

[14] S. S. Rao. *Optimization: Theory and Applications*. Wiley, New York, 1984.

[15] G. V. Reklaitis, A. Ravindran, and K. M. Ragsdell. *Engineering Optimization Methods and Applications*. New York : Wiley, 1983.

In: Evolutionary Machine Design: Methodology & Applications ISBN 1-59454-405-0
Editors: N. Nedjah & L. Mourelle, pp:165-191

Chapter 7

TOWARD EFFICIENT TOPOLOGICAL SYNTHESIS OF DYNAMIC SYSTEMS USING GENETIC PROGRAMMING

Jianjun Hu, Kisung Seo, Erik D. Goodman, Ronald Rosenberg[†]

Genetic Algorithm Research and Application Group (GARAGe),
Department of Computer Science and Engineering,
Michigan State University, East Lansing, MI, 48823, USA
(hujianju | ksseo)@cse.msu.edu, www.egr.msu.edu/

[†]Department of Mechanical Engineering, Michigan State University,
East Lansing, MI, 48823, USA
rosenber@egr.msu.edu, www.egr.msu.edu/~rosenber

Automated design synthesis has become a promising area with the availability of supercomputing power to desktop users, enabled by the emergence of grid computing. Successful stories of automated synthesis by genetic programming have been reported from areas including electrical circuits, controllers, and mechatronic systems. However, building a topologically open-ended evolutionary synthesis engine is still a tricky art, with few theoretical or empirical guidelines. Using a set of scalable benchmark problems, the eigenvalue placement problems, for bond-graph-based synthesis of mechatronic systems, this chapter investigates the representation issues and knowledge incorporation approaches critical for efficient automated synthesis of mechatronic systems by genetic programming. We showed that the encoding scheme or the function set can greatly affect the efficiency of the topology search, and that adding more high-level functions that encapsulate modules may inadvertently introduce undesirable bias into the search and then greatly decrease rather than increase the search speed for some types of problems, while speeding up the search for other types of problems, as predicted by the No Free Lunch theorem. We also demonstrated that seeding the genetic programming population with useful modules in a problem domain can improve the search efficiency. These guidelines may help users to make better decisions in real-world topologically open-ended dynamic system synthesis problems.

7.1 Introduction

Computational synthesis as a solution to topologically open-ended design synthesis has received increasing attention from many design areas [1]. Notably, many success stories with automated evolutionary synthesis by genetic programming (GP) have been recently reported, including automatically synthesized electric circuits infringing several recent patents [2], an automatically created general-purpose non-PID controller [3, 4] for which a patent is sought, mechatronic systems [13, 14] and digital circuits [5]. It can be observed that a large number of topologically open-ended design problems can be summarized as: given a set of heterogeneous functional building blocks, connection/combination rules or constraints, and the functional requirements, how can one synthesize a solution to achieve the desired system behavior, automatically or interactively? The difficulty lies in that one needs to identify the appropriate topology of the system as well as its appropriate parameters, simultaneously, from an extraordinarily large search space, to achieve the desired behavior.

Despite the apparent difficulty, the examples cited above have been offered as an existence proof of the adequacy of genetic programming for addressing that challenge in some areas of open-ended design innovation [4]. Compared to traditional single-point trajectory search techniques such as hill-climbing and simulated annealing, population-based genetic programming allows much more efficient exploration of topology search space by exploiting the potential modules embedded in the individuals of the population through its innovative crossover/recombination operator. Compared to genetic algorithms, genetic programming can be naturally used to evolve variable-length structures while genetic algorithms need special operators to implement this feature. Another distinct feature of genetic programming is that it provides an easy way for simultaneous parameter and topology search. In particular, by combining symbolic search and parameter search together, genetic programming can be used to evolve parameterized structures, which might be very tedious to implement with genetic algorithms.

Despite these apparent advantages of genetic programming in computational synthesis, critical issues remain concerning effective design of such a tool for open-ended topological exploration, leaving the prospective practitioner with many seemingly arbitrary decisions to make. While there is increasing concern over the scalability of generic evolutionary synthesis in applications such as evolvable hardware [6] and digital circuit design [7], there are few explicit theoretical and experimental studies in the context of topological search per se on issues like appropriate representations, appropriate levels of building blocks, topological operations employed in the search process, scalability, and balancing of topological and parameter search. One reason can be traced to the difficulty of establishing common benchmark problems, accessible to all researchers, requiring relatively small amounts of computational resources, and representative of multiple design domains.

In this chapter, we introduce a set of carefully designed open-ended system synthesis benchmark problems—eigenvalue placement problems—and investigate issues related to the evolvability, efficiency, and scalability of search-based automated topology synthesis—-in particular, by genetic programming. Specifically, we investigate how representation/encoding—choosing the function and terminal sets in genetic programming—affects the evolvability of the topology search, and how population seeding, as a means of knowledge incorporation, can speed up the synthesis of desired topologies. Our goal is to enable synthesis of high-performance systems with several dozen components within a few CPU-days of computing effort, rather than taking several days of computing by hundreds of PCs, as Koza typically uses [4]. In this chapter, systems to be synthesized are represented by bond graphs [8] – a multi-domain modeling scheme that can unify design domains such as analog circuits, mechatronic systems, and controllers. One of our test problems is called the eigenvalue placement problem, which has a tunable problem size in terms of the order of the dynamic system to be synthesized. To take a systematic divide-and-conquer strategy to investigate critical issues in evolutionary topology search by genetic programming, we begin by removing the parameter search from the evolutionary synthesis framework and examine only factors influencing the efficiency and scalability of topological search by the developmental genetic programming approach, which is widely adopted [4], [5], [13], [19] and represents one of best methods that have achieved significant novel inventions automatically through the evolutionary process [4].

The remaining sections of this chapter are organized as follows. Section 7.2 describes the basic framework for topologically open-ended synthesis of dynamic systems based on bond graphs and genetic programming, which has been extensively investigated in our previous studies. Section 7.3 proposes two advanced approaches for bond graph synthesis that employ properties of bond graph design space to remove redundancy. Section 7.4 introduces a benchmark problem with tunable sizes—the eigenvalue placement problem—for topologically open-ended synthesis. Section 7.5 investigates the relationship between representation/encoding, scalability, and search bias, along with two approaches for knowledge incorporation in topology synthesis by genetic programming: a) improving the function and terminal set, and b) seeding the initial population guided by domain knowledge. Finally, discussion on related issues and conclusions are provided in Sections 7.6 and 7.7, respectively.

7.2 Basic Framework for Bond Graph Synthesis

Bond Graph-Based Synthesis of Dynamic Systems by Genetic Programming: the Basic Framework

7.2.1 Bond Graphs

The bond graph is a multi-domain modeling tool for analysis and design of dynamic systems, especially hybrid multi-domain systems including mechanical, electrical, pneumatic, hydraulic, etc., components [8]. Bond graph models can describe the dynamic behavior of physical systems by the connection of idealized, lumped elements based on the principle of conservation of power.

Bond graphs consist of elements (nodes) and bonds (edges). There are several types of basic elements (building blocks), each of which performs analogous roles across energy domains. The first type – C, I, and R elements – are passive one-port elements that contain no sources of power, and represent capacitors, inductors, and resistors in the electrical domain and other equivalent elements in other domains. The second type, Se and Sf, are active one-port elements that are sources of power, and that represent effort sources and flow sources, respectively (for example, sources of voltage or current, respectively, in the electrical domain). The third type, TF and GY, are two-port elements, and represent transformers and gyrators, respectively. The transformer TF relates efforts to efforts and flows to flows, while gyrators GY relate the effort at one port to the flow at the other. Power is conserved in these elements. A fourth type, denoted as 0 or 1 on bond graphs, represents junctions, which are N-port elements. They serve to interconnect other elements into subsystems or system models. A 0-junction represents the generic parallel connections where all connected bonds have identical "effort" and the algebraic sum of flows is 0. A 1-junction represents generic serial connections, where the connected bonds have identical "flow" and the sum of efforts is 0. It should be noted that junctions are not physical entities; instead, they represent the relations among other building blocks, so a bond graphs is one kind of relational graph [9].

Rather than solely by physical function, the building blocks of a bond graph can also be classified according to both their allowable topological manipulations and their physical functions, which is more useful from the point of view of evolutionary synthesis. Table 7.1 lists the classifications:

Table 7.1. Classification of bond graph elements and their allowable operations

Type	**Allowable (Topological) Operations**
Bond (2-port)	can be modified by inserting a two-port element or module such as a transformer, gyrator, etc
1-port Element	can be modified by changing its function (resistor, inductor, or capacitor, or other one-port module)
2-port Element	can be modified by removing the element and connecting its bonds, or by separating one of its bonds and inserting a new two-port element (e.g., gyrator, transformer) into it.
Junction (N-port)	A junction can be modified by switching changing a 1-junction to a 0-junction or vice-versa; by attaching a one-port element, or by connecting it to another junction
Numeric	Numeric nodes used to size the elements of a bond graph. A numeric node can be replaced by another numeric node, either a random constant or a numeric expression sub-tree.

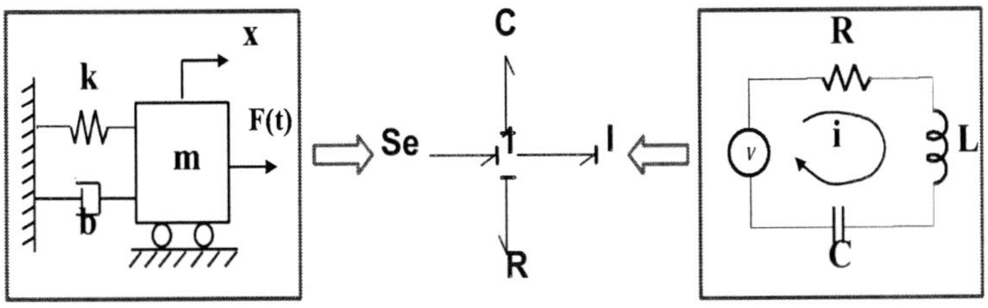

Figure 7.1. Bond graph representation of a mechanical system and an electric circuit. Left: a mechanical system; Right: an electric circuit; Middle: the equivalent bond graph representation of mechanical and electrical systems

One of the advantages of using bond graphs for open-ended design exploration is that complex loops typical in electric circuits can be transformed into tree-like structures by the bond graph's 1-junction (serial connection) and 0-junction (parallel connection) concepts. Details of notation and methods of system analysis related to the bond graph representation can be found in [8]. Much recent research has explored the bond graph as a tool for design [10]. Design of controllers by augmenting bond graphs with signals (as used in "block-diagram" representations) has also been practiced [11]. Figure 7.1 illustrates a bond graph that represents either of the accompanying electrical or mechanical systems.

7.2.2 Automated Synthesis of Bond Graphs by Genetic Programming

Genetic programming (GP) [12] is an extension of the genetic algorithm. The distinctive feature of genetic programming is its capability to evolve variable-length structures such as computer programs or dynamic systems, etc., so is widely used for topologically open-ended search.

In this chapter, a developmental strongly-typed genetic programming method is used as described in [3] to evolve a program tree, whose pre-ordered execution will grow a given minimal embryo bond graph into a complex design solution. Combining the advantages of bond graphs as a unified modeling tool for multi-domain systems and the topological search capability of genetic programming, we have proposed an automated design methodology (BG/GP) for synthesis of dynamic systems and, in particular, mechatronic systems [13], [14] (see Figure 7.2):

To evolve a dynamic system represented in a bond graph by genetic programming, there are five preparatory steps to follow [2], each of which is problem specific. The decisions made may strongly affect the evolvability of the genetic programming search:

1. Determine the architecture of the program tree: this determines if how many trees are used to represent one GP solution and if the Automatically-Defined-Function (ADF) feature is used or not. Here we only use one tree and no ADF.
2. Determine the embryo structure: the starting point of topological operation. Each embryo will have one or more modifiable sites where the topological operations can

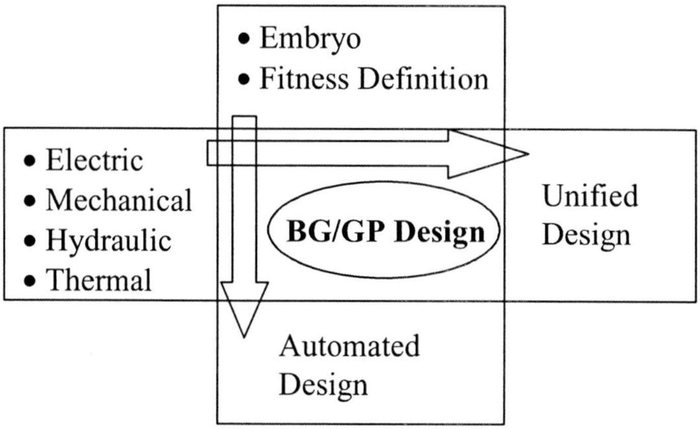

Figure 7.2. The BG/GP design methodology for automated synthesis of multi-domain mechatronic systems

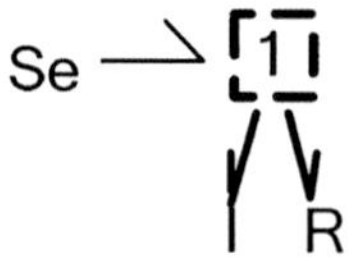

Figure 7.3. An embryo bond graph with one junction-type modifiable site at a 1-junction

be applied to grow the topology. Usually, a minimum embryo structure is used to remove strong biases that may come in through choosing the embryo. Embryo structure can also include an existing system to be subjected to evolutionary modification to improve its performance. This type of problem is called a redesign problem. This chapter will consider only the minimum embryo structures, not those aimed at redesign. The embryo used in this study is illustrated in Figure 7.3, which is composed of a 1-junction to which one inductor, one resistor, and an effort source are attached. The 1-junction here is labeled as a modifiable site - a place at which topology operations are allowed, enabling the embryo to be "grown" into a more complex system.

3. Select a GP terminal set and function set: these are the building blocks of GP programs for bond graph synthesis. Each program is represented as a syntax tree. In developmental GP for topology synthesis, the topological manipulation terminals and functions can be regard as a tree node with a single-input port and zero or more output ports. The input port reads in modifiable site information that specifies the position that the topological manipulation in the current node works on. The output ports specify possible modification points that subtree operations can work on. In contrast, for the mathematical functions and terminals, the branches are the input to the mathematical function, and the root of a subtree is the output of that node. The functions and terminals for the basic approach [13], [14] are summarized in Ta-

ble 7.2. (We omitted transformers and gyrators for simplicity without sacrificing the completeness of the representation):

4. Determine the fitness function of the solutions

5. Determine the running parameters of the search engine

Table 7.2. Definition of function set and terminal set. The operators with 0 arguments are all terminals

Name	#Args	Description
add_C	4	Add a C element to a junction
add_I	4	Add an I element to a junction
add_R	4	Add an R element to a junction
insert_J0	3	Insert a 0-junction in a bond
insert_J1	3	Insert a 1-junction in a bond
replace_C	2	Replace the current element with a C element
replace_ I	2	Replace the current element with an I element
replace_ R	2	Replace the current element with an R element
end_A	0	End terminal for add element
end_I	0	End terminal for insert junction
end_R	0	End terminal for replace element
+	2	Add two numeric nodes
-	2	Subtract two numeric nodes
*	2	Multiply two numeric nodes
/	2	Divide two numeric nodes
erc	0	Ephemeral random constant (ERC)

From Table 7.2, it is clear that the basic approach for bond graph synthesis by GP encapsulates each bond graph primitive in one or more functions or terminals. For example, capacitors can be added or removed from a bond graph using add_C or replace_C and 0-junctions or 1-junctions can be inserted into a bond graph using insert_J0 and insert_J1. The operations of insert_X and add_X functions are shown in Figure 7.4.

Given the embryo bond graph above, function and terminal sets, a simulator to evaluate bond graphs, and a GP search engine, we can evolve a population of better and better bond graph-generating GP trees and their corresponding phenotypes, the desired dynamic systems, by iteratively applying evaluation, crossover, mutation, and selection operators. This straightforward migration of genetic programming from electric circuit synthesis to bond graph synthesis has successfully evolved some interesting designs including analog filters [20], an improved typewriter drive mechanism [14], and an air pump [14].

However, scalability is still a major issue, and no very complex solutions to hard problems have been evolved. After close examination of the evolved solutions, it turns out

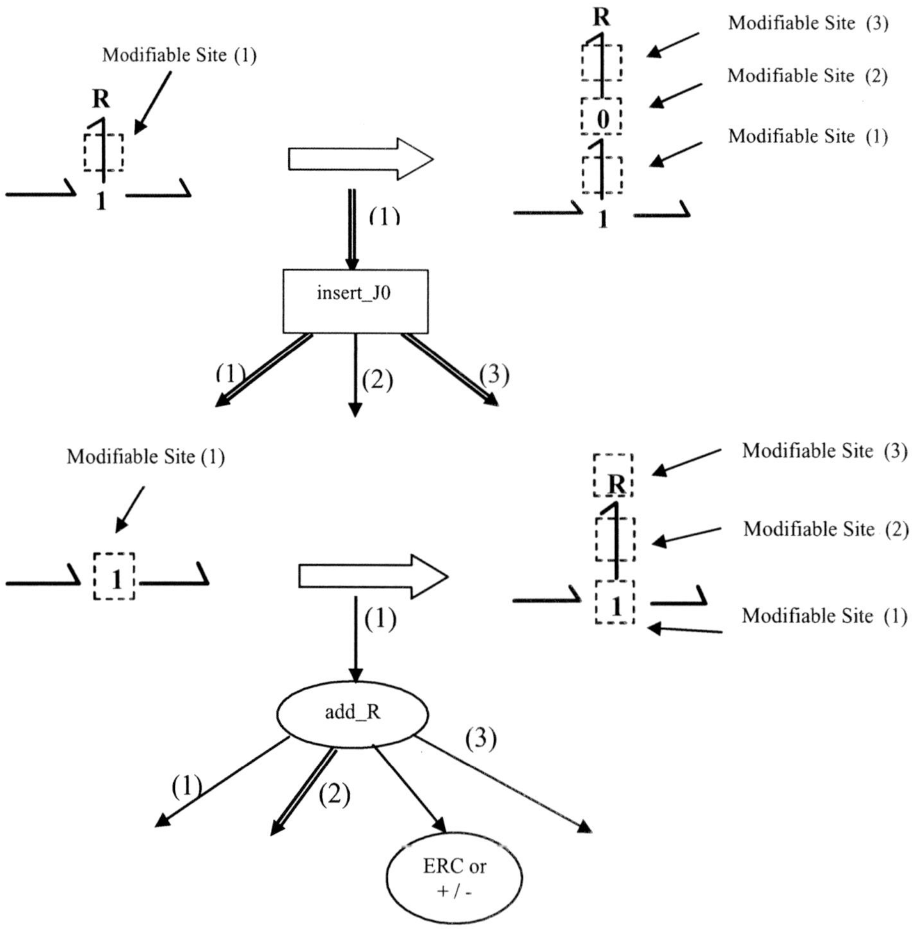

Figure 7.4. The operation of GP function insert_J0 (top) and add_R (bottom)

that the evolved solutions with this basic approach are usually highly redundant, with many physically meaningless local structures. We need to, and do, conduct a simplification procedure to remove those redundant structures (Figure 7.5). This redundancy is partially derived from the bond graph modeling method, in which the building blocks of 1-junction and 0-junction are not physical entities. For example, two adjacent 0-junctions or 1-junctions can be simplified to only one such junction. Another redundancy comes from the fact that multiple copies of the same element type, like C/I/R, can be attached to the same junction, but are equivalent to a single such element. Since redundancy may unnecessarily increase the search space, a modular set approach was proposed in [15], and is described in the next section. Some preliminary experiments showed that this modular set can effectively remove the redundancy phenomenon, but its performance gain is not clear. Although we know that factors such as the embryo, the function and terminal set, and the type of modifiable sites can all influence the search efficiency, we have no clear idea of precisely how they affect it

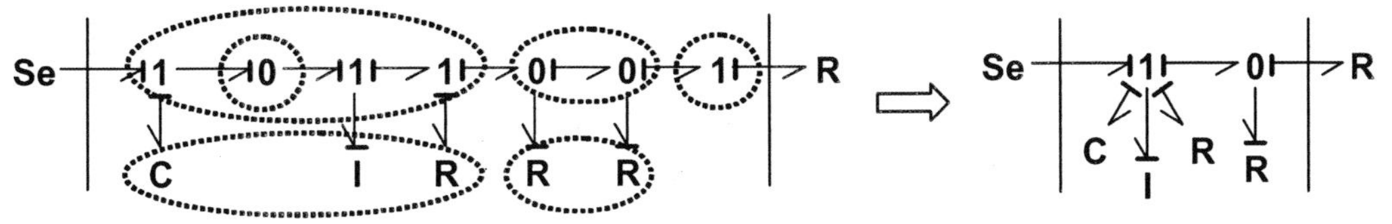

Figure 7.5. Example of redundant 0-and 1-junctions and R elements (left) in automatically generated bond graph model, and the equivalent model after simplification (right). The dotted lines represent the boundary of the blocks that can be merged or simplified.

and what we can do to make better decisions. The next section proposes two more advanced function and terminal sets for bond graph synthesis, which will be used to investigate the issue of how representation affects evolvability, in Section 7.4.

7.3 Bond Graph-Based Synthesis of Dynamic Systems by Genetic Programming: More Advanced Approaches

To remove, or at least lessen, the redundancy of the representation described above, two modular set approaches for bond graph synthesis are proposed in this section. They are based on the concept of causally-well-posed bond graphs: a bond graph in which two junctions of the same type (0- or 1-) are never adjacent to each other, each element (I/R/C) is connected to a junction and all I, R, or C elements attached to the same junction are coalesced to a maximum of three elements with the types of I, R, and C. Such bond graphs are physically meaningful, at least in some domain. These modular set approaches greatly reduce the number of GP functions while still ensuring the capacity to express all causally well-posed bond graphs expressible by the basic approach. In this section, these approaches are described, and then are used to investigate issues of representation and evolvability and scalability in Section 7.5.

7.3.1 Node-Encoding for Bond Graph Synthesis by Genetic Programming

In the node-encoding approach for bond graph synthesis by genetic programming, only one topological manipulation function (Add_J_CI_R) is used in the function set, augmented only by the growth termination terminal, EndNode (Figure 7.6). So the function and terminal set for node-encoding approach is:

$$F = \{Add\_J\_CI\_R, EndNode, ERC\} \tag{7.1}$$

where ERC represents a real number that can be changed by Gaussian mutation. In this section, in order to focus attention purely on the evolution of topology, all ERCs are fixed at a value of 1.0.

There is only one type of modifiable site, the junction (or node) site, in the node-encoding approach. Function Add_J_CI_R works by first checking the junction type of the

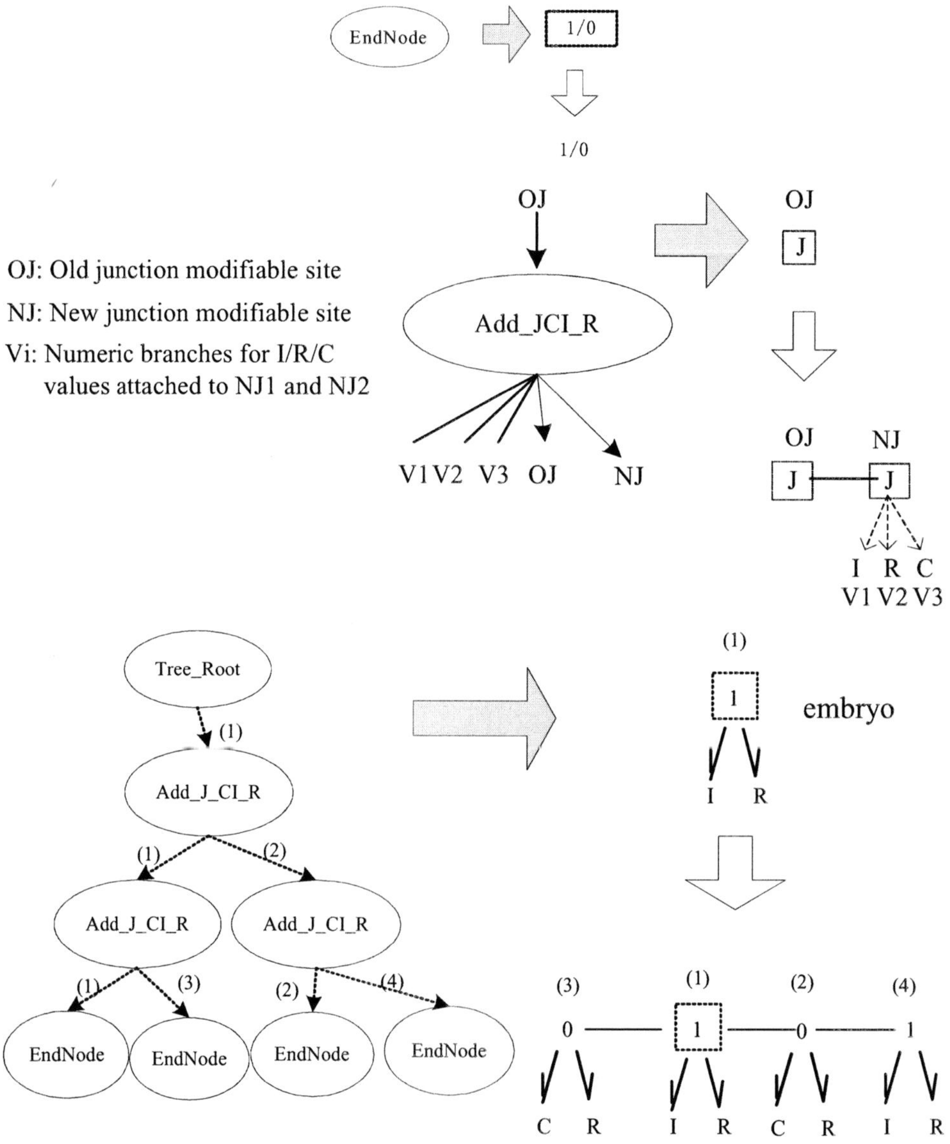

Figure 7.6. Top: the EndNode terminal simply stops the growth from the input modifiable site; Middle: the Add_JCI_R function; Bottom: an example of the GP tree, composed of topology operators applied to an embryo generates a bond graph after depth-first execution (numeric branches are omitted).

incoming modifiable site, if it is a 1-junction, it will attach a 0-junction to it, and vice-versa (Figure 7.6). The number of elements attached to a junction is determined by a two-bit flag inside the Add_J_CI_R node in the GP tree (Figure 7.7). A *flag mutation operator* is introduced to the genetic programming procedure to evolve these flag bits. To ensure the causality of the bond graphs developed by execution of the GP tree, we mandate that a 0-junction can have only a C element and/or an R element attached to it and a 1-junction can have only an I element and/or an R element attached to it. Each Add_J_CI_R function has two branches, with two junction modifiable sites and three numeric branches for establishing the values of the attached I/R/C elements. When the switch for an element (such as C) is off, the element is not present, and the corresponding numeric value is left unused. It is clear that the number of topology manipulation GP functions has decreased dramatically from 11 to 2. Preliminary experiments have shows that for some types of problems, this modular set can achieve better performance than the basic set [15].

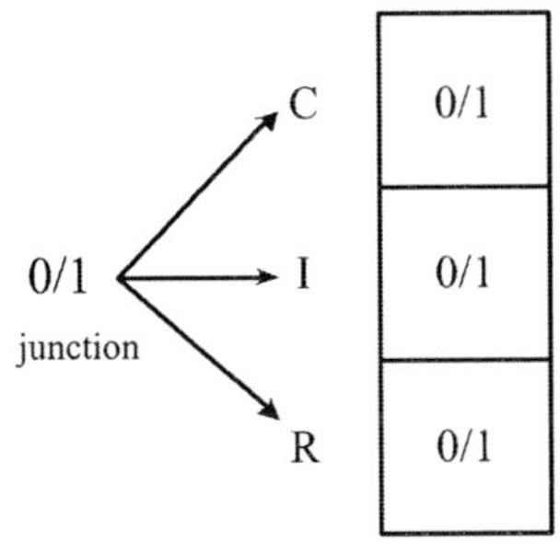

Figure 7.7. Switches for elements attached to junctions.

7.3.2 Hybrid-Encoding for Bond Graph Synthesis by Genetic Programming

One of the puzzles in genetic programming is that there are only vague guidelines as to how many and what types of functions and terminals are appropriate for a given problem, and whether adding more GP functions and terminals is helpful or not. One of the guidelines is that one should try to find a suitable high-level set of functions (encapsulating the common modules in a problem domain) plus a set primitive functions and terminals. It is believed that using only low-level functions may lead to extreme difficulty to evolve even essential modules in a problem domain. The function and terminal sets are usually chosen such that solutions can be constructed by a relatively small GP tree [14].

In the hybrid encoding approach proposed here, a high-level GP function Insert_J0C_J1I_R (Figure 7.8) is added to the function and terminal set of the node-encoding scheme described in the previous subsection. Then the function and terminal set of the hybrid encoding is: F= Add_J_CI_R, EndNode, Insert_J0C_J1I_R, EndBond, ERC. Instead of inserting one junction at a time as the Add_J_CI_R operator does, the Insert_J0C_J1I_R operator inserts a pair consisting of a 0-junction and a 1-junction, each with appropriate elements attached to it. The type of modifiable site at which this function may be applied is a bond. Since in simplified

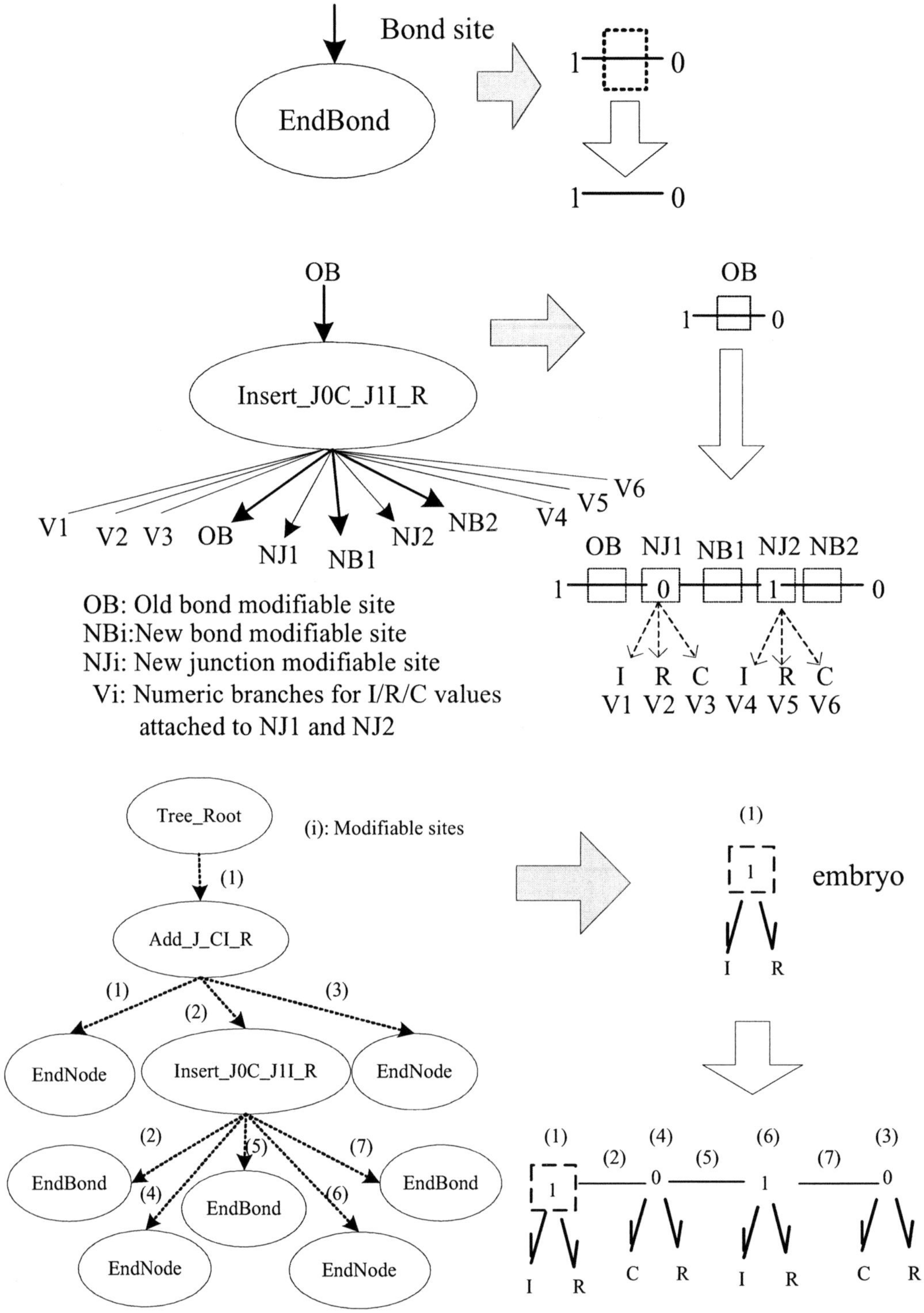

Figure 7.8. Function Insert_J0C_J1I_R and terminal EndBond in hybrid encoding approach for bond graph evolution. Top: EndBond terminates the growth at a modifiable site; Middle: Insert_J0C_J1I_R function and its effect Bottom: a GP tree with hybrid encoding and its result (numeric branches are omitted).

bond graphs, all junctions are adjacent only to junctions of the opposite type, this function continues to span the space of junction connections, and assures that the resulting bond graphs are not redundant. The hybrid encoding approach allows both the junctions (nodes) and the bonds (edges) to be modifiable sites, at which new structures could be inserted or attached. Such approaches are widely used by Koza and others [3], [19]. Our intuition is that this additional GP function may greatly improve the efficiency of evolutionary search. Figure 7.8 shows this additional function and the related terminal (EndBond) of the hybrid encoding, compared to node-encoding. A typical GP tree with this encoding scheme and the result of this GP tree after applying to an embryo are also provided in the same figure.

7.3.3 Encoding with a Realizable Function Set

In the hybrid encoding approach above, the high-level GP function Insert_J0C_J1I_R is designed according to the general properties of bond graphs rather than to a specific problem domain. However, in many cases, the modules in a given problem domain are usually very specific and then a problem-oriented set of GP functions might need to be designed, each encapsulating a particular type of module. For example, GP functions have been devised to model typical physical modules in resonators of MEMS design, which are then used to evolve physically feasible resonators represented as bond graphs [17]. Since this approach is used to evolve feasible solutions and is problem specific, it is hard to compare the efficiency of these types of problem-specific approaches with that of the basic approach discussed in Section 7.2.

7.4 The Eigenvalue Placement Problem: A Scalable Benchmark for Automated Topology Synthesis

Designing a good benchmark problem for investigating open-ended system synthesis is difficult for several reasons. The generic electrical circuit synthesis problem of Koza et al. [12], widely known as it is, requires a complicated simulation package such as SPICE, and the simulation complexity is fairly high. Other topology synthesis problems, such as molecular design, suffer from the lack of a "standard" and universally available simulation engine. Communication network design [18], neural network design [26], and other pure graph-oriented topology synthesis procedures [19], however, have quite different characteristics in terms of the search space and the fitness landscape from problems such as synthesis of dynamic systems. As a result, we introduce a set of bond graph-based benchmark problems for evaluating methods and identifying issues in automated evolutionary synthesis of mechatronic systems.

The benchmark problem proposed here is called the eigenvalue placement problem, in which an analog circuit represented as a bond graph model is to be synthesized (including its topology and sizing of components) to achieve a specific behavior, represented as the distribution of the eigenvalues of the system (Figure 7.9). The bond graph model domain to be used is composed of a set of inductors (I), resistors (R), capacitors (C), transformers

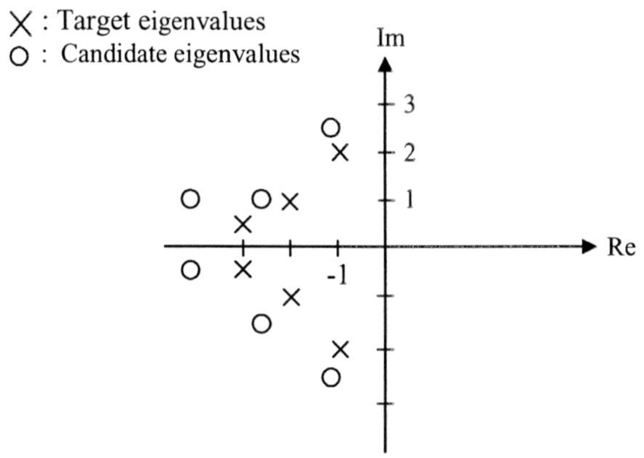

Figure 7.9. The eigenvalue placement problem.

(TF), gyrators (GY), and Sources of Effort (SE). Our synthesis task in the K-eigenvalue placement problem is to evolve a dynamic system with K eigenvalues that approximate a pre-specified set as closely as possible. By increasing the number of eigenvalues (K) (and, correspondingly, the order of the dynamic system), we can define a sequence of synthesis problems of increasing difficulty, for use in evaluating the scalability of various techniques. The problem difficulty can also be varied by choosing different sets of primitive building blocks (modules) to be used in the search process. In this chapter, we use a set of causally well-posed primitives (CWP), in which each junction has a resistor attached, 1-junctions always have an inductor attached, 0-junctions always have a capacitor attached, 0-junctions can only be adjacent to 1-junctions, and vice-versa. Such systems are readily realized in the form of mechanical systems, as well as in the electrical domain. The space of all possible topologies generated using these primitives consists of connected graphs without loops (i.e., trees), and the conditions are strong enough to guarantee that the corresponding systems satisfy causality constraints.

Given a bond graph model, the fitness evaluation is conducted as follows:

1. Derive the A matrix of the state space model from the bond graph model [8]

2. Compute the eigenvalues of the A matrix (code to do this is widely available, or a procedure converted from Matlab may be used, for example)

3. Match the resulting eigenvalues to the target eigenvalue set to compute a relative-distance-based error measure by Algorithm 7.1.

4. Calculate the fitness of the bond graph by normalizing that error measure into a fitness value (to be maximized) between 0 and 1 according the following scaling rule: if distance/order ¡0.1 then fitness = 0.1 /(0.1+distance/order) else fitness = 5.05 /(10+distance/order) where order is the number of energy-storing components (capacitors and inductors).

Algorithm 7.1 Calculating distance between two sets of eigenvalues

Input: target eigenvalue set (x_i^t, y_i^t), $i = 1, ..., O_t$, where O_t is the number of target eigenvalues; Candidate eigenvalue set (x_i, y_i), $i = 1, ..., O_c$, where O_c is the number of candidate eigenvalues.

Output: summed relative distances between two sets of eigenvalues

1. if order (cardinality) of candidate set O_c is different from that of target set, O_t then return ∞;
2. else
3. calculate the average length l_{ave} of target eigenvalues(distance from the origin), $l_{ave} = \sum_{i=1}^{O_t} l_i$, l_i is the length of i_{th} target eigenvalue;
4. label all eigenvalues as unmatched
5. *distance* $\leftarrow 0$
6. for i = 1 to O_t
7. find an unmatched candidate eigenvalue j, which is closest to target eigenvalue i;
8. label the candidate eigenvalue j as matched;
9. *distance* $\leftarrow$ *distance* + $\sqrt{(x_j - x_i^t)^2 + (y_j - y_i^t)^2} / l_{ave}$, where (x_j, y_j) is the candidate eigenvalue, and (x_i^t, y_i^t) is the current target eigenvalue i.;
10. end for
11. return *distance*;

end.

The fitness scaling measure in 4) above is chosen such that 50% of the fitness range is occupied by error measures greater than 0.1, and the remainder is used for error measures less than 0.1. It is continuous, with a single slope discontinuity, and approaches 1 asymptotically as the error measure approaches 0. Many evolutionary methods (using tournament or rank-based selection, for example) will not require or be sensitive to the scaling suggested in step 4, but some methods depend on an absolute fitness measure, and this is suggested for use in such cases, and also converts the fitness into the classical maximization form of evolutionary computation, without a singularity for an error of 0 (an exact match of candidates to the targets).

It is possible to use this problem formulation in at least two interesting ways. First, a set of eigenvalues may be generated arbitrarily, without knowledge of a system that would have such a set of eigenvalues. This provides an open-ended problem with no known answer and unknown properties. Second, it is possible, and often useful, to start from a known system, calculate its eigenvalues, and use that set as the target, thereby providing a target with at least one known optimal solution (error = 0, fitness = 1). This allows the user to readily assess the efficiency of the evolutionary design system as a global optimizer.

This problem formulation explicitly specifies the order of the system. It is useful and often pre-specified in real-world applications, as cost often correlates well with order. Alternative formulations could allow candidate systems of higher order than the target to receive finite error measures, but require that unmatched eigenvalues be outside the range of the target set, for example. Another interesting formulation of the problem, with many of the same properties but requiring much less computational effort, would use the coefficients of the characteristic polynomial of the A matrix as the targets to be matched by those coefficients of candidate systems, thereby avoiding the cost of numerically calculating the eigenvalues. However, systems with widely differing eigenvalues can possess only small differences in characteristic polynomials, so the authors have chosen here to study the eigenvalues themselves, with the hope of better illuminating structure/function relationships in the systems evolved.

7.5 Experimental Studies of Issues in Topologically Open-Ended Bond Graph Synthesis

In this section, we try to answer the following questions. First, we would like to investigate whether the representation (here, the design of function and terminal set) affects its performance on different types of synthesis tasks. In other words, is it necessary to design a special type of encoding for each type of problem? The second issue to study is the effect of introducing more high-level GP functions into the function set and whether it is helpful in all cases. Finally, we want to examine how to seed the initial GP population with typical modules to increase the search efficiency in evolutionary topological synthesis.

Automated evolutionary synthesis of dynamic systems involves the need to search simultaneously for the topology and parameters of the system. This is because the goodness of a topology cannot be assessed without assigning appropriate values to its parameters, and a set of parameters independent of the topology to which they are assigned defines no performance at all. However, to explore the issue of how topology encoding affects the search efficiency, it is preferable to look at a reduced sub-problem that eliminates the requirement for parameter searching by making all parameters identical at unity (i.e., all resistors, capacitors, and inductors have numerical parameters of 1.0). To ensure that the target optimum solutions indeed exist, the target eigenvalue sets are determined from assorted topologies with unit parameters for all of their components. Since parameter search is very expensive for high-order eigenvalue problems, this topology-only search defines a much simpler problem, but can still illuminate some properties of the topology search for more general problems. The function set primitives used here restrict the resulting bond graphs to having C components attached to each and only 0-junctions and I components attached to each and only 1-junctions, which results in systems readily realizable in any energy domain and which need not be checked for being causally well-posed. Each junction also has an R component attached. Of course, this is only a sub-problem of the more general case in which I components might optionally be attached to 0-junctions and C components to 1-junctions, as well.

7.5.1 Search Bias of Representation in Topologically Open-Ended Synthesis

The first issue of evolutionary synthesis in an unfamiliar domain is the encoding, which should be studied to determine whether the representation biases the genetic search. If there is no domain knowledge available, it is better to use an unbiased search so as not to restrict the range of the search in an attempt to increase efficiency; otherwise, a special problem-specific representation might be employed. For each specific representation, it is important to evaluate its search bias for different types of problems to ensure its appropriateness in the problem domain. In this section, we evaluate the search bias of the node-encoding approach for synthesis of bond graphs as described in Section 7.2.

Three representative target topologies with different sizes are selected to compare the average search effort of the node-encoding approach. The first topology is a bush, in which 0-junctions are attached to a central 1-junction. The third topology type is a chain, consisting of alternating 1-junctions and 0-junctions. The second is a mixed topology type, which is neither bush nor chain. Table 7.3 gives examples of order 8 (since there are many possible intermediate topologies, only one of them is selected for evaluation). As described in Section 7.4, we assume that each 0-junction has one capacitor (C) and one resistor (R) attached, each with fixed size parameters of 1.0, and each 1-junction has one inductor (I) and one resistor (R) attached, each sized at 1.0.

Figure 7.10 shows the search effort to find the target topologies of each type for 8, 12, 16, 18, and 20-eigenvalue problems, using a generational GP with population size 500 for 8- and 12-eigenvalue problems, and 1000 for 16- and higher-order eigenvalue problems (with 20 runs for each target). Other primary parameters for the GP runs were as follows:

crossover rate: 0.4; mutation rate: 0.05; tournament selection with tournament size: 7; subtree swap mutation: 0.55 (this operator chooses two separate subtrees of the same individual and swaps them, preserving system order); initialization: ramped-half-and-half

Table 7.3. Three types of target bond graph topologies (the attached C, I, and R elements are omitted for simplicity)

<table>
<tr><th>target topology type</th><th>structure</th></tr>
<tr><td>bush topology</td><td>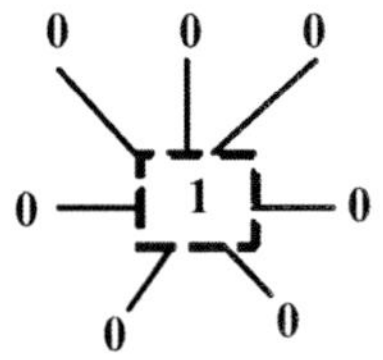</td></tr>
<tr><td>intermediate topology</td><td>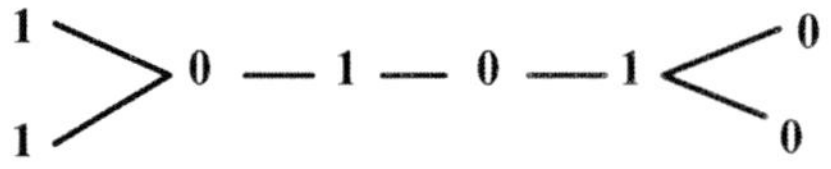</td></tr>
<tr><td>chain topology</td><td>1 — 0 — 1 — 0 — 1 — 0 — 1 — 0</td></tr>
</table>

initialization to generate random trees with maximum depth of 5. Maximum evaluations: 100,000 for 8- and 12-eigenvalue problems, 200,000 for 16-, 18-, and 20-eigenvalue problems.

To see the effectiveness of genetic programming-based topology search, let us first consider the sizes of the topology-only search spaces of various orders, expressed in terms of distinct bond graph junction structures, which have been enumerated [21]. Since each 0-junction or 1-junction in the causally well-posed function set used has a determined set of attached components (the 1-junction has I and R, while the 0-junction has C and R), and since the embryo contains a fixed 1-junction, counting the junction topologies also counts the distinct bond graph topologies, and the number of junctions and order of system are identical. For systems of order four, there are only two possible bond graphs. For order 8, there are 23 different bond graphs; for 12, there are 551; for 16, there are 19,320, for 18 there are 128,340, and for 20, there are 823,065). It is obvious that the search space increases quickly with increasing numbers of components. However, since multiple GP trees map to the same bond graph topology, the *genotype* search space is actually much larger – that is, there are multiple encodings for each distinct bond graph.

From Figure 7.10, it is evident that the GP method tested can easily find the target topologies for 8- to 20-eigenvalue problems. For example, the 20-eigenvalue problem has 823,065 possible topologies, and the search procedure found the target topology with an average of 46,651 evaluations. We also found that the node-encoding approach was a somewhat biased away from finding bush topologies. For all problems with order greater than 16, node-encoding used about 50% more evaluations to find the bush target topologies.

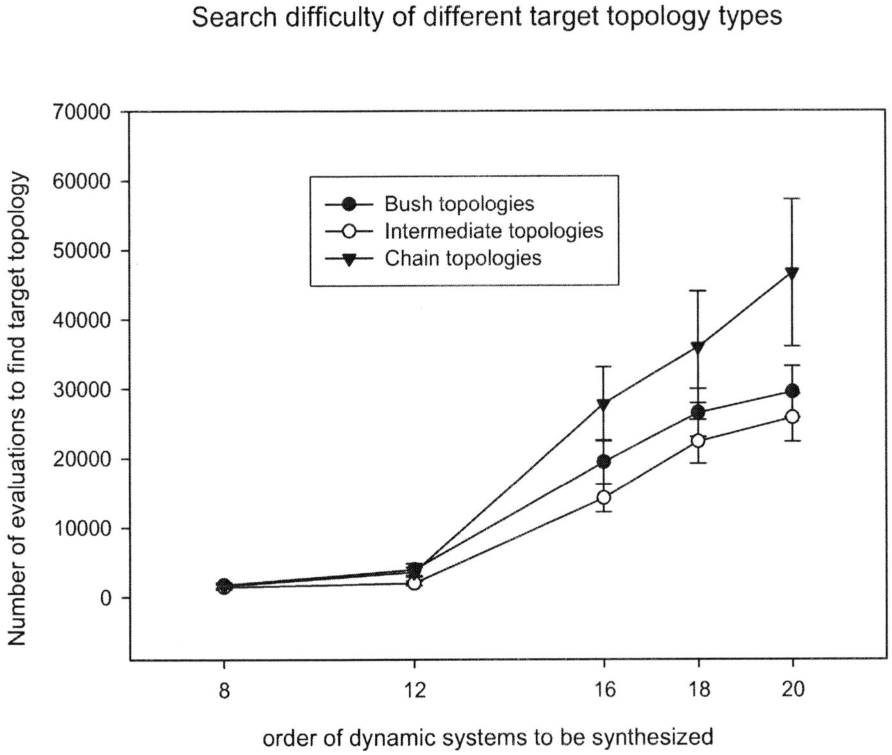

Figure 7.10. Search effort to find three types of target topologies for 8-, 12-, 16-, 18, 20-eigenvalue problems with the node-encoding approach, averaged over 20 runs

Superficially, it may be surprising that the intermediate topologies take the fewest evaluations to find the targets; however, because genetic programming starts from an initial population with a myriad topologies, it seems to have been easier to find an intermediate topology than those strongly biased target topologies like chains and bushes, which represent two extreme bond graph topologies. Generally speaking, node encoding solved all the 20-eigenvalue problems. This experiment demonstrated the bias of the function and terminal set that skewed its efficiency in solving certain types of problems. This is reminiscent of the underpinnings of the well-known No-Free-Lunch theorem [22].

7.5.2 Representation and Scalability: How Function Set Affects Efficiency

Another difficult decision in genetic programming-based synthesis is how to determine an appropriate function and terminal set. In practice, there is generally some domain knowledge available. For example, some types of components or modules appear often in specific types of problems. One straightforward way is to encapsulate many high-level modules into the function set and let genetic programming decide which kinds of modules to use in the final design. It is expected that more GP functions should help the search by providing more flexibility, or that, at least, they will not hurt the search.

To evaluate the effect of adding more high-level modules on search efficiency, we launched the same set of experiments of synthesizing three types of topologies of different orders with the hybrid encoding approach described in Section 7.5.1. The hybrid-encoding approach simply adds a new GP function Insert_J0C_J1I_R (Figure 7.8) to the function and terminal set F={EndNode, Add_J_CI_R, ERC} of the node-encoding approach used in the previous section. This new function is expected to speed up the search for chain topologies, since it inserts a 1-0 junction pair into a bond. Since node-encoding is a complete set that is able to represent all the target bond graphs, this new set F'= {EndNode, Add_J_CI_R, Insert_J0C_J1I_R, EndBond, ERC} is also complete. We used the same set of parameters as in the previous section for the GP experiments. The experimental results are shown in Figure 7.11.

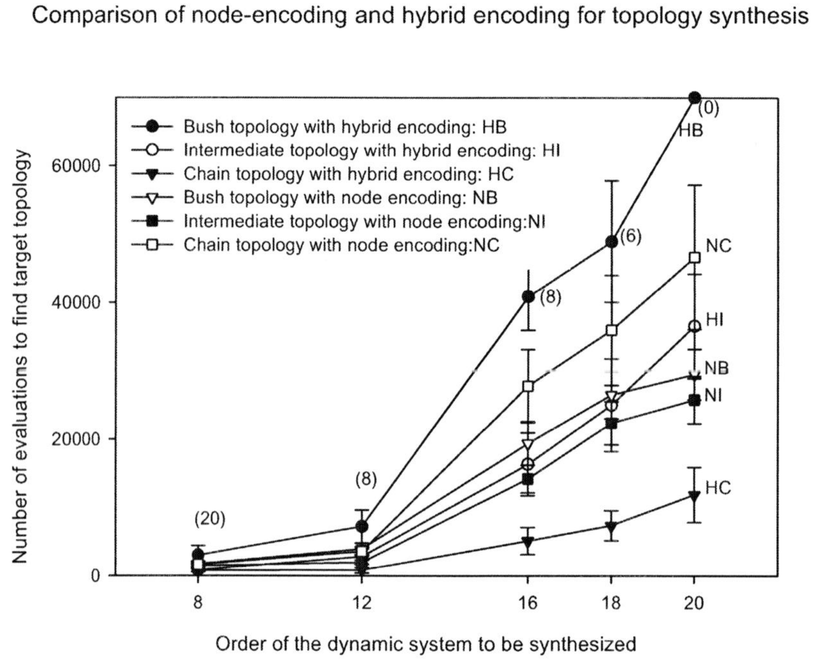

Figure 7.11. Comparison of hybrid encoding with node encoding approach for three types of target topologies for 8-, 12-, 16-, 18-, and 20-eigenvalue problems, each averaged over 20 runs. The numbers in brackets are the numbers of runs that successfully found the bush topology, using the hybrid encoding. The unlabelled experiments always found target topologies within 200,000 evaluations.

The first observation of Figure 7.11 is that hybrid encoding has reduced the number of evaluations needed to find the chain topology (see curve labeled HC) by a factor of three.

However, this improvement is not surprising, since inserting a junction pair into bonds can quickly construct a chain. What is more surprising is that the hybrid encoding—the simple adding of the Insert_J0C_J1I_R function—made this approach quite unsuccessful in evolving bush topologies, which is in sharp contrast with the improvement on chain topologies. Actually, even for 12-eigenvalue problems, the hybrid encoding only found the target bush topology in 8 runs out of 20. It is also interesting that the hybrid encoding had similar performance to node-encoding on the intermediate topologies, though with a few more evaluations. Node encoding was clearly more robust than hybrid encoding, when judged across all topologies tested.

Hybrid encoding with the GP function Insert_J0C_J1I_R allows all constructs including the bonds and junctions of the bond graph to become modifiable sites, and thus might be expected to allow more rapid or effective evolution. However, experimental results showed that this is not the case. While the hybrid encoding approach sometimes succeeded on the 8- to 18-eigenvalue problems, its bias made it unable to scale to the 20-eigenvalue problem for bush target topologies.

Seeking the source of the difficulty revealed that the hybrid-encoding approach could find a topology fairly similar to the target topology quite quickly. However, since there were two types of modifiable sites in the genome (bond and junction modifiable sites), it was highly constrained in local manipulations of the genome, because of gene incompatibility – a bond modifiable GP tree node cannot be exchanged with a junction modification GP tree node. In this case, to remove a undesirable GP node without deteriorating its fitness is extremely difficult, and then no significant genetic operations can help the search jump out of local optima. It thus lacks sufficient local topology modification capability, at least in a probabilistic sense. The superficial flexibility in the phenotype space with all possible modifiable sites hides the rigidity in the genotype manipulation capability. In contrast, the node-encoding approach allows very flexible genotype manipulation, and thus is able to achieve better results.

It is apparent that the hybrid encoding method is comparable to the node-encoding approach for the easy 8-eigenvalue problems when searching for intermediate and chain topologies, but at the cost of slower search on the bush topology caused by its bias, while the unbiased node-encoding achieves similar performance for all types of topologies. Adding more high-level modules may thus be quite harmful for synthesizing some types of topologies. We also found that if one can devise a good function set based on the characteristics of the solution space, it is possible to achieve striking speed-up in search efficiency simply by modifying the representation alone.

7.5.3 Population Seeding and the Efficiency of Topology Search

While designing a good GP function set based on problem knowledge is a good strategy for topology synthesis by genetic programming, another approach for knowledge incorporation in evolutionary synthesis is to seed the initial population with individuals possessing certain domain-relevant properties. Nachbar [23], for example, seeded his initial populations with different types of components whose proportions were extracted from existing molecule designs. To evaluate the impact of various population initialization methods, a set of topology transformation experiments was conducted here. We started from an initial population with identical individuals (bond graph constructor trees) whose execution generated an identical source topology—-e.g., an initial population consisting entirely of the bush topology. Then we evolved this initially uniform population toward a target topology. The experimental results are summarized in Table 7.4, with means and standard deviations. Each source-target pair experiment was repeated 20 times, all with same running parameters as in Section 7.5.1.

Table 7.4. Topological transformation with different initial homogenous populations

Source topology	Target topologies (mean ±std. dev) evaluations		
	Bush	Intermediate	Chain
bush	N/A	2825 (±411)	3433 (±396)
intermediate	2348 (±471)	N/A	1864 (±359)
chain	3183 (±294)	2227 (±273)	N/A

Table 7.4 shows some interesting, but not too surprising observations. Since bush and chain topologies represent the two extreme types of the topology space, transformation between them is most difficult, while transformation from the selected initial intermediate to either chain or bush is much easier. As the intermediate topology is *between* bush and chain topologies in some sense, our results confirmed that seeding with a more similar topology will speed up the evolution. If one does not have any idea what the topology of the final solution looks like, it thus appears advisable to use one or more intermediate topologies as starting points. Another observation is that genetic programming is able to break the symmetry in the initial population and evolve toward the target topology even if it starts with the opposite topology type, such as evolving from bush to chain.

7.6 Discussion

Experiments in previous sections showed that there is a strong relationship between representation/encoding, evolvability, and scalability of topologically open-ended synthesis by genetic programming. As is generally true, the evolvability of topology search depends strongly on the correlation of the topology with its fitness. The less rugged and deceptive the fitness landscape, with respect to changes caused by single applications of genetic operators, the easier the problem will be to solve. By watching the solutions evolve toward the target topology, we see a correlation between topologies and their functional behavior in the eigenvalue location problems. We saw above that the 8- to 20-eigenvalue problems were solved fairly quickly. Identifying the target bush topology from 823,065 possible topologies using only 29,506 evaluations illustrates the capability of GP for topology search. Next, we used the same experimental settings to try to solve 24-eigenvalue problems (with a search space cardinality of 39,299,897), except that the population size was increased to 2,000, maximum number of evaluations to 500,000, and the maximum tree depth to 30. Unfortunately, the current node encoding approach failed to find the target bush topology in any of 10 runs. This hints at one of the most severe problems of current genetic programming-based systems, the lack of scalability, especially considering that we have removed parameter search in our experiments here, which would add additional difficulty to the synthesis engine.

This failure can be attributed to several causes. One is the high epistasis and multimodality of the topology search space. The resulting low neutrality and sparseness of intermediate solutions make it extremely difficult to find the target topology. However, an interesting phenomenon is observed—that genetic programming usually can quickly find a reasonable good topology with high similarity to the target. But after that, there is not sufficient guiding information to fine-tune similar topologies into the target solution. One factor is that this genetic programming system for topology synthesis lacks effective local topology mechanisms as discussed in Section 7.5.2. Moreover, the standard genetic programming, with its random crossover and mutation, is random in its choice of directions to explore, and perhaps that is too unstructured to succeed in such cases. For example, it would be desirable that, after identifying a basic framework of a possible solution, more exploration be allocated to local topology search while leaving the framework undisturbed. However, current GP randomly chooses crossover/mutation points, thus often leading to random scrambling, most of which destroys the framework discovered so far and wastes search effort. In the genotype space, we observe, for example, that although one near-optimal solution discovered was only one swap away from the target topology, GP did not find the target, because the probability to swap the two given branches is extremely low.

Current standard genetic programming has inherent difficulty to increase its scalability for solving large design synthesis problems. This may explain the huge computational effort (several days running with hundreds of PCs) that Koza has used for discovering controllers with a hundred or so components. We conjecture that mechanisms for discovering and "freezing" useful frameworks and building blocks are needed. Local topology search capability also needs to be improved to allow effective exploitation in local neighborhoods. One promising solution to these problems might be to apply the mechanisms of biological development to the synthesis process, which has attracted a lot of recent attention [24], [25], [27]. However, these developmental techniques have not yet evolved results competitive with standard genetic programming.

7.7 SUMMARY

We have introduced a well-defined scalable benchmark problem for studying automated synthesis of dynamic systems—the eigenvalue placement problem, based on the bond graph representation. For this problem, we have found that similar topologies of bond graphs lead to somewhat similar behaviors in terms of their eigenvalue distributions. This correlation between structure and function of the problem is important for efficient topology search. Without some significant correlation, such inverse problems are essentially intractable.

Using genetic programming as the topology search engine, and on a fixed-parameter reduced version of the problem, we investigated the properties of the topologically open-ended synthesis of bond graphs by genetic programming, which has quite different properties from other (parametric) search problems, including low neutrality, high multi-modality, discreteness, and lack of information to guide local topology search. We found that standard genetic programming, with node-encoding only, could easily solve up-to-20-eigenvalue problems, but did not scale well to 24-eigenvalue problems (with a search space of 39,299,897) or higher. Two encoding schemes, node-encoding and hybrid (node and edge) encoding were compared, as applied to 8-, 12-, 16-, 18-, and 20-eigenvalue problems. The result was that node encoding was much better than the hybrid encoding in terms of scalability and robustness. It turned out that incompatibility of the "genes" in the hybrid encoding introduced too strong a bias for efficient solution of the bush topology problem. However, this bias enabled it to find chain topologies very efficiently. It showed that arbitrarily introducing many high-levels GP functions may introduce strong bias to make it hard to solve certain types of problems, while speeding the solution of other types of problems. With topology transforming experiments, we confirmed that appropriate population seeding is beneficial to the search process. If faced with an unfamiliar problem, it appears to be better to seed the population with diverse topologies. Here, we have intentionally neglected parameter search, which we have treated elsewhere in the context of topology search [28]. However, more systematic examination of the interaction between topology and parameter search is needed. For example, the neutrality introduced by parameter search may facilitate, rather than block, topology search.

Our experiments showed that current developmental genetic programming is powerful for topological search in design innovation. But it still lacks some essential mechanisms to scale up to even larger dynamic system synthesis problems, at least unless enormous population sizes and numbers of evaluations are used. One promising direction appears to be introduction of mechanisms for framework or module discovery and reuse, especially those mechanisms inspired by the biological developmental principles [27], [29]. A second is a local genotype operator that exploits the locality of topology. Another possible improvement may come from smarter crossover and mutation operators, rather than the random swapping and mutation of GP sub-trees.

Bibliography

[1] Antonsson, E.K. and J. Cagan. *Formal Engineering Design Synthesis*, Cambridge University press, Cambridge. (2001).

[2] Koza, J. R., M. A., Keane, M. J., Streeter. What's AI Done for Me Lately? Genetic Programming's Human-Competitive Results. *IEEE Intelligent Systems*,**18** (03), 25-31 (2003).

[3] Koza, J. R., M. A., Keane, J., Yu, F. H III,Bennett, and W., Mydlowec. Automatic creation of human-competitive programs and controllers by means of genetic programming. *Genetic Programming and Evolvable Machines*. **1** (1-2) 121 - 164. (2000)

[4] Koza, J. R., M. A., Keane, M. J., Streeter, W., Mydlowec, J., Yu, and G., Lanza. *Genetic Programming IV: Routine Human-Competitive Machine Intelligence*. Kluwer Academic Publishers. (2003)

[5] Miller, J. F., D. Job, and V. K. Vassilev. Principles in the Evolutionary Design of Digital Circuits – Part I . *Journal of Genetic Programming and Evolvable Machines*, Vol. 1, No. 1, 2000, pp. 8-35. (2000).

[6] Gordon, T.G.M and P.J., Bentley. Towards Development in Evolvable Hardware. In *Proceedings of the 2002 NASA/DoD Conference on Evolvable Hardware*, Washington D.C., U.S.A., July 15-18, 2002, pp. 241-250. (2002)

[7] Vassilev V. K. and J. F., Miller. Scalability Problems of Digital Circuit Evolution. in *Proceedings of the 2nd NASA/DOD Workshop on Evolvable Hardware*, IEEE Computer Society, pp. 55-64, (2000).

[8] Karnopp D. C., D. L., Margolis and R. C.,Rosenberg *System Dynamics: Modeling and Simulation of Mechatronic Systems*. Third Edition. New York: John Wiley & Sons, Inc., (2000)

[9] Polya, G. *Mathematical Discovery*. **1**, Wiley, New York, (1962)

[10] Tay E., Flowers W. and Barrus J. Automated Generation and Analysis of Dynamic System Designs, *Research in Engineering Design*, **10** (1), 15 – 29, (1998)

[11] Youcef-Toumi K. Modeling, Design, and Control Integration: A necessary Step in Mechatronics, IEEE/ASME Trans. *Mechatronics*, **1**(1), 29-38, (1996)

[12] Koza, J. R. et al., *Genetic Programming III: Darwinian Invention and Problem Solving*, Morgan Kaufmann, San Francisco, (1999).

[13] Seo, K., J. Hu, Z. Fan, E. D. Goodman, and R. C. Rosenberg. Automated Design Approaches for Multi-Domain Dynamic Systems Using Bond Graphs and Genetic Programming. *The International Journal of Computers, Systems and Signals*, vol.3, no.1, pp.55-70, (2002).

[14] Seo, K., Z., Fan, J. Hu, E. D. Goodman, and R. C. Rosenberg. Toward an Automated Design Method for Multi-Domain Dynamic Systems Using Bond Graphs and Genetic Programming. *Mechatronics*, V. 13, Issues 8-9, pp. 851-885, (2003).

[15] Seo, K., Z. Fan, J. Hu, E. Goodman, and R. Rosenberg. Dense and Switched Modular Primitives for Bond Graph Model Design. *Proc. Genetic and Evolutionary Computing Conference*, Chicago, Springer, Lecture Notes in Computer Science, 1764-1775, (2003).

[16] Goodman, E. D., K. Seo, Z. Fan, J. Hu, R. C. Rosenberg. Automated Design of Mechatronic Systems: Novel Search Methods and Modular Primitives to Enable Real_World Applications. In *Proc. of 2003 NSF Design, Service and Manufacturing Grantees and Research Conference*, Birmingham, Alabama, January 6-9,(2003).

[17] Fan, Z, K. Seo, J. Hu, R. Rosenberg, and E. Goodman. System-Level Synthesis of MEMS via Genetic Programming and Bond Graphs. In *Proc. Genetic and Evolutionary Computing Conference*, Chicago, Springer, Lecture Notes in Computer Science, pp. 2058-2071, (2003).

[18] Dengiz, B., Altiparmak, F. & Smith, A.E. Local search genetic algorithm for optimal design of reliable networks. *IEEE Transactions on Evolutionary Computation*, **1**(3), pp.179-188, September, (1997)

[19] Luke, S., and L. Spector. Evolving Graphs and Networks with Edge Encoding: Preliminary Report. In Koza, John R. (editor), *Late-Breaking Papers at the Genetic Programming 1996 Conference*. Palo Alto, CA., (1996)

[20] Fan, Z., J. Hu, K. Seo, E. D. Goodman, R. C. Rosenberg, and B. Zhang. Bond Graph Representation and GP for Automated Analog Filter Design. In *Proc. of Genetic and Evolutionary Computation Conference Late-Breaking Papers*, E. Goodman, ed., ISGEC Press, San Francisco, 2001, pp. 81-86. (2001)

[21] Harary, F. and E. Palmer. *Graphical Enumeration*. Academic Press, New York. (1973)

[22] Wolpert, D.H. and Macready, W.G. No free lunch theorems for optimization. *IEEE Transactions on Evolutionary Computation*, **4**: 67-82, (1997).

[23] Nachbar, N.B. Molecular Evolution: Automated Manipulation of Hierarchical Chemical Topology and Its Application to Average Molecular Structures. *Genetic Programming and Evolvable Machines* **1**(1): 57-94, (2000)

[24] Miller, J. F. and P. Thomson. A Developmental Method for Growing Graphs and Circuits . In Proc. Of Fifth International Conference on Evolvable Systems: From Biology to Hardware. Proceedings published as *Lecture Notes in Computer Science*, Vol. 2606, pp. 93-104 , Tyrrell, Andy M., Haddow P., Torrensen J.(Eds.)., (2003)

[25] Timothy G.W. Gordon. Exploring Models of Development for Evolutionary Circuit Design. In CEC2003, the Congress on Evolutionary Computation, Canberra, Australia, December 8-12, (2003)

[26] Stanley, K.O and Miikkulainen,R. Evolving Neural Networks through augmenting topologies. *Evolutionary Computation* **10**(2):99-127, (2002).

[27] Stanley, K.O. and Risto Miikkulainen. A Taxonomy for artificial embryogeny. *Artificial Life*, **9**(2):93-130, (2003).

[28] Hu, J., K. Seo, S. Li, Z. Fan, R. C. Rosenberg, E. D. Goodman. Structure Fitness Sharing (SFS) for Evolutionary Design by Genetic Programming. In *Proceedings of the Genetic and Evolutionary Computation Conference*, GECCO-2002, pp. 780-787, New York, (2002).

[29] Miller, J. F. and P. Thomson. A Developmental Method for Growing Graphs and Circuits. *Proc. of Fifth International Conference on Evolvable Systems: From Biology to Hardware,2003*.Or Lecture Notes in Computer Science, Vol. 2606, pp. 93-104 , Tyrrell, Andy M., Haddow P., Torrensen J.(Eds.)., (2003).

In: Evolutionary Machine Design: Methodology & Applications ISBN 1-59454-405-0
Editors: N. Nedjah & L. Mourelle, pp:193-215

Chapter 8

THE ROLE OF SIMULATED EVOLUTION IN BIOINFORMATICS

Andy Auyeung, Ajith Abraham

Department of Computer Science, Oklahoma State University,
Stillwater, OK 74078, USA
(wingha@cs.okstate.edu, ajith.abraham@ieee.org
http://www.cs.okstate.edu/~wingha, http://ajith.softcomputing.net

Bioinformatics is a fast growing field in the scientific community. It involves a wide range of problems, for example, DNA sequence analyses, RNA secondary structure predictions, phylogenetic analyses and microarray analyses (just to name a few). Furthermore, new problem domains are constantly evolving, such as proteomics and biomedical applications. In fact, many of these problems are very complex in nature and are often hard to solve by conventional methods. We have learned that Evolutionary Computing (EC) is a powerful optimization technique that solves complex problems and it has been proven successful in various application domains. Therefore, in this chapter, we introduce EC applications in Bioinformatics. The chapter first gives an overview of some key concepts and classical problems in Bioinformatics. Then, it is followed by two case studies, where the problem's background, the mathematical formulation, the EC representation and the performance of the methods are presented in details.

8.1 INTRODUCTION

8.1.1 The Precursor of Bioinformatics

The origin of Bioinformatics can be traced back to the first discovery of modern genetics. In 1854, Gregor Johann Mendel (is now known as the father of genetics) conducted a study on heredity of a garden pea called *Pisum sativum*. The study was to breed a population of the garden pea with different physical characteristics, such as seed shapes, seed colors and flower colors. Then the variations of these characteristics were observed in their offspring. Mendel discovered some regular patterns from the offspring by breeding parents with selected characteristics. After some careful analyses on these patterns, Mendel established two fundamental principles of genetics, which are now known as the Mendel's first and second law.

Another milestone of genetics is the discovery of DeoxyriboNucleic Acid (DNA) as genetic material. However, the discovery was not straightforward. First, in 1928, Frederick Griffith discovered an unknown agent that transforms a pneumonia causing bacteria called *Streptococcus pneumoniae* from R-type (which is harmless) to S-type (which is highly infectious). This unknown agent was believed to be responsible for the transformation of the genetic material in the bacteria. In 1940s, Oswald T. Avery and his colleagues proposed that this transformation agent was indeed DNA. Later in 1953, Alfred D. Hershey and Martha Chase provided more evidence to confirm Avery's discovery. A few years later, RiboNucleic Acid (RNA) was discovered to be the genetic material of viruses.

8.1.2 Modern Bioinformatics

The rapid growth of Bioinformatics was triggered by the introduction of the DNA sequencing technique. Walter Gilbert and Frederick Sanger were rewarded the Nobel Prize in Chemistry in 1980 for their contribution to nucleic acid sequencing. In 1981, the first complete genome sequencing was done on a circular genome of the human mitochondrion. Since then, many more genomes have been sequenced. In addition, the sequencing procedure became more time and cost effective. In 1990, the Human Genome Project (HGP) was initiated in the United States and was led by the National Institutes of Health (NIH) and the Department of Energy (DOE). After 13 years, the completion of the Human Genome Project was announced in 2003.

Bioinformatics has now become a large field with cross-expertise, such as molecular biology, genetics, biochemistry, computer science and statistics. Furthermore, this field continues to grow and evolve different sub-fields, such as proteomics and biomedical applications. In fact, more and more sub-fields are expected to evolve in the next 10 to 20 years.

8.1.3 Goal and Layout

In this chapter, we will introduce how Evolutionary Computing (EC) can be used to solve problems in Bioinformatics. First we will discuss some important concepts in Bioinformatics. We will also introduce some key Bioinformatics problems and their mathematical formulations. Finally, we will provide two case studies and see how they can be solved using EC.

8.2 AN OVERVIEW OF BIOINFORMATICS

8.2.1 Important Concepts in Bioinformatics

The cell is the fundamental unit of life (with the exception of viruses). Some organisms are single-cell and some are multi-cell. For example, a human being is composed of billions of cells. Although, all the cells are genetically identical, they can differentiate into different types of cells with different functionality to work together as a system. These complex systems not only require mechanisms that regulate the cells to work together, but also require mechanisms that regulate the processes within a cell. As a result, these intra-cellular and inter-cellular regulations in turn define the organism. In fact, all this information is encoded in the genetic material and is passed down in generations. For many organisms, DNA is the genetic material, which contains all the essential information about this organism. RNA and protein are important intermediates that carry out the 'instructions' written in DNA. Below we will discuss DNA, RNA and protein in detail and explain the relationships between them.

The DeoxyriboNucleic Acid is where the genetic information is stored. The DNA is a chain of small molecules called nucleotides. Each nucleotide is composed of three molecular components, a five-carbon sugar, a phosphate group and a nitrogenous base. In addition, there are four types of nitrogenous bases: adenine (A), thymine (T), guanine (G) and cytosine (C). Figure 8.1 gives the molecular diagram of a DNA strand. The genetic information is encoded by alternating these four bases in the DNA strand. Moreover, this genetic information is usually represented as a DNA sequence, a string composed of characters from the alphabet {A, T, G, C}. A DNA strand is oriented, where one end is called the 5'-end (five prime end) and the other end is called the 3'-end (three prime end). Notice that some DNA strands are linear and some are circular. Regardless of the starting point of a DNA strand, the convention is to write the DNA sequence from the 5'-end to the 3'-end. That is, if we write TCGTA, the left end is the 5'-end and the right end is the 3'-end, i.e. 5'-TCGTA-3'. The length of a DNA strand can vary from a few thousands base pairs to a few millions base pairs in different organisms. DNA strands come in pairs and they are called complementary strands. Two complementary DNA strands complement of each other in the opposite orientation. Base A and base T are complements of each other, while base G and base C are complements. Two complementary DNA strands are bonded together in the shape of a double-helix by hydrogen bonds. Figure 8.2 shows the double-helix complementary structure of DNAs. In fact, there are other higher level structures of the DNA strand, such as the supercoilng structure. Except during some cellular events (such as transcription or duplication), DNA strands are coiled and packed up with a special type of protein called histone. This super-structure is visible under the electron micrograph and it is called the chromosome.

The RiboNucleic Acid is similar to the DNA. In RNA, the five-carbon sugar has a hydroxyl group (OH) attached to the 2' carbon, instead of a hydrogen atom (H) as in the DNA. Besides, the base thymine (T) is replaced by uracil (U) in the RNA. But unlike the DNA, the RNA is usually single stranded. However, its complementary property sometimes is exhib-

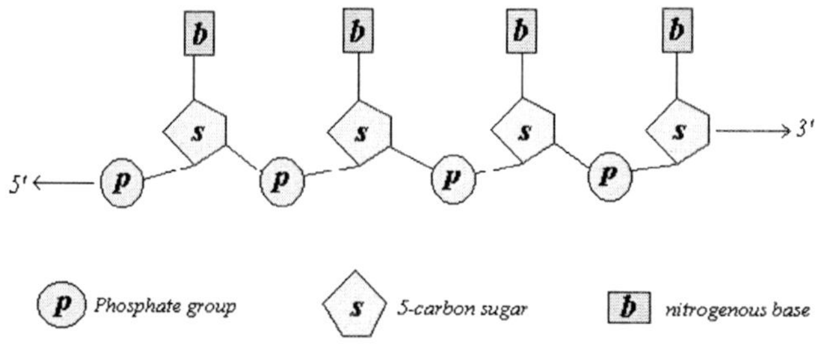

Figure 8.1. The Molecular Structure of DNAs

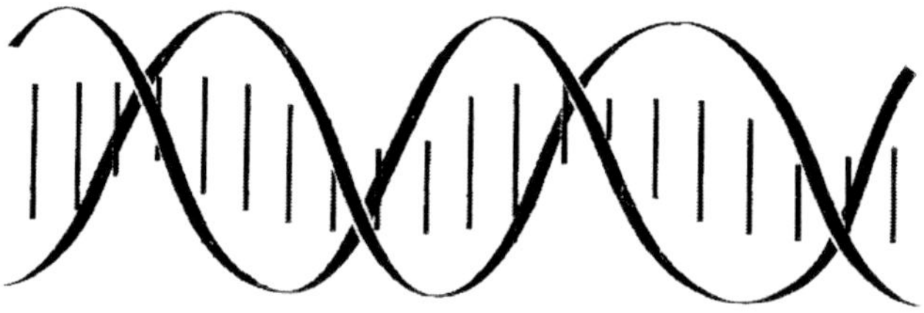

Figure 8.2. The Double Helix Structure of DNAs

ited within itself. That is, it 'folds up' itself when there are two segments in the RNA strand that are complementary or close to complementary. This characteristic is very important because it gives the RNA shape, which is crucial to its functionality. There are actually different types of RNAs, for example, the messenger RNA (mRNA), the transfer RNA (tRNA) and the ribosomal RNA (rRNA). One major function of the RNA is to synthesize proteins. The process is as follows. First, a segment of the DNA is 'copied' into the form of a RNA according to the complementary property. This process is called the transcription. Then, the RNA serves as the template that has encoded information carried from the DNA to produce a protein. This process is called translation.

The protein is essential for carrying out most of the mechanisms in the cell. The regulation of these mechanisms is indeed controlled by producing different proteins and in different quantities at different times. The protein is composed of a chain of amino acids. There are twenty different kinds of amino acids. Each amino acid is encoded by three RNA bases, and we call these three RNA units a codon. Since there are four different kinds of bases in RNA (and DNA), there a total of are sixty-four different combinations of codons. Therefore, some codons actually encode the same amino acid. Also, notice that some codons do not encode any amino acid, which is called the stop codon. The stop codon indicates the termination of the amino acid chain during the process of translations. Figure 8.3 shows the codon/amino acid mapping table. Figure 8.4 shows the relationships of DNAs, RNAs and proteins in transcriptions and translations.

A gene is a segment of the DNA that encodes proteins (i.e. a DNA segment that is

UUU	Phe (F)	UCU	Ser (S)	UAU	Tyr (Y)	UGU	Cys (C)
UUC		UCC		UAC		UGC	
UUA	Leu (L)	UCA		UAA	Stop	UGA	Stop
UUG		UCG		UAG		UGG	Trp (W)
CUU	Leu (L)	CCU	Pro (P)	CAU	His (H)	CGU	Arg (R)
CUC		CCC		CAC		CGC	
CUA		CCA		CAA	Gln (Q)	CGA	
CUG		CCG		CAG		CGG	
AUU	Ile (I)	ACU	Thr (T)	AAU	Asn (N)	AGU	Ser (S)
AUC		ACC		AAC		AGC	
AUA		ACA		AAA	Lys (K)	AGA	Arg (R)
AUG	Met (M)	ACG		AAG		AGG	
GUU	Val (V)	GCU	Ala (A)	GAU	Asp (D)	GGU	Gly (G)
GUC		GCC		GAC		GGC	
GUA		GCA		GAA	Glu (E)	GGA	
GUG		GCG		GAG		GGG	

Stop Codon   Start Codon

Figure 8.3. The Codon/Amino Acid Mapping Table

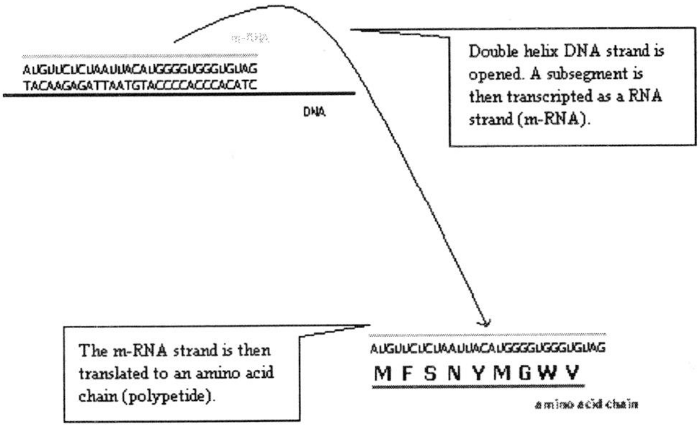

Figure 8.4. The Relationships of DNAs, RNAs and Proteins in Transcriptions and Translations

transcripted to a RNA and in turn determines the protein synthesis). The genome is the whole set of DNAs in a cell. Although there are DNAs in some cell organelles, the term genome usually refers to the set of DNAs that serves as the genetic material.

The relationships, regulations and mechanisms between DNAs, RNAs and proteins are very complex and we understand very little of it. With the basic concepts in mind, below we will look at some of the major research areas in Bioinformatics, namely the problems of sequence alignments, multiple sequence alignments and functional site identifications.

8.2.2 Sequence Alignments

The sequence alignment is a computational model that is used to estimate the relationship between two biological sequences, such as DNA sequences and protein sequences. The alignment is used to model the imperfect matching between two sequences due to some biological events, such as mutations, additions or deletions of nucleotides. Regardless of the types of sequences to align, the basic concepts of alignments are essentially the same. Therefore, in this section the DNA sequence alignment is used to illustrate the idea.

Given two DNA sequences s_1 and s_2 {A, T, G, C}*, where * represents the kleene star, we want to extend them into s'_1 and s'_2 by inserting a special symbol '_', such that and have the same length. The special symbol '_' is used to represent an imaginary base that is missing from the sequence (or is added to the other sequence) due to a biological event. Therefore, our task is to find a pair of s'_1 and s'_2 that matches the best. That is let,

s_1 = AGTTGCA and s_2 = GTGCGA, then s'_1 and s'_2 can be:

$$\begin{array}{lcllllllll} s'_1 & = & A & G & T & T & G & C & \_ & A \\ s'_2 & = & \_ & G & \_ & T & G & C & G & A \end{array}$$

Once we decided what s'_1 and s'_2 are, we can then evaluate how much they are alike. We first line up s'_1 and s'_2. Then, we reward each position that has a matched base pair and penalize each position that has a mismatched base pair. We assign a $+1$ score for a matched base pairs and a -1 score for a mismatched base pairs. From the above alignment of s_1 and s_2, there are five matched base pairs and three mismatched base pairs. Therefore, it has an alignment score of $5-3=2$. Note that we do not want to have any position that has '_' on both s'_1 and s'_2 because it is biologically uninformative. Therefore, we could assign a negative infinity score for the position that has a ' _' pair. As a result, the higher the alignment score is, the more s'_1 and s'_2 are alike.

In reality, the scoring scheme of matched and mismatched base pair is not that simple. Often, the scoring is based on the statistical observation of how likely it is for a certain base to undergo biological events. For computational purpose, we assume that there is a scoring function $f(a,b)$, where a and b are either a base in {A, T, G, C} or '_', that defines the score of a position of s'_1 and s'_2. Therefore, the alignment score of a pair of s_1' and s_2' can be defined as $\sum_{i=1}^{l} f(s'_{1i}, s'_{2i})$, where l is the length of s'_1 (and s'_2), and s'_{1i} is the symbol at position i of s'_1 (similarly for s'_{2i}). As a result, we can describe the sequence alignment problem as follows. Given two sequences s_1 and s_2, find a pair of s'_1 and s'_2 that has the maximum alignment score.

The sequence alignment problem can be solved in $O(mn)$ time, where m and n are the length of s_1 and s_2 respectively. The $O(mn)$ time algorithm uses a dynamic programming to find the optimal alignment. We should clarify that the way we define the alignment score is just one of the many ways to do that. In fact, there are different models to evaluate the alignment score. For example, one idea is that two contiguous '_' should not be penalized the same as two separate '_'. Therefore, the concept of gap penalty was introduced.

8.2.3 Multiple Sequence Alignments

Sometimes, we want to investigate the relationships between a group of sequences. For example, a protein family is a group of proteins that are similar to each other. Moreover, a consensus sequence is a sequence that represents the motif of a protein family. The multiple

Table 8.1. Putative Promoter Sequences Preceding the Messenger Start Point

GCATATAAAGT	mouse β^{maj} globin
GGGCATAAAAC	rabbit β globin
AGTTATATTAT	mouse λI Ig
GACTATAAAGC	rat insulin I & II
GGCTATAAAAG	adenovirus late
GGCTATATATT	chicken ovalbumin
TTGTATATATT	chicken ovomucoid
GTGTATAAAAA	S. purpuratus H2B
CAGTATAAAAT	B. mori silk fibroin

sequence alignment can be used to extract the consensus sequence of a protein family. The concept of multiple sequence alignment is similar to that of the sequence alignment. Given a group of sequences $s_1, s_2, \ldots, s_k$. We want to find a set of $s'_1, s'_2, \ldots, s'_k$ (all with equal length), such that $\sum_{i=1}^{k}\sum_{j=1}^{k} A(s'_i, s'_j)$ is maximized, where $A(s'_i, s'_j)$ is the maximum alignment score of s'_i and s'_j.

Although the multiple sequence alignment problem is defined similarly to the sequence alignment problem, the multiple sequence is in fact an NP-complete problem. Therefore, heuristic approaches are often used to solve this problem.

8.2.4 Functional Site Identifications

A site is a short segment of a DNA sequence that has a special function, for example, a starting site of transcription and a gene regulation region (called promoter). Often, we might know some instances of a site, and from this information, we want to identify whether a given short segment is possibly an instance of this site. For example, Table 8.1 below are different putative promoter sequences preceding the messenger start point.

With the set of known instances, now we can create a profile for this site. We first create a 4 by l table T, where l is the length of this site. Each row in this table is labeled by a base and each column is labeled by a position of this site. In addition, an entry $T[b,i]$ is the number of occurrences of base b at position i. Therefore, for our example, we obtain Table 8.2 below.

Sometimes, it is more convenient to calculate in terms of probability instead of number of occurrences. Therefore, if we translate the table values into a probability (that is, divide the value by the total occurrences), we have a probability table T'. Table 8.3 below is the table T' for our example.

Now we can test an unknown short sequence against the profile (represented in T') for this site. For example, given an unknown short sequence s = GGCTATAAAAG, the probability that s is an instance of the putative promoter is:

Table 8.2. Number of Occurrences of Bases at each Position

	1	2	3	4	5	6	7	8	9	10	11
A	1	2	1	0	9	0	9	6	8	5	1
T	1	2	1	8	0	9	0	3	1	2	5
G	6	4	4	0	0	0	0	0	0	2	2
C	1	1	3	1	0	0	0	0	0	0	1

Table 8.3. Probability of Occurrences of Bases at each Position

	1	2	3	4	5	6	7	8	9	10	11
A	0.11	0.22	0.11	0	1	0	1	0.67	0.89	0.56	0.11
T	0.11	0.22	0.11	0.89	0	1	0	0.33	0.11	0.22	0.56
G	0.67	0.44	0.44	0	0	0	0	0	0	0.22	0.22
C	0.11	0.11	0.33	0.11	0	0	0	0	0	0	0.11

$$(0.67)(0.44)(0.33)(0.89)(1)(1)(1)(0.67)(0.89)(0.56)(0.22) = 0.0064.$$

It is easy to observe that the probability of the unknown instance will be small when the site is long. In order to normalize the measure, we can calculate the maximum (max) and the minimum (min) probability of an unknown short sequence. For example,

$$max = (0.67)(0.44)(0.44)(0.89)(1)(1)(1)(0.67)(0.89)(0.56)(0.56) = 0.022, \text{ and}$$

$$min = (0.11)(0.11)(0.11)(0)(0)(0)(0)(0)(0)(0)(0.11) = 0.$$

Therefore, the normalized score is:

$$(0.0064 - min)/(max - min) = (0.0064 - 0)/(0.022 - 0) = 0.29.$$

Also, notice that this method does not tell us whether 0.29 is high or low. Therefore, more statistical techniques are needed to solve this problem, such as using the concept of expected value.

8.2.5 Evolutionary Computing Applications in Bioinformatics

Many EC solutions have been introduced to solve problems in Bioinformatics. For example, Chellapilla and Fogel [8] proposed an evolutionary programming approach to the multiple sequence alignment problem (see multiple sequence alignment above). Later, Thomsen and his colleagues [28] extended the approach by using Clustal alignment to optimize the initial population. Platt and Dix [24] employed genetic algorithm to construct the restriction map; that is the map that indicates the relative positions of different genes on a DNA. Ando and Iba [1] used genetic algorithm to infer the gene regulatory model. Indeed, EC has also applied in many other problems such as RNA structure predictions [26], DNA motif discoveries [21], protein classifications [9] and so forth [12, 19, 20]. This chapter explains two EC applications in specific. The first case study uses EC to estimate the genome reversal distance for un-oriented genomes [2]. The second case study uses EC to find a largest compatible subset from phylogenetic data [3].

8.3 First Case Study: Genome Reversal Distance Estimation

8.3.1 Introduction

The mitochondria is a cell organelle that releases energy for the rest of the cell to consume. This organelle in fact contains a small set of DNAs for its own purpose (note that it is not the primary genetic material). In the late 1980s, Jeffrey Palmer and his colleagues discovered a gene shuffling pattern among different mitochondria genomes. This pattern is now known as the genome rearrangement.

The genome rearrangement describes a mechanism in which the genes order in the mitochondrial genome is constantly under rearrangement. Therefore, if we can estimate the rearrangement distance between two genomes, we can estimate the relationship between them. The reversal is the most commonly seen mechanism of the genome rearrangement. Figure 8.5 shows the estimated transformation from *Tobacco* to *Lobelia fervens* by reversals. Due to this discovery, two mathematical models were proposed, signed permutations and unsigned permutations [5, 6, 23]. For unsigned permutations, a genome is modeled as a permutation π with an order n (i.e. a permutation of $\{1, 2, \ldots, n\}$), where n is the number of gene blocks in the genome. Let the permutation $\pi = \pi[1]\ \pi[2]\ \ldots \pi[n]$, the reversal operation $\rho(i, j)$ rearrange π into $\pi[1] \ldots \pi[i-1]\ \pi[j-1] \ldots \pi[i]\ \pi[j] \ldots \pi[n]$. For a signed permutation π', each $\pi'[k]$ has either a positive or a negative sign. Each reversal operation $\rho(i, j)$ not only rearranges π' but also negates the sign of $\pi'[k]$ for $i \leq k < j$. The problem of estimating reversal distance between two genomes is formulated as sorting the permutation by reversal operations. That is, given π (or π'), we want to find a sorting sequence that uses the minimum number of reversal to sort π (or π') into the identity permutation (i.e. the permutation, $1\ 2 \ldots n$ for unsigned permutations, and $+1\ +2 \ldots +n$ for signed permutations). We called the minimum number of reversals the reversal distance, denoted by $d(\pi)$ (or $d(\pi')$). Figure 8.6 provides an example of both the unsigned and the signed permutation and their sorting paths.

The problem of sorting signed permutations can be solved in $O(n^2)$ time [18]. Moreover, the problem of finding the reversal distance of a signed permutation can be solved in $O(n)$ time [4]. However, both sorting and finding the reversal distance of an unsigned permutation have been proven to be NP-hard [7]. Therefore, the EC approach can be used to search for the near-optimal solution.

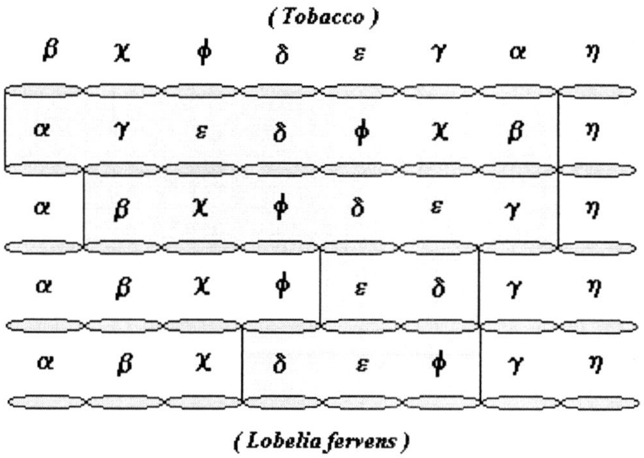

Figure 8.5. The Estimated Transformation from *Tobacco* to *Lobelia fervens* by Reversals

Unsigned	Signed
4 1 3 2	+4 -1 +3 -2
⇩	⇩
1 4 3 2	+1 -4 +3 -2
⇩	⇩
1 2 3 4	+1 +2 -3 +4
	⇩
	+1 +2 +3 +4

Figure 8.6. An Example of the Unsigned and the Signed Permutation and their Sorting Paths

The EC approach requires an effective representation. A naïve representation may have a huge searching space, yet encounter the problem of invalid solutions. Fortunately, our knowledge of signed permutations can in fact provide us an effective EC representation for unsigned permutations. Below, we look at some background on unsigned and signed permutations.

8.3.2 The Breakpoint Graph

An unsigned permutation can be modeled by a breakpoint graph. For each gene (a number in the permutation), we create a node. The idea of the breakpoint graph is to mark the desired and realistic relationship between these nodes in the permutation. For each pair of the nodes, we draw a black edge between them if they are adjacent in the permutation, and we draw a red edge between them if they are adjacent in the identity permutation. In order to model the orientation, we expand the unsigned permutation to have a zero at the front and a n+1 at the end. An example is shown in Figure 8.7. It has been shown that

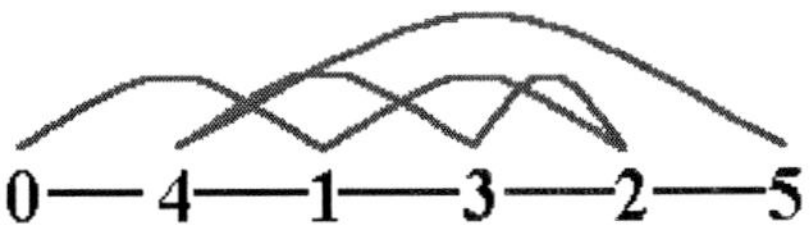

Figure 8.7. The Breakpoint Graph for the Unsigned Permutation 4 1 3 2

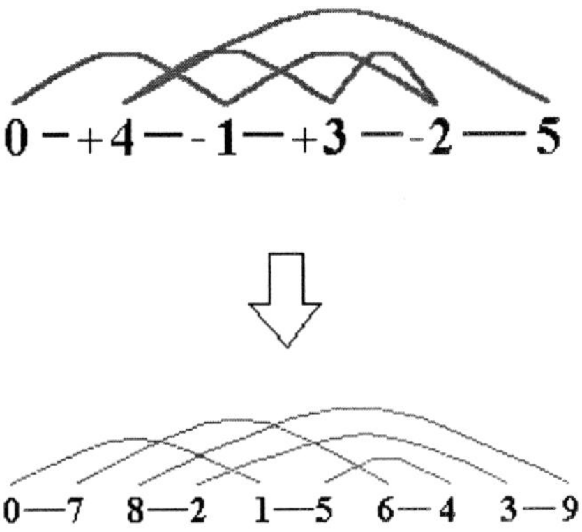

Figure 8.8. The Breakpoint Graph for the Signed Permutation +4 -1 +3 -2

given a cycle decomposition of the breakpoint graph, any reversal can at most change the number of cycles by one. Besides, it has also been shown that given a cycle decomposition of the breakpoint graph, the corresponding shortest sorting sequence can then be found in polynomial time. Thus, the key problem is to find a cycle decomposition that provides the shortest sorting sequence for the unsigned permutation. However, the problem of finding an optimal cycle decomposition is NP-hard.

On the other hand, sorting signed permutations can be solved easily by using the breakpoint graph. First we create the breakpoint graph as above. Then for each gene node i, we split it into two nodes $2i$-1 and $2i$, with ascending order if i is positive, descending order otherwise. Also, note that node 0 and n+1 (the nodes we artificially added) are replaced by node 0 and $2n$+1 respectively. An example is shown in Figure 8.8. The advantage is that now each node has exactly one red edge and one black edge associated with it. Because there is only one cycle decomposition of this breakpoint graph, the problem can now be solved in polynomial time. Many algorithms have been proposed to find the sorting sequence. There is an $O(n^2)$ time algorithm that finds the shortest sorting sequence. In addition, there is an $O(n)$ time algorithm that finds the reversal distance.

8.3.3 The Evolutionary Computing Solution

The idea of the EC approach [2] is to view all the possible cycle decomposition of the unsigned permutation as the signed permutations that have the same gene order. Except the node 0 and n+1, every node in the breakpoint graph has degree 2 for red edges and also for black edges. So, a cycle decomposition is used to define the (color) alternating paths. However, there is a corresponding signed permutation that actually defines the same alternating paths. Therefore, we can now turn our focus on the signed permutation instead of the cycle decomposition. We define the set $Signed(\pi)$ be the set of signed permutations that have the same gene order as π. For example, when π is 2 1, then $Signed(\pi)$ is $\{$-2 -1, -2 +1, +2 -1, +2 +1$\}$. Thus, the size of $Signed(\pi)$ is 2^n. Furthermore, the following two observations are required for our EC approach.

Observation 1. Each $\pi' \in Signed(\pi)$ can deduce a valid sorting sequence for π.

Proof. Let sorting sequence ρ sort π' into identity (i.e. $\pi'_\rho = id$). Because $|\,\pi'[i]\,| = \pi[i]$, then $\pi'_\rho[i] = \pi_\rho[i]$, for all i. Thus, ρ can also sort π (i.e. $\pi_\rho = id$). □

Observation 2. There exists a $\pi^* \in Signed(\pi)$ that deduces an optimal sorting sequence for π.

Proof. Let ρ be a sorting sequence for π that uses minimum number of reversals. For each $\pi[k]$, let $count[k]$ be the number of times that $\pi[k]$ is included in reversals of ρ, i.e. $\rho(i,j)$ $i \leq k < j$. Then π^* is as follows. $\pi^*[k]$ has a positive sign if $count[k]$ is even, otherwise it has a negative sign. Because $|\,\pi'[i]\,| = \pi[i]$, $\pi_\rho[i] = |\,\pi'_\rho[i]\,|$, for all i. In addition, all $\pi'_\rho[i]$, must be positive. Therefore, ρ can also sort π^* and the reversal distance for π^* is equal to the reversal distance for π. □

From the two observations, we can see that the problem can be solved in $O(2^n n)$ time. That is to find the reversal distance for all 2^n corresponding π'. Let π^* be the π' that has the minimum reversal distance. Then the sorting sequence of π is the sorting sequence of π^*. However, it is not feasible to go through all 2^n π'. Therefore, genetic algorithms can be used to find π^*. We can expect the genetic algorithm to find a π' with low reversal distance. In fact, the result is an upper bound for the reversal distance of π.

The chromosome of the genetic algorithm is a binary string with length n, which represents the signs of the signed permutation. From observation 1, we know that any instance of the chromosome gives a valid solution. Therefore, it allows us to use generic bitwise crossover and mutation operations. Due to the bitwise chromosome representation and simple genetic operations, least computation is required which results in fast generations. The fitness can be some functions of $d(\pi')$, such as $\frac{1}{d(\pi')}$. Note that this fitness function requires $O(n)$ time. Figure 8.9 gives a comparison between the EC approach and a heuristic approach [10]. In this experiment, single bit mutation and single point crossover operations were used.

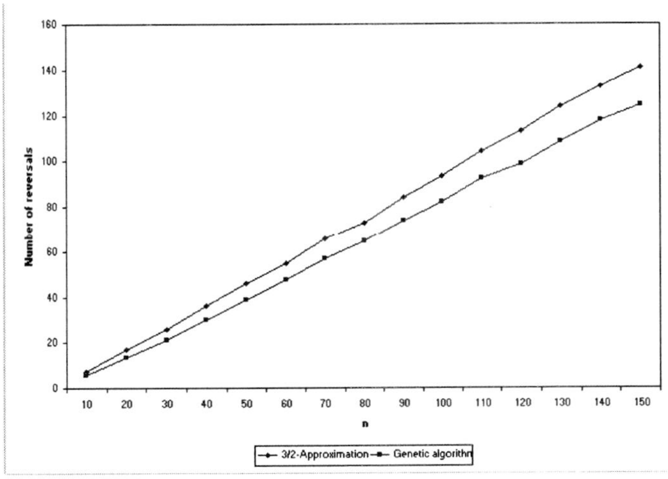

Figure 8.9. A Comparison of the Evolutionary Approach and a $\frac{3}{2}$-approximation Approach

Often, some information about the solution allows us to apply another heuristic or even prune out some search space without risking the loss of the global optimal. In fact, it has been proven that there exists a sorting sequence that does not break any sorted substring with length longer than 2. (Note that this observation is for substring straightly greater than 2. For example, when we optimally sort the permutation 3 4 1 2, one of the sorted 2-lengthed substrings (i.e. 3 4 or 1 2) has to be broken.) Therefore, for any long sorted substring, we can compress it into one number and according to whether it is ascendingly sorted or descendingly sorted, we can remove such bit from the chromosome and always assign it a positive or negative sign. Furthermore, there are different error bounded heuristics proposed. We can use these heuristic algorithms to enhance the quality of the initial population. For example, the idea of the $\frac{3}{2}$-approximation algorithm is to maximize the number of 2-lengthed (color) alternating cycles. Therefore, we can adapt the idea by initiating the population of different signed permutations that maximize some r-length alternating cycles (e.g. r=1, 2 or 3).

8.3.4 Open Problems

Sorting permutations by reversals is only one of the many mathematical models of the genome rearrangement. In fact, this model is the simplest one. Below we introduce two somewhat more realistic models of the genome arrangement problem. Both problems are very complex in nature and have no known efficient algorithm in general thus far.

Sorting Words by Reversals. Not all genes are uniquely existing in the genome. Sometimes, copies of the genes can be found in different locations in the genome. Sorting words by reversals is the mathematical model to address this reality. A word w is a string in *Gene**, where $Gene = \{1, 2, \ldots, n\}$. Without loss of generality, we assume that all elements in *Gene* are exhibited in w. This model is similar to the sorting permutations model, only that some genes can be duplicated. The problem is to find a sorting path using the minimum number of reversals to sort a genome π to a genome θ, where $\pi, \theta \in Gene^*$.

Sorting A permutations by Reversals. Another variation is sorting A permutations by reversals. This model addresses the fact that there are special sites for rearrangements. Rearrangements only occur when the beginning and the end of the subsequence allow binding for the responsible enzymes. Therefore, we now have special symbols (sites) from the set $A = \{a, b, c, \ldots\}$ which indicates different sites of the genes. For example, $3aa1baa4a52b$ is an A-permutation of 31452 with $A = \{a, b\}$. The reversal is valid only between two identical sites (i.e. $a - a$ or $b - b$). The problem is to first identify whether the A permutation is sortable, then to find a minimum sorting path.

8.4 Second Case Study: The Largest Compatible Subset Problem for Phylogenetic Data

8.4.1 Introduction

The theory of evolution hypothesizes that all organisms evolved from a single source, a simple organism. Therefore, under this hypothesis there is a relationship between every two species. One way to interpret this relationship is to look at the phenotypes (the features that can be observed) of the species. We call them the characters of the species. Furthermore, we expect that the more characters two species share, the closer relationship they have. The study of phylogenetics (phylogeny) is to understand these evolutionary relationships between the species. Different models have been proposed to model the evolutionary relationships between the species from different types of experimental data [16]. The perfect phylogeny [15] is a tree-based model that uses binary characters to infer phylogeny. Due to the noisy nature of the experimental data, conflicts are often found between subsets of the experimental data. Therefore, it is important to extract the motif from the imperfect data. The largest compatible subset problem is that given a set of experimental data, we want to discard the minimum such that the remaining are compatible.

In the case of the perfect phylogeny, the conflicts between subsets of data come pairwise [13,14]. In other words, the compatibility between subset A and subset B are independent of other subsets. Moreover, if A is incompatible with B, B is also incompatible with A. From this condition, we model the incompatibility between subsets of data by a graph, where each vertex represents a disjointed data subset, and an edge (u, v) indicates that vertex u and v are incompatible.

In the context of a graph $G = (V, E)$, where V is the set of vertices and E is the set of edges, the largest compatible subset problem [11] is to find a subset $U' \subseteq V$, such that $(u, v) \notin E, \forall u, v \in U'$ and $\mid U' \mid$ is maximum. Equivalently, we can find a subset $V' \subseteq V$ such that $\forall (u, v) \in E$, then either $u \in V'$ or $v \in V'$ (or both) and $\mid V' \mid$ is minimum. In fact, this problem has ready been studied in graph theory and is called the vertex cover problem [22].

However, the vertex cover problem has been proven to be NP-complete [17]. Therefore, the EC approach can be used to search for the near-optimal solution.

Again, a well-designed representation is critical for the EC approach. We can encode the chromosome to be a possible V'. But, there are $\sum_{i=1}^{n} \binom{n}{i}$ possible V'. Besides, some V' are in fact invalid. Here we would introduce an EC approach [3] that uses some knowledge on the vertex cover for special graphs to reduce the complexity. We also need a scheme to avoid invalid chromosomes. First, we present an overview on the perfect phylogeny and the vertex cover problem.

8.4.2 The Perfect Phylogeny

The perfect phylogeny is a phylogenetic model that uses binary characters. An m by n 0-1 matrix M records the exhibition of the n characters in the m species. That is $M[i,j] = 1$ if and only if species i exhibits character j, and zero otherwise. The definition of a perfect phylogenetic tree for matrix M is as follows. A rooted tree T is a perfect phylogenetic tree of M if it satisfies:

1. T has exactly m leaves;
2. each of the m species labels exactly one leaf of T;
3. each of the n characters labels exactly one edge of T; and
4. for any leaf l, the unique path from the root node to l contains labels that specify all the characters that l (its corresponding species) has.

Figure 8.10 shows an example of a matrix M and its perfect phylogenetic tree T. Not all matrices are perfect phylogeny. For any two characters c_i and c_j, let o_i and o_j be the species who exhibit c_i and c_j respectively. The matrix M is a perfect phylogeny if and only if o_i and o_j are either disjoint or one contains the other, for every i, j. In other words, character c_i and c_j are incompatible when o_i and o_j are overlapped. The incompatibility between the characters in M can be visualized by a conflict graph, where each vertex represents a character and each edge represents a conflict. Figure 8.11 shows an example of M that is not a perfect phylogeny and its conflict graph.

In practice, most experimental data is not a perfect phylogeny. Therefore, we want to extract a matrix M' from M, such that M' is a perfect phylogeny. The largest compatible subset problem for the perfect phylogeny is that given an m by n matrix M, find an m by n' matrix M' by removing columns from M, such that n' is maximum and M' is a perfect phylogeny. In the context of the conflict graph, we want to find the largest subset of vertices U' to keep, such that the resulting graph is edge free.

	c_1	c_2	c_3	c_4	c_5
s_1	1	1	0	0	0
s_2	0	0	1	0	0
s_3	1	1	0	0	1
s_4	0	0	1	1	0
s_5	0	1	0	0	0

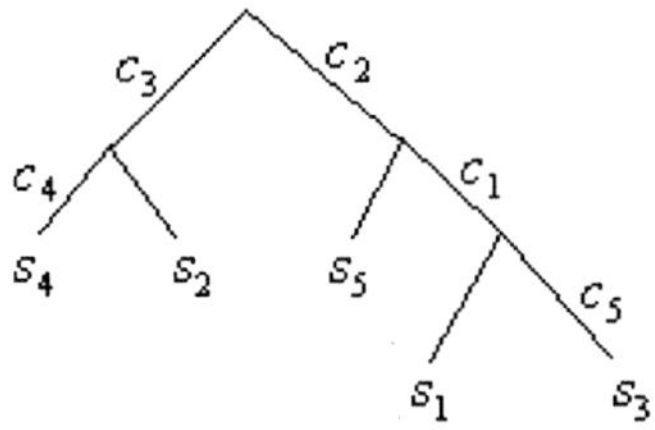

Figure 8.10. An Example of a Matrix and its Perfect Phylogenetic Tree

	c_1	c_2	c_3	c_4	c_5
s_1	1	1	0	0	0
s_2	0	0	1	0	1
s_3	1	1	0	0	1
s_4	0	0	1	1	0
s_5	0	1	0	0	1

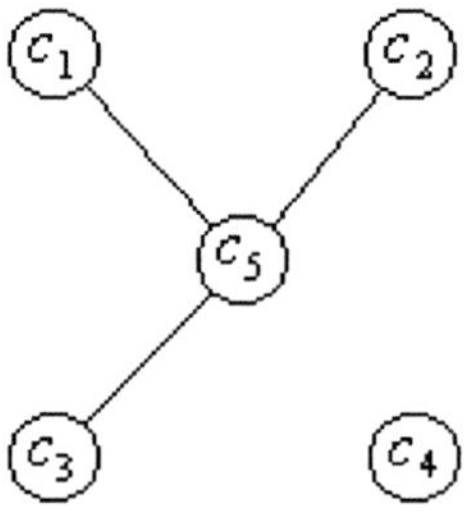

Figure 8.11. An Example of a Matrix that is not Perfect Phylogeny and its Conflict Graph

8.4.3 The Vertex Cover Problem

The largest compatible subset problem actually has already been studied in the form of the vertex cover problem in the graph theory. A vertex cover of a graph $G = (V, E)$ is a set $V' \subseteq V$ such that if (u, v) is an edge of G, then either $u \in V'$ or $v \in V'$ (or both). The vertex cover problem is to find a vertex cover that minimize $\mid V' \mid$.

The largest compatible subset problem and the vertex cover problem are actually dual. The largest compatible subset problem is to find the largest subset U' to keep, such that the remaining graph is edge free, while the vertex cover problem is to find the smallest subset V' that covers all edges. That is $U' = V - V'$.

The vertex cover problem has been proven to be NP-complete. Therefore, there is no efficient algorithm to solve it (and the largest compatible subset problem too). As a result, different heuristic algorithms have been proposed to find a near-optimal solution for the vertex cover problem. For example, Algorithm 8.1 will produce a vertex cover that is at most twice the size of the optimal vertex cover.

Although there is no efficient algorithm to solve the vertex cover problem in general, the optimal solution can easily be found if the graph is composed of disjointed simple cycles and trees. The optimal vertex cover for a graph that is a simple cycle can be obtained by taking alternating vertices on the cycle starting from an arbitrary vertex. The optimal vertex cover for a graph that is a tree can be found by Algorithm 8.2.

Algorithm 8.1 A 2-approximation algorithm for the Vertex Cover Problem

Input. $G = (V, E)$
Output. Vertex cover

```
1.  V' = 0
2.  while (E is not empty)
3.      Pick an arbitrary edge (u, v) ∈ E
4.      V' = V' ∈ u, v
5.      Remove (u, v) and all edges incident on u or v from E
6.  return V'
```

Algorithm 8.2 A linear-time algorithm to find Optimal Vertex Cover

Input. $G = (V, E)$
Output. Optimal vertex cover for a tree

```
1.  while (E is not empty)
2.      Pick an arbitrary leaf node u in G
3.      Let v be the parent node of u
4.      V' = V' ∪ {v}
5.      Removing v and all edges incident on v from G
6.  return V'
```

8.4.4 The Evolutionary Computing Solution

The idea of the EC approach is to encode the vertex cover by a binary string, where each bit corresponds to a vertex in the graph. When a vertex u has a 1-bit, it represents including u in V' and (conceptually) excluding u from V' otherwise. However, the optimal presence can actually be found for the rest of the vertices once the presence of some 'critical vertices' is determined. Therefore, our representation of the chromosome is only composed of the set of critical vertices. We define the set of critical vertices to be the set $C \subseteq V$, where $\{u \in V \mid u$ has the edge degree larger than two and u belongs to a cycle in $G\}$. The following lemma shows the definition of critical vertices is sufficient to decompose an arbitrary graph into a graph that composes of only simple cycles or/and trees.

Lemma 1. The set of non-critical vertices spans a graph G' that is composed of only simple cycles or/and trees.

Proof. If there exist a component in G' that is not a simple cycle nor a tree, then there must exist a vertex u that belongs to a cycle and has degree larger than two. But the set of non-critical vertices $(V - C)$ is the set of vertices that have the degree less than three or it does not belong to any cycle in G, thus it contradicts the assumption. □

Once the presence of the critical vertices is determined, the rest of the vertices can easily be determined by the methods discussed in the last section. However, some critical vertices can in fact be adjacent to each other. Thus, the effect of a vertex u with a 0-bit does not immediately exclude u from V', but it does immediately include all adjacent vertices of u from V'. Algorithm 8.3 shows how the vertex cover is interpreted from a chromosome.

Algorithm 8.3 An algorithm to construct the Vertex Cover from a chromosome.

Input. $G = (V, E)$
Output. Vertex cover from a chromosome

$V' = V$
for each critical vertex u
    if (u has 1-bit)
        remove u and all edges incident on u from G
    else // u has 0-bit
        remove all edges and vertices incident on u from G
Use Algorithm 2 to find vertex cover on tree components and
remove them from G
Remove alternating vertices on simple cycles from G,
starting from an arbitrary vertex
$V' = V' - V$
return V'

Once again, the EC representation and interpretation of the solution provides a better search space because it reduces the size of the search space and it ensures that all instances are valid solutions. Generic genetic operators can then be used. The fitness function can be some functions of $|V'|$, such as $\frac{1}{|V'|}$. Figure 8.12 gives a comparison between the EC approach and a heuristic approach. In this experiment, again single bit mutation and single point crossover operations were used.

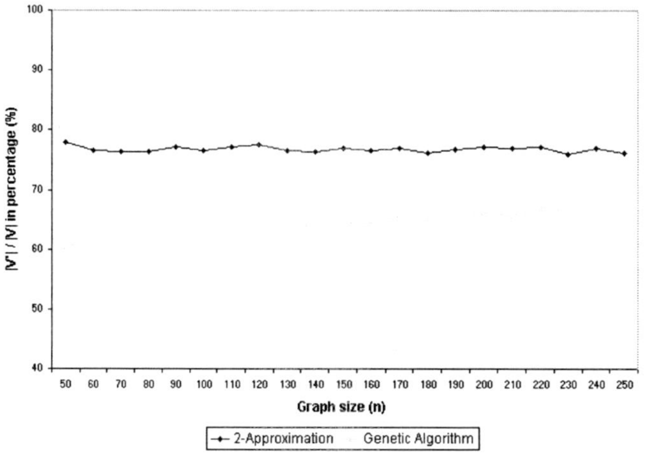

Figure 8.12. A Comparison of the Evolutionary Approach and a 2-approximation Approach

The concept of critical vertices is the key to reduce the problem size. Figure 8.13 shows the average number of critical vertices in different graph sizes. We can see that the concept of critical vertices reduces the problem size to about half, that is $(\frac{\sqrt{2}}{2})^n$ times of the search space.

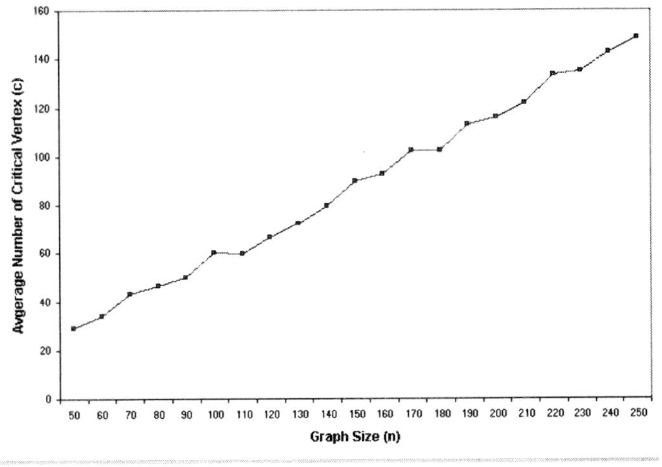

Figure 8.13. The Average Number of Critical Vertices for Various Graph Size

8.4.5 Open Problems

Although the largest compatible subset problem for the perfect phylogeny demonstrates the fundamental concept of the compatibility problem, other variations of the models require some adaptations of the representations. Below we look at two similar compatibility problems.

Weighted Data. Sometimes, data subsets are not equally important. Biology experts might weight data subsets according to their source and characteristics. Therefore, we assign a weight for each vertex in the graph. Then, the problem is to find a vertex cover V' that minimizes the total weight, i.e. $\sum_{v \in V'} weight(v)$. Notice that this problem is inherently an NP problem, because its special case, when all weights are equal to one, is indeed the vertex cover problem.

Non-pairwise Conflicts. Sometimes, the conflicts are not in pairwise form. Therefore, we need to extend the graph definition to the hypergraph. A hypergraph is a graph that its edges can have more than two end-points. Therefore, a conflict exists between a group of species can be represented by an edge in the hypergraph. Furthermore, by removing any vertex of this group, the conflict can be resolved. Similarly, this problem is inherently an NP problem because when all edges have exactly two end-points, it is same as the vertex cover problem.

8.5 Summary

This chapter introduced Evolutionary Computing applications in Bioinformatics. We reviewed some major events and explained some key concepts of Bioinformatics. We also gave an overview of some of the important problems. Furthermore, two case studies were presented in detail with the problem's background, the EC solution, the experimental results and the open problems.

Bibliography

[1] S. Ando and H. Iba, Inference of Gene Regulatory Model by Genetic Algorithms, T*he IEEE Congress on Evolutionary Computation*, **1**: pp. 712-719, 2001

[2] A. Auyeung and A. Abraham, Estimating Genome Reversal Distance by Genetic Algorithm, *The IEEE Congress on Evolutionary Computation*, pp. 1157-1161, 2003

[3] A. Auyeung and A. Abraham, The Largest Compatible Subset Problem for Phylogenetic Data, *The Genetic and Evolutionary Computation Conference*, 2004

[4] D. A. Bader, B. M. E. Moret and M. Yan, A Linear-Time Algorithm for Computing Inversion Distance between Signed Permutations with an Experimental Study, *Journal of Computational Biology*, **8**(5): pp. 483-491, 2001

[5] A. Bergeron, A Very Elementary Presentation of the Hannenhalli-Pevzner Theory, *The Twelfth Annual Symposium on Combinatorial Pattern Matching*, pp. 106-117, 2001

[6] P. Berman and S. Hannenhalli, Fast Sorting by Reversal, *The Seventh Annual Symposium on Combinatorial Pattern Matching*, 1075: pp. 168-185, 1996

[7] A. Caprara, Sorting by Reversals is Difficult, *The First International Conference on Computational Molecular Biology*, pp. 75-83, 1997

[8] K. Chellapilla and G. B. Fogel, Multiple Sequence Alignment Using Evolutionary Programming, *The IEEE Congress on Evolutionary Computation*, **1**: pp. 445-452, 1999

[9] S. Chiba, K. Sugawara and T. Watanabe, Classification and Function Estimation of Protein by using Data Compression and Genetic Algorithms, *the IEEE Congress on Evolutionary Computation*, **2**: pp. 839-844, 2001

[10] D. A. Christie, A 3/2-Approximation Algorithm for Sorting by Reversals, *The Ninth Annual ACM-SIAM Symposium on Discrete Algorithms*, pp. 244-252, 1998

[11] W. Day and D. Sankoff, Computational Complexity of Inferring phylogenies by Compatibility, *Systematic Zoology*, **35**(2): pp. 224-229, 1986

[12] R. Deaton, R. C. Murphy, J. A. Rose, M. Garzon, D. R. Franceschetti and S. E. Stevens Jr., A DNA Based Implementation of an Evolutionary Search for Good Encodings for DNA Computation, *The IEEE International Conference on Evolutionary Computation*, pp. 267-271, 1997

[13] G. F. Estabrook, C. Johnson and F. R. McMorris, A Mathematical Foundation for Analysis of Cladistic Character Compatibility, *Math Bioscience*, **29**: pp. 181-187, 1976

[14] G. F. Estabrook and F. R. McMorris, When are Two Qualitative Taxonomic Characters Compatible, *Journal of Mathematical Biology*, **4**: pp. 195-200, 1977

[15] D. Gusfield, Efficient Algorithm for Inferring Evolutionary History, *Networks*, **21**: pp. 19-28, 1991

[16] D. Gusfield, *Algorithm on Strings Trees, and Sequences - Computer Science and Computational Biology*, Cambridge University Press, 1997

[17] E. Halperin, Improved Approximation Algorithm for the Vertex Cover Problem in Graphs and Hypergraphs, *SIAM Journal of Computing*, **31**(5): pp. 1608-1623, 2002

[18] H. Kaplan, R. Shamir and R. E. Tarjan, Faster and Simpler Algorithm for Sorting Signed Permutations by Reversals, *The Eighth Annual ACM-SIAM Symposium on Discrete Algorithms*, pp. 344-351, 1997

[19] S. Kikuchi, D. Tominaga, M. Arita, K. Takashi and M. Tomita, Dynamic modeling of genetic networks using genetic algorithm and S-system, *Bioinformatics* **19**(5): pp. 643-650, 2003

[20] A. Meade, D. Corne and R. Sibly, Applying Evolutionary Computation to Understanding the Insertion Behavior of LINE-1 Retrotransposons in Human DNA. *The IEEE Congress on Evolutionary Computation*, pp. 836-843, 2000

[21] A. Meade, D. Corne and R. Sibly, Discovering Patterns in Microsatellite Flanks with Evolutionary Computation by Evolving Discriminatory DNA Motifs. *The IEEE Congress on Evolutionary Computation*, pp. 1-6, 2002

[22] V. T. Paschos, A Survery of Approximately Optimal Solution to Some Covering and Packing Problems, *ACM Computing Surveys*, **29**(2): pp. 171-209, 1997

[23] P. A. Pevzner, *Computational Molecular Biology An Algorithmic Approach*, MIT Press, 2001

[24] D. M. Platt and T. I. Dix, Construction of Restriction Maps Using a Genetic Algorithm, *The Twenty-Sixth International Conference on System Sciences*, **1**: pp. 756-762, 1993

[25] P. J. Russell, *iGenetics*, Benjamin Cummings, 2002

[26] A. B. Shapiro, J. C. Wu, D. Bengali and M. J. Potts, The Massively Parallel Genetic Algorithm for RNA Folding: MIMD Implementation and Population Variation. *Bioinformatics* **17**(2): pp. 137-148, 2001

[27] J. Tao, X. Ying and M. Q. Zhang, *Current Topics in Computational Molecular Biology*, MIT Press, 2002

[28] R. Thomen, G. B. Fogel, T. Krink, A Clustal Alignment Improver using Evolutionary Algorithms, *The IEEE Congress on Evolutionary Computation*, **1**: pp. 121 -126, 2002

Index

Reviewer List